Translations of Mathematical Monographs *Volume 13*

ADDITIVE THEORY
of
PRIME NUMBERS

by

L. K. Hua

AMERICAN MATHEMATICAL SOCIETY
PROVIDENCE, RHODE ISLAND
1965

堆壘素數論

華　羅　庚

Institute of Mathematics, Chinese Academy of Sciences
Peking, 1957

Translated from the Chinese by N. H. NG

Translation aided by support to the Emmanuel College Research Center from the Air Force Cambridge Research Laboratories, L. G. Hanscom Field, Bedford, Massachusetts under contract Number AF 19(604)-8505.

Library of Congress Card Number 65-23103

Printed in the United States of America

TABLE OF CONTENTS

Foreword vii

Preface to the present edition ix

Preface to the 1953 Chinese edition ix

Preface to the Russian edition x

Preface originally intended for the Russian edition xi

Explanatory remarks xiii

Chapter I. Trigonometric sums 1

§1. Statement of a theorem and a Fundamental Lemma 1

§2. Proof of the theorem from the Fundamental Lemma 1

§3. Proof of the Fundamental Lemma for the case $l = 1$ (Mordell) 3

§4. Some lemmas 4

§5. Proof of the Fundamental Lemma 5

§6. Corollaries 7

§7. Finite Fourier series 9

§8. Formulation and proof of Theorem 2 10

Chapter II. Estimates for sums involving the divisor function $d(n)$ 11

§1. Formulation of Theorem 3 11

§2. Van der Corput's lemma 11

§3. Lemmas pertaining to the number of solutions of congruences 14

§4. Proof of the theorem 16

§5. Further lemmas 17

Chapter III. Mean-value theorems for certain trigonometric sums (I) 19

§1. Formulation of Theorem 4 19

§2. Certain lemmas pertaining to inequalities 19

§3. Proof of the theorem 22

§4. Weyl's lemma 23

Chapter IV. Vinogradov's mean-value theorem and its corollaries 26

§1. Description of the theorem 26

§2. Lemmas 27

§3. Proof of the theorem 30

§4. Corollary 36
§5. Lemmas on convex functions 37
Chapter V. Mean-value theorems for certain trigonometric sums (II) 40
§1. Formulation of Theorems 7 and 8 40
§2. Remarks concerning theorems A_k (i.e., Theorem 8) 41
§3. An estimate of two integrals by means of symmetric functions 42
§4. A further lemma 46
§5. Proof of the theorems 47
§6. Proof of the theorems (continued) 52
§7. The relation between a single sum and the mean value 56
§8. Estimates for trigonometric sums 62
Chapter VI. Trigonometric sums depending on prime numbers 66
§1. Formulation of Theorem 10 66
§2. Certain essential lemmas 66
§3. Proof of the theorem 73
Chapter VII. An asymptotic formula for the number of solutions of the Waring-Goldbach problem 78
§1. Formulation of Theorem 11 78
§2. Certain lemmas 79
§3. Farey's dissection 85
§4. An estimate of the absolute value of an integral taken over E 86
§5. Lemmas concerning $\mathfrak{M}(h, g)$ 87
§6. An estimate of the absolute value of an integral taken over $\mathfrak{M}(h, g)$ 89
§7. Lemmas essential for the proof of the theorem 90
§8. Proof of the theorem 94
§9. Proof of the theorem (conclusion) 96
Chapter VIII. Singular series 100
§1. Formulation of Theorem 12 100
§2. Lemmas pertaining to trigonometric sums 100
§3. Lemmas pertaining to congruences 103
§4. Positiveness of the singular series 106
§5. Corollaries of Theorems 11 and 12 108
Chapter IX. A further study of the Waring-Goldbach problem 109
§1. Introduction 109
§2. Davenport's lemma 112

§3. Proof of Theorem 13 114
§4. Appendix 117
Chapter X. Indeterminate equations in prime unknowns 124
§1. Introduction 124
§2. Lemmas necessary for the proof of Theorem 16 124
§3. Results related to Tarry's problem 130
§4. Formulation of Theorem 16 139
§5. Proof of the theorem 140
§6. Appendix 149
Chapter XI. A further study of the problem of the preceding chapter 157
§1. Introduction 157
§2. A study of the condition of positive solvability 157
§3. Singular series and the condition of congruent solvability 162
§4. Some lemmas 170
§5. A lemma 171
§6. A further lemma 173
Chapter XII. Other results 175
§1. Introduction 175
§2. Definitions 175
§3. Formulation of a conjecture 176
§4. Application of the method of Chapters X and XI to a general problem 178
§5. Statement of a further conjecture 178
§6. Further results 179
Appendix 181

FOREWORD

This book is a summing up of the methods of study of the additive theory of prime numbers by Academician Vinogradov of Soviet Russia and the author, with discussions centering on Vinogradov's mean-value theorem and its improvement by the author.

The author combines the methods of study of the Goldbach problem and the Waring problem, the latter being extended by letting the summands be polynomials with integral coefficients in which the variables are restricted to prime values. He also limits the variables in Tarry's problem to assuming only prime values, and at the same time carries out broader discussions on indeterminate equations in unknown primes.

In its original form this book was first published in the Russian language [1)] in the Soviet Union in 1947. In 1953 the Chinese edition [2)] was published by the Chinese Academy of Sciences. In its present form the book is completely revised and supplemented, with great changes made in the contents, as in §5 of Chapter IV, §§6 and 8 of Chapter V, and the entire Chapter IX, which have been completely rewritten. Large parts of a number of other sections have also been rewritten, and an Appendix is added.

---

1) In the Trudy of the Steklov Mathematical Institute 22 (1947).

2) Editor's note. A German translation, based on the Russian edition of 1947 and the Chinese edition of 1953, was published, under the title *Additive Zahlentheorie*, by B. G. Teubner, Leipzig, 1959.

PREFACE TO THE PRESENT EDITION

The publication of a revised edition has enabled the auther to make a number of improvements and to add supplements to the book. §5 of Chapter IV, §§6 and 8 of Chapter V, and the entire Chapter IX were rewritten, and many other chapters and sections were partly rewritten.

After reading this book and a few other contemporary publications, such as the author's "Certain results in the additive theory of numbers," which will soon be published in Acta Mathematica Sinica, the reader will understand the basic principles of the modern additive theory of numbers and will be able to embark upon research. But it must be remembered that this book is merely an individual piece of work designed to describe one branch of the theory. To improve his comprehension of the subject, the reader should also acquaint himself with a more general treatment (for example, the author's "Introduction to number theory" (Chinese), Science Publishing Co., Peking, 1957; MR 20 #829).

The author takes this opportunity to express his thanks to his colleagues Yue Min-yi (Yüeh Min-i), Wang Yuan (Wang Yuan), Wu Fang (Wu Fang), Wei Dao-zheng (Wei Tao-cheng) and Chen Jing-run (Ch'en Ching-jun), who have pointed out errors or have rendered other assistance. Without their cooperation, this edition could not have been published at this early date.

L. K. Hua
July 7, 1957, Peking

PREFACE TO THE 1953 CHINESE EDITION

It has been twelve years since the completion of the first draft and six years since the publication of the Russian edition. During these years the problem of publishing the book has been such that the protracted delay finally caused the original draft [1] to disappear without leaving a trace. To-day, after being urged to

1) Note by the editor of the Russian edition. In this original draft, which was written in English, the term "exponential sum" was used instead of "trigonometric sum."

do so by the Chinese Academy of Sciences, I had to translate the book from the Russian edition in order to send it to the publishers.

The twelve years were not idle; the scientific developments within these years were very great, and therefore to present only the Russian translation would have been inadequate to deal with the current situation. I rewrote several chapters, especially Chapter V, in which I included the creative work of Academician Vinogradov between 1942 and 1947 and my work in 1947.

Upon completion of my work, I was indeed well content. This was not only because my book could be published in my mother country, but especially because the unbreakable Sino-Soviet friendship which we had longed for in the past was realized. Without the encouragement of the Chinese Academy of Sciences, this book could not have been reprinted, and I extend my sincere gratitude to them. The members of the Institute of Mathematics all shared the responsibility of proof reading and editing, and the great number of persons who participated in various ways makes it impossible for me to thank them individually here.

L. K. Hua
May 1953, Peking

PREFACE TO THE RUSSIAN EDITION

After several years of war the author, who had been invited by Academician Vinogradov to make a tour of Soviet Russia, was delighted to learn that a Russian translation of the essay he had written in the years 1940 and 1941 had been sent to the publishers. In 1942, Academician Vinogradov had already made his method more precise, a fact of which the author was unaware before his arrival in Moscow. This precision strengthened the theorem on the mean value (Theorem 7, this book) and thus made it possible to improve Theorems 8, 9, 11, 13, 17 and others. For example, Theorem 11 is also true for $s \geq 10k^2 \log k$, while Theorem 13 also holds for $s \geq s_0 \sim 4k \log k$, and so forth.

In conclusion, the author extends his gratitude to Professors B. I. Segal and D. A. Vasil′kov for their translation of this book into Russian.

L. K. Hua
April 17, 1946, Moscow

PREFACE ORIGINALLY INTENDED FOR THE RUSSIAN EDITION [1)]

This book contains a description of new findings in the additive theory of prime numbers. The basic principles of this field of study were established by Academician I. M. Vinogradov and further developed by the author. The work of Vinogradov, which has opened up new paths for development, is simplified, changed and redescribed in Chapters V and VI. Apart from Lemma 7.14, no specialized knowledge is necessary for reading this book.

The greater part of the book is the work of the author, systematically described here for the first time.

The author wishes to express his profound gratitude to Academician Vinogradov.

Assistance rendered by his colleagues Min Si-hao (Min Szu-hao) and Zhong Kai-lai (Chung K′ai-lai) in preparing the draft is gratefully acknowledged by the author.

In conclusion, the author wishes to express his deep gratitude to the Soviet Academy of Sciences for its favorable reception of his work. In these difficult days we are especially happy to see the results of our scientific study win the approval of the highest authority of a people to whom we are bound by the closest ties of friendship. This kind of cultural cooperation will always be treasured and is especially meaningful at the present time. It is respectfully hoped that the publication of this book will strengthen the true friendship and mutual affection of our two great peoples.

National Tsinghua University

L. K. Hua
Feb. 18, 1941, Kunming, China

---

1) This book was sent to the editorial department of special publications of the Institute of Mathematics in 1941, but the publication was delayed as a result of the war.

EXPLANATORY REMARKS

The book has no general introduction but the first section of each chapter gives a description of the principal results of that chapter. The following symbols are frequently used:

z is a real number, $[z]$ is the greatest integer in z, and $\{z\}$ is the distance from z to the nearest integer.

$$e(z) = e^{2\pi i z}. \qquad e_q(x) = e^{2\pi i x/q}.$$

k denotes a positive integer, P is a "sufficiently large" positive number, and $L = \log P$.

$\max(a, b, \cdots, g)$ denotes the largest number among $a, b, \cdots, g$ and $\min(a, b, \cdots, g)$ denotes the smallest.

As usual, $a|b$ means that a divides b, and $a \nmid b$ means that a does not divide b. In this book, p is frequently used for a prime number, and $p^l \| n$ means that $p^l | n$ but $p^{l+1} \nmid n$.

The expression $c(a, b, \cdots, g)$ denotes a positive number which depends on $a, b, \cdots, g$, and ϵ denotes an arbitrary small positive number; these numbers are not necessarily the same every time they occur.

The expression $f(x) = O(\phi(x))$ or $f(x) \ll \phi(x)$ means that $|f(x)| \leq c(a, b, \cdots, g)\phi(x)$.

In stating the theorems, we shall not use the symbols $\ll$ and O but an inequality of the above form. In the proofs and lemmas, if the symbol $\ll$ or O is used, the constant implied in it depends only on the $a, b, \cdots, g$ involved in the description of the theorem.

The meaning of any particular symbol will not necessarily be the same in all parts of the book.

CHAPTER I

TRIGONOMETRIC SUMS

§1. STATEMENT OF A THEOREM AND A FUNDAMENTAL LEMMA

Theorem 1. *Let $f(x)$ denote a polynomial with integral coefficients*

$$f(x) = a_k x^k + \cdots + a_1 x + a_0.$$

If $(a_k, \cdots, a_1, q) = 1$, then

$$\left| \sum_{x=1}^{q} e^{2\pi i f(x)/q} \right| \leqslant c_1(k, \varepsilon) q^{1-\frac{1}{k}+\varepsilon},$$

where ϵ is an arbitrary positive number.

For brevity we introduce the following notation:

$$a = \frac{1}{k}, \quad e_q(x) = e^{2\pi i x/q}$$

and

$$S(q, f(x)) = \sum_{x=1}^{q} e_q(f(x)).$$

Fundamental Lemma (Lemma 1.1). *If $p \nmid (a_k, \cdots, a_1)$, then*

$$|S(p^l, f(x))| \leqslant c_2(k) p^{l(1-a)}.$$

§2. PROOF OF THE THEOREM FROM THE FUNDAMENTAL LEMMA

Lemma 1.2. *Let $\nu(q)$ denote the number of distinct prime factors of q. Let $d(q)$ denote the number of positive divisors of q. Then*

$$2^{\nu(q)} \leqslant d(q) \leqslant c_3(\varepsilon) q^{\varepsilon}.$$

Proof. If the prime $p > 2^{1/\epsilon}$, then

$$\frac{d(p^l)}{p^{l\varepsilon}} = \frac{l+1}{p^{l\varepsilon}} \leqslant \frac{l+1}{2^l} = \frac{l+1}{(1+1)^l} \leqslant \frac{l+1}{l+1} = 1.$$

But if the prime $p \le 2^{1/\epsilon}$ and $l \ge 1$, then

$$\frac{d(p^l)}{p^{l\varepsilon}} = \frac{l+1}{p^{l\varepsilon}} \leqslant \frac{l+1}{2^{l\varepsilon}} \leqslant \frac{l+1}{l\varepsilon \log 2} \leqslant \frac{2}{\varepsilon \log 2}.$$

Let $q = p_1^{l_1} \cdots p_s^{l_s}$, where $p_1, \cdots, p_s$ are the distinct prime factors of q; then

$$\frac{d(q)}{q^\varepsilon} = \prod_{p|q} \frac{d(p^l)}{p^{l\varepsilon}} \leqslant \prod_{p \leqslant 2^{1/\varepsilon}} \frac{2}{\varepsilon \log 2} = c_3(\varepsilon).$$

The first inequality is obviously true.

Lemma 1.3. *If* $(q_1, q_2) = 1$ *and* $f(0) = 0$, *then*

$$S(q_1 q_2, f(x)) = S(q_1, f(q_2 x)/q_2)\, S(q_2, f(q_1 x)/q_1).$$

Proof. Let $x = q_1 y + q_2 z$. If y and z run through a complete set of residues modulo q_2 and q_1 respectively, then x runs through a complete set of residues modulo $q_1 q_2$. Obviously we have

$$e_{q_1 q_2}(f(q_1 y + q_2 z)) = e_{q_2}(f(q_1 y)/q_1) e_{q_1}(f(q_2 z)/q_2),$$

and

$$\begin{aligned} S(q_1 q_2, f(x)) &= \sum_{x=1}^{q_1 q_2} e_{q_1 q_2}(f(x)) \\ &= \sum_{y=1}^{q_2} \sum_{z=1}^{q_1} e_{q_2}(f(q_1 y)/q_1) e_{q_1}(f(q_2 z)/q_2) \\ &= S(q_1, f(q_2 x)/q_2)\, S(q_2, f(q_1 x)/q_1). \end{aligned}$$

Proof of theorem. We can assume without loss of generality that $a_0 = 0$. Let $q = p_1^{l_1} \cdots p_s^{l_s}$, where $p_1, \cdots, p_s$ are all the distinct prime factors of q. By Lemma 1.3,

$$S(q, f(x)) = \prod_{p|q} S\left(p^l, \frac{f(q x/p^l)}{q/p^l}\right),$$

and by Lemma 1.1, we obtain

$$\left| S(q, f(x)) \right| \leqslant c_2^{\nu(q)} q^{1-a}.$$

Further, by Lemma 1.2 (we can assume that $c_2 > 1$),

$$c_2^{\nu(q)} = (2^{\nu(q)})^{\log c_2/\log 2} \leqslant c_1(k, \varepsilon) q^\varepsilon.$$

From this the theorem follows at once.

§3. PROOF OF THE FUNDAMENTAL LEMMA FOR THE CASE $l = 1$ (Mordell)[1)]

We can assume without loss of generality that $p > k$ and $a_0 = 0$. For brevity we use Σ_x to mean $\Sigma_{x=1}^{p}$. Then we have

$$\sum_{a_k} \cdots \sum_{a_1} \left| \sum_x e_p(a_k x^k + \cdots + a_1 x) \right|^{2k}$$

$$= \sum_{x_1} \cdots \sum_{x_k} \sum_{y_1} \cdots \sum_{y_k} \sum_{a_k} \cdots \sum_{a_1} e_p(a_k(x_1^k + \cdots + x_k^k - y_1^k - \cdots - y_k^k)$$

$$+ \cdots + a_1(x_1 + \cdots + x_k - y_1 - \cdots - y_k)) = p^k N,$$

where N denotes the number of distinct solutions of the congruences

$$x_1^h + \cdots + x_k^h \equiv y_1^h + \cdots + y_k^h \pmod p, \quad 1 \leqslant h \leqslant k, \quad 1 \leqslant x, \quad y \leqslant p. \tag{1}$$

Note that in order to arrive at this conclusion we have used the following formula:

$$\sum_{x=1}^{q} e_q(h x) = \begin{cases} q & \text{if } q \mid h, \\ 0 & \text{if } q \nmid h. \end{cases}$$

By a well-known theorem on symmetric functions, we can deduce from (1) that

$$(x - x_1) \cdots (x - x_k) \equiv (x - y_1) \cdots (x - y_k) \pmod p.$$

Hence we see that $y_1, \cdots, y_k$ are obtained by permutation of $x_1, \cdots, x_k$ (mod p). Therefore,

$$N \leqslant k!\, p^k.$$

Hence we obtain

$$\sum_{a_k} \cdots \sum_{a_1} \left| S(p, a_k x^k + \cdots + a_1 x) \right|^{2k} \leqslant k!\, p^{2k}. \tag{2}$$

Obviously, for all λ ($\not\equiv 0 \pmod p$) and all μ, we have

$$|S(p, f(x))| = |S(p, f(\lambda x + \mu) - f(\mu))|.$$

The sums of this form all occur in the left side of (2). We shall now find the number of distinct sums $S(p, f(\lambda x + \mu) - f(\mu))$ obtained from all the different polynomials

1) Quart. J. Math. Oxford Ser. 3 (1932), 161–167.

$f(\lambda x + \mu) - f(\mu)$. If the coefficients of two polynomials are congruent to each other (mod p), then these two polynomials are congruent to modulus p. We can assume without loss of generality that $p \nmid a_k$. If $f(\lambda x + \mu) - f(\mu)$ and $f(x)$ are congruent to modulus p, we obtain

$$a_k \lambda^k \equiv a_k, \qquad k a_k \lambda^{k-1} \mu + a_{k-1} \lambda^{k-1} \equiv a_{k-1} \pmod p.$$

The number of distinct λ satisfying $\lambda^k \equiv 1 \pmod p$ is $\leq k$. For a fixed λ, μ is uniquely determined. Therefore, among the polynomials of the form $f(\lambda x + \mu) - f(\mu)$, there are at most k which are congruent with $f(x)$ to modulus p.

Hence we obtain altogether $p(p-1)$ polynomials

$$f(\lambda x + \mu) - f(\mu), \qquad 1 \leqslant \lambda \leqslant p-1, \qquad 1 \leqslant \mu \leqslant p,$$

of which at least $p(p-1)/k$ are not congruent with one another. Therefore

$$a\, p(p-1) |S(p, f(x))|^{2k} \leqslant k!\, p^{2k},$$

i.e.,

$$|S(p, f(x))| \leqslant \left(\frac{k \cdot k!}{p(p-1)}\right)^{\frac{1}{2}a} p \leqslant (2k \cdot k!)^{\frac{1}{2}a} p^{1-a} \leqslant k p^{1-a}. \qquad (3)$$

§4. SOME LEMMAS

Lemma 1.4. *Suppose that* $s(x)$ *is a polynomial with integral coefficients* mod p, α *is a root of multiplicity* m *of* $s(x) \equiv 0 \pmod p$, *and* $p^u \| s(px + \alpha)$.[1] *If we let* $t(x) = p^{-u} s(px + \alpha)$, *then the congruence*

$$t(x) \equiv 0 \pmod p$$

has at most m *roots.*

Proof. We can assume without loss of generality that $\alpha = 0$. Then

$$s(x) = x^m s_1(x) + p s_2(x),$$

where $s_1(0) \not\equiv 0 \pmod p$ and the degree of $s_2(x)$ is lower than m. Also, $s_1(x)$ and $s_2(x)$ are both polynomials with integral coefficients. Hence we obtain

$$s(px) = p^m x^m s_1(px) + p s_2(px).$$

Since the coefficient $p^m s_1(0)$ of x^m is not divisible by p^{m+1}, it follows that $u \leq m$. Consequently, since the degree of $p^{-u} s(px)$ is $\leq m \pmod p$, the lemma

---

1) $p^u \| g(x)$ denotes that p^u divides all the coefficients of $g(x)$ but p^{u+1} does not.

is proved.

Lemma 1.5. *Suppose that*

$$f(x) = a_k x^k + \cdots + a_1 x,$$

and $p \nmid (a_k, \cdots, a_1)$. *If* p^σ *exactly divides all the coefficients of* $f(\mu + py) - f(\mu)$, *then*

$$1 \leqslant \sigma \leqslant k.$$

Proof. Suppose that $\sigma \geq k + 1$. Then since p^σ divides all the coefficients of $f(\mu + py) - f(\mu)$, we see that

$$p^\sigma \left| \frac{p^h}{h!} f^{(h)}(\mu), \qquad 1 \leqslant h \leqslant k. \right.$$

That is, for any h, we always have

$$p^{k+1} \left| \frac{p^h}{h!} f^{(h)}(\mu), \right.$$

whence we obtain

$$p \left| \frac{1}{h!} f^{(h)}(\mu). \right.$$

Hence we obtain $p \mid a_k$, $p \mid a_{k-1}, \cdots, p \mid a_1$. This contradicts the assumption that $p \nmid (a_k, \cdots, a_1)$.

§5. PROOF OF THE FUNDAMENTAL LEMMA

The Fundamental Lemma can be restated, in general, in the following clearer and more precise form:

Lemma 1.6. *Let* $f(x) = a_k x^k + \cdots + a_1 x + a_0$. $p \nmid (a_k, \cdots, a_1)$. *Then*

$$|S(p^l, f(x))| \leqslant k^3 p^{(1-a)l}.$$

Proof. Let t be the highest power of p which divides $(ka_k, \cdots, 2a_2, a_1)$. Further, suppose that $\mu_1, \cdots, \mu_r$ are the distinct roots of the congruence

$$f'(x) \equiv 0 \pmod{p^{t+1}}, \qquad 0 \leqslant x < p.$$

Suppose also that their multiplicities are $m_1, \cdots, m_r$ respectively. Letting $m_1 + \cdots + m_r = m$, it is easily seen that $m \leq k - 1$. This lemma is obviously a direct consequence of the inequality

$$|S(p^l, f(x))| \leqslant k^2 \max(1, m) p^{(1-a)l}. \tag{4}$$

Let us now prove the latter inequality by mathematical induction.

Since $p \nmid (a_k, \cdots, a_1)$ and $p^t \| (ka_k, \cdots, 2a_2, a_1)$, we must therefore have $p^t \le k$.

1) Suppose that $l < 2(t+1)$. If $t = 0$, we have $l = 1$. This is a case already discussed. If $t \ge 1$, we obviously have

$$|S(p^l, f(x))| \leqslant p^l \leqslant p^{l(1-a)} \cdot p^{(2t+1)a} \leqslant p^{l(1-a)} k^{(2+1/t)a} \leqslant k^2 p^{l(1-a)},$$

and thus the lemma is established.

2) Suppose that $l \ge 2(t+1)$. Write

$$S(p^l, f(x)) = \sum_{\nu=1}^{p} \sum_{\substack{0 \leqslant x \leqslant p^l - 1 \\ x \equiv \nu \pmod p}} e_{p^l}(f(x)) = \sum_{\nu=1}^{p} S_\nu .$$

If ν is not one of the μ_i, let

$$x = y + p^{l-t-1}z, \qquad 0 \leqslant y < p^{l-t-1}, \qquad 0 \leqslant z < p^{t+1},$$

from which we obtain

$$\begin{aligned} S_\nu = \sum_{\substack{0 \leqslant x < p^l \\ x \equiv \nu \pmod p}} e_{p^l}(f(x)) &= \sum_{\substack{0 \leqslant y < p^{l-t-1} \\ y \equiv \nu \pmod p}} \sum_{0 \leqslant z < p^{t+1}} e_{p^l}(f(y) + y^{l-t-1} z f'(y)) \\ &= \sum_{\substack{0 \leqslant y < p^{l-t-1} \\ y \equiv \nu \pmod p}} e_{p^l}(f(y)) \sum_{z=0}^{p^{t+1}-1} e_{p^{t+1}}(z f'(y)) = 0, \end{aligned} \tag{5}$$

the last equality being the result of $f'(y) \not\equiv 0 \pmod{p^{t+1}}$.

If $\nu \doteq \mu_i$, we define σ_i as in Lemma 1.5 and obtain

$$\begin{aligned} S_{\mu_i} = \sum_{\substack{x=1 \\ x \equiv \mu_i \pmod p}}^{p^l} e_{p^l}(f(x)) &= \sum_{y=1}^{p^{l-1}} e_{p^l}(f(\mu_i + py)) \\ &= e_{p^l}(f(\mu_i)) \sum_{y=1}^{p^{l-1}} e_{p^{l-\sigma_i}}(p^{-\sigma_i}(f(\mu_i + py) - f(\mu_i))) . \end{aligned}$$

Let $g_i(x) = p^{-\sigma_i}(f(\mu_i + px) - f(\mu_i))$. By Lemma 1.5, we know that

$$\begin{aligned} |S_{\mu_i}| &= p^{\sigma_i - 1} |S(p^{l-\sigma_i}, g_i(x))| \\ &\leqslant p^{\sigma_i(1-a)} |S(p^{l-\sigma_i}, g_i(x))| . \end{aligned} \tag{6}$$

From (5) and (6) we obtain

$$|S(p^l, f(x))| \leqslant \sum_{i=1}^{r} p^{\sigma_i(1-a)} |S(p^{l-\sigma_i}, g_i(x))| \,. \tag{7}$$

If $l > \max(\sigma_1, \cdots, \sigma_r)$, we obtain from (7), by induction and by Lemma 1.4,

$$|S(p^l, f(x))| \leqslant \sum_{i=1}^{r} m_i\, p^{\sigma_i(1-a)}\, k^2\, p^{(l-\sigma_i)(1-a)} < m k^2\, p^{l(1-a)} \,.$$

If $l \le \max(\sigma_1, \cdots, \sigma_r)$, then $l \le k$ and

$$|S(p^l, f(x))| \leqslant \sum_{i=1}^{r} p^{\sigma_i - 1}\, p^{l-\sigma_i} \leqslant k\, p^{l(1-a)} \,.$$

Hence the Fundamental Lemma is completely proved.

Therefore the proof of Theorem 1 is also complete.

§6. COROLLARIES

Before we begin the discussion of certain consequences of the Fundamental Lemma we should first introduce the concept of a polynomial with integral values.

Definition. If for any integer x the value of a polynomial $f(x)$ is also an integer, then the polynomial is called a polynomial with integral values.

Lemma 1.7. *Let*

$$\nu!\, F_\nu(x) = x(x-1) \cdots (x-\nu+1) \,.$$

Then the necessary and sufficient condition that a given polynomial be a polynomial with integral values is that it can be expressed in the form

$$a_k F_k(x) + \cdots + a_1 F_1(x) + a_0$$

where $a_k, \cdots, a_1, a_0$ *are all integers.*

Proof. Obviously $F_\nu(x)$ is a polynomial with integral values and therefore $a_k F_k(x) + \cdots + a_1 F_1(x) + a_0$ is also.

Conversely, any polynomial can always be expressed as

$$f(x) = b_k F_k(x) + \cdots + b_1 F_1(x) + b_0 \,.$$

By successively substituting $x = 0, 1, 2, \cdots, k$ in this equation we see that if $f(x)$ is a polynomial with integral values, then all the b's are necessarily integers.

Now let us discuss the corollaries of the theorem and the Fundamental Lemma contained in this chapter.

Corollary 1.1. *Let $f(x)$ be a polynomial of the kth degree with integral values, and let us denote the least common denominator of its coefficients by d. Suppose that $p^t \| d$, and assume that not all the numerators of the coefficients of the nonconstant terms of $f(x)$ are multiples of p. Then*

$$\left| \sum_{x=1}^{p^{l+t}} e_{p^l}(f(x)) \right| \leqslant c_4(k) p^{l(1-a)}.$$

Proof. Since $d \mid k!$, this corollary follows at once.

Corollary 1.2. *Let $f(x)$ be a polynomial of the kth degree with integral values, and let the least common denominator of its coefficients be d. Suppose that for any prime factor p of q not all the numerators of the coefficients of the nonconstant terms of $f(x)$ are multiples of p. Then*

$$\left| \sum_{x=1}^{\bar{q}} e_q(f(x)) \right| \leqslant c_5(k, \varepsilon) q^{1-a+\varepsilon},$$

where $\bar{q} = q \cdot \prod_{\substack{p \mid q \\ p^t \| d}} p^t$.

Corollary 1.3. *With the same hypotheses as in Corollaries 1.1 and 1.2, we have*

$$\left| \sum_{\substack{x=1 \\ p \nmid x}}^{p^{l+t}} e_{p^l}(f(x)) \right| \leqslant c_6(k) p^{(1-a)l}$$

and

$$\left| \sum_{\substack{x=1 \\ (x, q)=1}}^{\bar{q}} e_q(f(x)) \right| \leqslant c_7(k, \varepsilon) q^{1-a+\varepsilon}.$$

Proof. We confine ourselves to the proof of the first inequality, since the second follows immediately from it. Obviously we have

$$\sum_{\substack{x=1 \\ p \nmid x}}^{p^{l+t}} e_{p^l}(f(x)) = \sum_{x=1}^{p^{l+t}} e_{p^l}(f(x)) - \sum_{x=1}^{p^{l+t-1}} e_{p^l}(f(px)).$$

Write

$$df(x) = a_k x^k + \cdots + a_1 x + a_0, \quad p \nmid (a_k, \cdots, a_1).$$

Let p^u be the highest power of p which divides all the coefficients of

$(f(px) - f(0))\,d$. Obviously $1 \le \mu \le k$. Therefore, when $l \ge \mu$,

$$\left|\sum_{x=1}^{p^{l+t-1}} e_{p^l}(f(px))\right| = \left|\sum_{x=1}^{p^{l+t-1}} e_{p^{l-\mu}}(p^{-\mu}(f(px)-f(0)))\right|$$
$$\leqslant p^{\mu-1}\cdot c_4(k)p^{(l-\mu)(1-a)}$$
$$\leqslant c_4(k)p^{l(1-a)-1+\mu a} \leqslant c_4(k)p^{l(1-a)}.$$

If $l < \mu \le k$, we obviously have

$$\left|\sum_{x=1}^{p^{l+t-1}} e_{p^l}(f(px))\right| \leqslant p^{l+t-1} \leqslant k!\,p^{l-1} \leqslant k!\,p^{(1-a)l}.$$

§7. FINITE FOURIER SERIES

Lemma 1.8. *Let*

$$S = \sum_{q'<n\leqslant q''} e(n\alpha), \qquad e(x) = e^{2\pi ix}.$$

Then we obtain

$$|S| \leqslant \min\left(q''-q', \frac{1}{2\{\alpha\}}\right),$$

where $\{\alpha\}$ *denotes the difference between* α *and the nearest integer. In other words,* $\{\alpha\} = \min(\alpha - [\alpha], [\alpha] + 1 - \alpha)$.

Proof. Obviously we have the inequality $|S| \le q'' - q'$. If $\alpha \ne [\alpha]$, let $Q = q'' - q'$. Then we have

$$\left|\sum_{q'<n\leqslant q''} e(n\alpha)\right| = \left|\sum_{n=0}^{Q-1} e(n\alpha)\right| = \left|\frac{1-e(Q\alpha)}{1-e(\alpha)}\right| \leqslant \frac{2}{|1-e(\alpha)|}$$
$$= \frac{1}{|\sin \pi\alpha|} \leqslant \frac{1}{2\{\alpha\}}.$$

(If $0 \le \xi \le 1/2$, then $\sin \pi\xi > 2\xi$, and therefore $|\sin \pi\xi| \ge 2\{\xi\}$.)

Lemma 1.9. *Let* $g(x)$ *be a function having* q *as a period, and*

$$g(x) = \begin{cases} 1 & \text{when } 0 < x \leqslant m, \\ 0 & \text{when } m < x \leqslant q. \end{cases}$$

Then

$$g(x) = \frac{m}{q} + \frac{1}{q}\sum_{n=1}^{q-1} e_q(nx)\sum_{t=1}^{m} e_q(-nt).$$

Proof. Obviously $g(x)$ can be expressed as

$$g(x)=\frac{1}{q}\sum_{n=1}^{q}e_q(nx)\sum_{t=1}^{m}e_q(-nt)$$
$$=\frac{m}{q}+\frac{1}{q}\sum_{n=1}^{q-1}e_q(nx)\sum_{t=1}^{m}e_q(-nt).$$

§8. FORMULATION AND PROOF OF THEOREM 2

Theorem 2. *Suppose that $f(x)=a_kx^k+\cdots+a_1x+a_0$ is a polynomial with integral coefficients. Letting $(a_k,\cdots,a_2,q)=d$, we have*

$$\left|\sum_{x=1}^{m}e_q(f(x))-\frac{m}{q}S(q,f(x))\right|\leqslant c_8(k,\varepsilon)q^{1-a+\varepsilon}d^a.$$

Further, when $1\le m\le q$, we have

$$\left|\sum_{x=1}^{m}e_q(f(x))\right|\leqslant c_9(k,\varepsilon)q^{1-a+\varepsilon}d^a.$$

Proof. We know by Lemma 1.9 that

$$\sum_{x=1}^{m}e_q(f(x))=\sum_{x=1}^{q}e_q(f(x))g(x)$$
$$=\frac{m}{q}S(q,f(x))+\frac{1}{q}\sum_{x=1}^{q}e_q(f(x))\sum_{n=1}^{q-1}e_q(nx)\sum_{t=1}^{m}e_q(-nt).$$

Thus (by Lemma 1.8) we obtain

$$\left|\sum_{x=1}^{m}e_q(f(x))-\frac{m}{q}S(q,f(x))\right|\leqslant\frac{1}{q}\sum_{n=1}^{q-1}\frac{1}{2\left\{\frac{n}{q}\right\}}\left|\sum_{x=1}^{q}e_q(f(x)+nx)\right|.$$

Setting $(d,a_1+n)=q'$, we see by Theorem 1 that

$$\frac{1}{q}\sum_{n=1}^{q-1}\frac{1}{2\left\{\frac{n}{q}\right\}}\left|\sum_{x=1}^{q}e_q(f(x)+nx)\right|\leqslant\frac{1}{q}\sum_{q'|d}\sum_{\substack{n=1\\a_1+n\equiv0\,(\mathrm{mod}\,q')}}^{q-1}\frac{1}{2\left\{\frac{n}{q}\right\}}\left|\sum_{x=1}^{q}e_{q/q'}\left(\frac{f(x)+nx}{q'}\right)\right|$$
$$\ll\frac{1}{q}\sum_{q'|d}\sum_{\substack{n=1\\a_1+n\equiv0\,(\mathrm{mod}\,q')}}^{q-1}\frac{1}{\left\{\frac{n}{q}\right\}}q'\left(\frac{q}{q'}\right)^{1-a+\epsilon}$$
$$\ll q^{1-a+\epsilon}\Bigg(\sum_{q'|d}q'^a\Bigg(\sum_{\substack{1\leqslant n\leqslant q/2\\a_1+n\equiv0\,(\mathrm{mod}\,q')}}\frac{1}{n}+\sum_{\substack{1\leqslant n\leqslant q/2\\a_1-n\equiv0\,(\mathrm{mod}\,q')}}\frac{1}{n}\Bigg)\Bigg)$$
$$\ll q^{1-a+\epsilon}\sum_{q'|d}q'^{\,a}\ll q^{1-a+\epsilon}d^a.$$

CHAPTER II

ESTIMATES FOR SUMS INVOLVING THE DIVISOR FUNCTION $d(n)$

§1. FORMULATION OF THEOREM 3

The object of this chapter is to prove the following theorem.

Theorem 3. *Let $f(x_1, x_2, \cdots, x_n)$ be a polynomial of the kth degree with integral coefficients, and suppose that the greatest common divisor of all the coefficients is* 1. *Then*

$$\sum_{\substack{x_1=1\\ f(x_1,\cdots,x_n)\neq 0}}^{P} \cdots \sum_{x_n=1}^{P} d^l(|f(x_1,\cdots,x_n)|) \leqslant c_1(k,n,l)\, A\, (\log X)^{c_2(k,n,l)},$$

where X is the maximum value of $|f(x_1, \cdots, x_n)|$ with $1 \leq x_1, \cdots, x_n \leq P$ and $A = \max(P^n, X^{n/k})$.

Note that c_1 and c_2 are independent of the coefficients of $f(x_1, \cdots, x_n)$. From this theorem it is easy to deduce a broader conclusion as follows:

Let $f(x_1, \cdots, x_n)$ denote a polynomial of the kth degree with integral coefficients. Let m denote the greatest common divisor of all its coefficients. Then

$$\sum_{\substack{x_1=1\\ f(x_1,\cdots,x_n)\neq 0}}^{P} \cdots \sum_{x_n=1}^{P} d^l(|f(x_1,\cdots,x_n)|) \leqslant c_1(k,n,l)\, A\, (\log X)^{c_2(k,n,l)}\, d^l(m).$$

The proof of Theorem 3 depends on van der Corput's lemma (§2) and on results concerning the trigonometric sums of Chapter I.

§2. VAN DER CORPUT'S LEMMA [1)]

Lemma 2.1. *Suppose that there exist positive numbers A and γ such that*

$$\sum_{\substack{y=1\\ v|y}}^{X} T(y) \leqslant A \prod_{\sigma=1}^{s} \frac{x(p_\sigma, \alpha_\sigma)}{p_\sigma}, \qquad v = p_1^{\alpha_1} \cdots p_s^{\alpha_s} \leqslant X^{\gamma},$$

---

1) *Une inégalité relative au nombre des diviseurs*, Nederl. Akad. Wetensch. Proc. 42 (1939), 547–553; MR 1, 41.

with $T(y) \geq 0$, $x(p_\sigma, \alpha_\sigma) \geq 0$; *also*

$$\sum_{\alpha=1}^{\infty} (\alpha+1)^{(1+2/\gamma)l} x(p, \alpha) \leqslant C,$$

where C *is independent of the prime* p. *Further, when* $v = 1$, $s = 0$, *we have the inequality*

$$\sum_{y=1}^{X} T(y) \leqslant A.$$

Then

$$S = \sum_{y=1}^{X} d^l(y) T(y) \leqslant c_3(l, C, \gamma) A (\log X)^C.$$

Proof. Write y as $y = P_1 P_2 \cdots P_m w$, where P runs through all prime factors of y greater than X^γ. Let v_1 denote the greatest factor of w which is not greater than X^γ, let v_2 denote the greatest factor of w/v_1 which is not greater than X^γ, and so forth. Suppose that this process ends at the nth step; then y can be expressed as

$$y = P_1 \cdots P_m v_1 \cdots v_n.$$

The n in question will be called the index of y, and $v_1, \cdots, v_n$ will be called the characteristic factors of y.

Obviously, we have $v_{n-1} \geq X^{\gamma/2}$. Hence we obtain

$$X^{\gamma m} \leqslant P_1 \cdots P_m \leqslant X, \quad X^{\frac{1}{2}(n-1)\gamma} \leqslant v_1 \cdots v_{n-1} \leqslant X,$$

and accordingly

$$m \leqslant \frac{1}{\gamma}, \qquad n \leqslant 1 + \frac{2}{\gamma}.$$

Since $d(\lambda\mu) \leq d(\lambda) d(\mu)$, we see that

$$d(y) \leqslant 2^m d(v_1) \cdots d(v_n) \leqslant 2^{1/\gamma} d(v_1) \cdots d(v_n).$$

Obviously we have

$$d^l(y) \leqslant \begin{cases} 2^{l/\gamma} & \text{if } n = 0, \\ 2^{l/\gamma} \max_\nu d^{ln}(v_\nu) \leqslant 2^{l/\gamma} \sum_{\nu=1}^{n} d^{ln}(v_\nu) & \text{if } n > 0. \end{cases}$$

Write

$$S = \sum_{y=1}^{X} d^l(y) T(y) = \sum_{0 \leqslant n \leqslant 1+2/\gamma} U_n,$$

where U_n denotes the part of this sum which is taken over the integers y with index n.

When $n = 0$,

$$U_0 \leqslant 2^{l/\gamma} \sum_{y=1}^{X} T(y) \leqslant 2^{l/\gamma} A.$$

If $1 \leq n \leq 1 + 2/\gamma$, then

$$U_n \leqslant 2^{l/\gamma} \sum_{\nu=1}^{n} U_{n\nu},$$

in which

$$U_{n\nu} = \sum_{y=1}^{X}{}' d^{ln}(v_\nu) T(y),$$

where $\sum_{y=1}^{X}{}'$ means summation over the integers y with index n, and v_ν is the νth characteristic factor. Since $2 \leq v_\nu \leq X^\gamma$, it follows that

$$U_{n\nu} \leqslant \sum_{2 \leqslant v \leqslant X^\gamma} d^{ln}(v) \sum_{y=1}^{X}{}'' T(y),$$

where $\sum_{y=1}^{X}{}''$ means summation over those integers y with index n that have v as their νth characteristic factor. Therefore,

$$\sum_{y=1}^{X}{}'' T(y) \leqslant \sum_{\substack{y=1 \\ v \mid y}}^{X} T(y) \leqslant A \prod_{\sigma=1}^{s} \frac{x(p_\sigma, a_\sigma)}{p_\sigma}.$$

Since $d(v) = (\alpha_1 + 1)(\alpha_2 + 1) \cdots (\alpha_s + 1)$, we see that

$$U_{n\nu} \leqslant A \sum_{2 \leqslant v \leqslant X^\gamma} \prod_{\sigma=1}^{s} \frac{(a_\sigma + 1)^{ln} x(p_\sigma, a_\sigma)}{p_\sigma}$$

$$\leqslant A \prod_{p \leqslant X^\gamma} \left(1 + \sum_{a=1}^{\infty} \frac{(a+1)^{ln} x(p, a)}{p}\right)$$

$$\leqslant A e^R \leqslant c_3' A e^{c \log \log X} \leqslant c_3' A (\log X)^c,$$

where $R = c \sum_{p \leq X^\gamma} 1/p$. Substituting this in the expressions for U_n and S, we accordingly obtain the lemma.

(Note that in the proof we have used the equality

$$\sum_{p \leq X} \frac{1}{p} = \log \log X + O(1),$$

which is a consequence of the prime number theorem; of course it is also a consequence of Lemma 7.14.)

§3. LEMMAS PERTAINING TO THE NUMBER OF SOLUTIONS OF CONGRUENCES

Lemma 2.2. *Let $f(x_1, \cdots, x_n)$ be a polynomial of the kth degree with integral coefficients. Further, suppose that not all its coefficients are multiples of* p. *Then the number of solutions of the congruence*

$$f(x_1, \cdots, x_n) \equiv 0 \pmod{p^a}$$

is $\leq c_4(k, n) p^{n\alpha - 1}$.

Proof. 1) When $n = 1$, this lemma is obviously true, since the number of roots of the congruence

$$f(x) \equiv 0 \pmod{p}$$

does not exceed k, and therefore the number of solutions of the original congruence is $\leq kp^{\alpha - 1}$.

2) Write the congruence $f(x_1, \cdots, x_n) \equiv 0 \pmod{p^{\alpha}}$ as

$$f_s(x_1, \cdots, x_{n-1}) x_n^s + \cdots + f_0(x_1, \cdots, x_{n-1}) \equiv 0 \pmod{p^a}.$$

We shall prove the lemma by mathematical induction. Suppose that the lemma is true for $n - 1$ variables. Then we may assume that the number of solutions of

$$f_s(x_1, \cdots, x_{n-1}) \equiv 0 \pmod{p^a}$$

is $O(p^{(n-1)\alpha - 1})$. But when $f_s(x_1, \cdots, x_{n-1}) \not\equiv 0 \pmod{p^{\alpha}}$ the number of values of x_n is not greater than $O(p^{\alpha - 1})$. Therefore, the number of solutions of the congruence in question is $\leq c_4(k, n) p^{n\alpha - 1}$.

Lemma 2.3. *By the hypotheses of Lemma 2.2, the number of solutions of the congruence*

$$f(x_1, \cdots, x_n) \equiv 0 \pmod{p^a}$$

is $\leq c_5(k, n)(\alpha + 1)^{n-1} p^{n\alpha - \alpha a}$, *where* $a = 1/k$.

Proof. 1) When $n = 1$, the number of solutions of the congruence

$$f(x) \equiv 0 \pmod{p^a}$$

is equal to

$$\frac{1}{p^a} \sum_{h=1}^{p^a} \sum_{x=1}^{p^a} e_{p^a}(h f(x)), \qquad e_q(x) = e^{2\pi i x/q}.$$

Let

$$f(x) = a_k x^k + \cdots + a_1 x + a_0.$$

If $p|(a_k, \cdots, a_1)$ with $p \nmid a_0$, then this congruence is insolvable and the lemma obviously holds. Now suppose that $p \nmid (a_k, \cdots, a_1)$. By Lemma 1.1,

$$\left| \frac{1}{p^a} \sum_{h=1}^{p^a} \sum_{x=1}^{p^a} e_{p^a}(h f(x)) \right| \leqslant \frac{1}{p^a} \sum_{h=1}^{p^a} \left| \sum_{x=1}^{p^a} e_{p^a}(h f(x)) \right| =$$

$$= \frac{1}{p^a} \sum_{\lambda=0}^{a} \sum_{\substack{h=1 \\ p^\lambda \| h}}^{p^a} \left| \sum_{x=1}^{p^a} e_{p^a}(h f(x)) \right| = O\left(\frac{1}{p^a} \sum_{\lambda=0}^{a} p^{a-\lambda} \cdot p^\lambda \cdot p^{(a-\lambda)(1-a)} \right)$$

$$= O\left(p^{a(1-a)}\right),$$

where we have used

$$\sum_{\lambda=0}^{a} p^{-\lambda(1-a)} = O(1).$$

2) Induction. Write the congruence

$$f(x_1, \cdots, x_n) \equiv 0 \pmod{p^a}$$

as

$$g_k x_n^k + \cdots + g_0 \equiv 0 \pmod{p^a}, \quad g_\nu = g_\nu(x_1, \cdots, x_{n-1}).$$

Let us now discuss those systems of integers $x_1, \cdots, x_{n-1}$ for which either

$$p^\lambda \| (g_k, \cdots, g_0), \qquad a > \lambda > 0, \tag{1}$$

or $p^a | (g_k, \cdots, g_0)$. In the latter case, the number of solutions is

$$O\left((a+1)^{n-2} p^{(n-1)a - aa} p^a\right) = O\left((a+1)^{n-2} p^{na - aa}\right).$$

Now let us discuss case (1). The coefficients in at least one of the g's, call it g_μ, are not all multiples of p. Suppose by induction that the number of solutions satisfying

$$g_\mu \equiv 0 \pmod{p^\lambda}, \qquad 0 \leqslant x_\nu < p^a, \qquad 1 \leqslant \nu \leqslant n-1$$

is at most

$$O\left((a+1)^{n-2} p^{(n-1)(a-\lambda)+(n-1)\lambda-\lambda a}\right) = O\left((a+1)^{n-2} p^{(n-1)a-\lambda a}\right),$$

i.e., the number of sets of $x_1, \cdots, x_{n-1}$ satisfying (1) is $O((a+1)^{n-2} p^{(n-1)a-\lambda a})$. For each set $x_1, \cdots, x_{n-1}$ which satisfies (1) the congruence

$$\frac{g_k}{p^\lambda} x_n^k + \cdots + \frac{g_0}{p^\lambda} \equiv 0 \pmod{p^{a-\lambda}}, \quad 0 < x_n \leqslant p^a,$$

is satisfied by not more than $O(p^{\lambda+(a-\lambda)(1-a)}) = O(p^{a-(a-\lambda)a})$ values of x_n.

Therefore the number of solutions of the congruence in the lemma that satisfy (1) is

$$O\left((a+1)^{n-2} p^{(n-1)a-\lambda a} p^{a-(a-\lambda)a}\right) = O\left((a+1)^{n-2} p^{na-aa}\right).$$

Obviously this conclusion is also true when $\lambda = 0$. Therefore the number of solutions of the congruence in the lemma is

$$O\left(\sum_{\lambda=0}^{a} (a+1)^{n-2} p^{na-aa}\right) = O\left((a+1)^{n-1} p^{na-aa}\right).$$

§4. PROOF OF THE THEOREM

Take $T(y)$ in Lemma 2.1 to be the number of solutions of

$$|f(x_1, \cdots, x_n)| = y, \qquad 1 \leqslant x_\nu \leqslant P.$$

Then we obtain

$$\sum_{\substack{x_1=1 \\ f(x_1, \cdots, x_n) \neq 0}}^{P} \cdots \sum_{x_n=1}^{P} d^l(|f(x_1, \cdots, x_n)|) = \sum_{y=1}^{X} d^l(y) T(y),$$

where X is the maximum value of $|f(x_1, \cdots, x_n)|$ for $1 \le x_1, \cdots, x_n \le P$.

Let $y = a$ and

$$x(p, a) = \begin{cases} O(1) & \text{when } a \leqslant k, \\ O\left((a+1)^{n-1} p^{1-aa}\right) & \text{when } a > k. \end{cases}$$

Then

$$\sum_{y=1}^{X} T(y) = \sum_{x_1=1}^{P} \cdots \sum_{x_n=1}^{P} 1 = P^n \leqslant A.$$

Furthermore

$$\sum_{\substack{y=1 \\ v|y}}^{X} T(y) \leqslant \left(\frac{P}{v} + 1\right)^n M,$$

where M is the number of solutions of

$$f(x_1, \cdots, x_n) \equiv 0 \pmod{v}.$$

But the number of solutions of this congruence is the product of those of the congruences

$$f(x_1, \cdots, x_n) \equiv 0 \pmod{p_\sigma^{\alpha_\sigma}}, \qquad \sigma = 1, \cdots, s.$$

Therefore by Lemmas 2.2 and 2.3 we have

$$\sum_{\substack{y=1 \\ v|y}}^{X} T(y) = O\left(\left(\frac{P}{v}+1\right)^n \prod_{\sigma=1}^{s} p_\sigma^{n\alpha_\sigma} \frac{\chi(p_\sigma, \alpha_\sigma)}{p_\sigma}\right)$$

$$= O\left(A \prod_{\sigma=1}^{s} \frac{\chi(p_\sigma, \alpha_\sigma)}{p_\sigma}\right).$$

Since

$$\sum_{\alpha=1}^{\infty} (\alpha+1)^{(1+2/\gamma)l} \chi(p, \alpha)$$

$$= O\left(\sum_{\alpha \leqslant k} (\alpha+1)^{(1+2k)l} + \sum_{\alpha > k} (\alpha+1)^{(1+2k)l+n-1} p^{1-\alpha\alpha}\right) = O(1),$$

our theorem is accordingly proved.

§5. FURTHER LEMMAS

For future reference we shall prove two more precise results regarding the divisor function $d(n)$.

Lemma 2.4. *Let t be a positive integer; then*

$$\sum_{0<z\leqslant P} \frac{(d(z))^t}{z} \leqslant c_6(t) (\log P)^{2^t}.$$

Proof. When $t = 0$, the statement is obviously valid. Now suppose that it is valid for $t-1$. Then

$$\sum_{0<z\leqslant P} \frac{(d(z))^t}{z} = \sum_{0<z\leqslant P} \frac{(d(z))^{t-1}}{z} \sum_{\lambda|z} 1 = \sum_{0<\lambda\leqslant P} \sum_{\substack{0<z\leqslant P \\ \lambda|z}} \frac{(d(z))^{t-1}}{z}$$

$$\leqslant \sum_{0<\lambda\leqslant P} \frac{(d(\lambda))^{t-1}}{\lambda} \sum_{0<\mu\leqslant P/\lambda} \frac{(d(\mu))^{t-1}}{\mu} \leqslant (c_6(t-1))^2 (\log P)^{2^t}.$$

Lemma 2.5. *Let t be a positive integer; then*

$$\sum_{0<z\leqslant P} (d(z))^t \leqslant c_7(t) P (\log P)^{2^t-1}.$$

Proof. By Lemma 2.4 and by induction, we know that

$$\sum_{0<z\leqslant P} (d(z))^t = \sum_{0<z\leqslant P} (d(z))^{t-1} \sum_{\lambda|z} 1 = \sum_{0<\lambda\leqslant P} \sum_{\substack{0<z\leqslant P \\ \lambda|z}} (d(z))^{t-1}$$

$$\leqslant \sum_{0<\lambda\leqslant P} (d(\lambda))^{t-1} \sum_{0<\mu\leqslant P/\lambda} (d(\mu))^{t-1}$$

$$= O\Big(\sum_{0<\lambda\leqslant P} (d(\lambda))^{t-1} \frac{P}{\lambda} (\log P)^{2^{t-1}-1}\Big) = O\Big(P (\log P)^{2^t-1}\Big).$$

CHAPTER III

MEAN-VALUE THEOREMS FOR CERTAIN TRIGONOMETRIC SUMS (I)

§1. FORMULATION OF THEOREM 4

Theorem 4. *Let $f(x)$ denote a polynomial of the kth degree with integral values, and set*

$$T(\alpha) = \sum_{x=1}^{P} e(f(x)\alpha).$$

Then when $1 \le \nu \le k$, we have

$$\int_0^1 |T(\alpha)|^{2^\nu} d\alpha \leqslant c_1(k, \nu) P^{2^\nu - \nu} (\log P)^{c_2(k,\nu)} d^{\nu-1}(u),$$

where u is the greatest common divisor of the numerators of the coefficients of $f(x)$, and the notation $c(k, \nu)$ indicates that c depends only on k and ν and not on the coefficients of $f(x)$.

Remark. Since

$$g(\lambda) = \log\left(\int_0^1 |T(\alpha)|^\lambda d\alpha\right)$$

is a convex function, we can obtain an inequality for certain λ. To be more specific, when $2^\nu < \lambda \le 2^{\nu+1}$, we have the inequality

$$\int_0^1 |T(\alpha)|^\lambda d\alpha \leqslant \left(\int_0^1 |T(\alpha)|^{2^\nu} d\alpha\right)^{2-2^{-\nu}\lambda} \left(\int_0^1 |T(\alpha)|^{2^{\nu+1}} d\alpha\right)^{2^{-\nu}\lambda-1}.$$

Since this result will not be used later, no attempt will be made here to prove it.

§2. CERTAIN LEMMAS PERTAINING TO INEQUALITIES

Lemma 3.1. *If $\alpha + \beta = 1$, $\alpha > 0$, $\beta > 0$, $s \ge 0$, $t \ge 0$, then*

$$s^\alpha t^\beta \leqslant s\alpha + t\beta. \tag{1}$$

More generally, if $\alpha_1 + \cdots + \alpha_n = 1$, $\alpha_1 > 0, \cdots, \alpha_n > 0$, $s_1 \ge 0, \cdots, s_n \ge 0$, then

$$s_1^{\alpha_1}\cdots s_n^{\alpha_n}\leqslant s_1\alpha_1+\cdots+s_n\alpha_n. \tag{2}$$

Proof. 1) When $x>1$, $0<m<1$, we have

$$x^m-1=m\int_1^x y^{m-1}\,dy\leqslant m\int_1^x dy=m(x-1).$$

Taking $x=s/t$ $(s>t)$, $m=\alpha$ and $1-m=\beta$, we obtain (1).

2) We know from (1) that (2) is valid when $n=2$. Now let us proceed by induction. Suppose that (2) is valid for $n-1$. Then

$$s_1^{\alpha_1}\cdots s_n^{\alpha_n}=\left(s_1^{\frac{\alpha_1}{1-\alpha_n}}\cdots s_{n-1}^{\frac{\alpha_{n-1}}{1-\alpha_n}}\right)^{1-\alpha_n}s_n^{\alpha_n}\leqslant\left(s_1^{\frac{\alpha_1}{1-\alpha_n}}\cdots s_{n-1}^{\frac{\alpha_{n-1}}{1-\alpha_n}}\right)(1-\alpha_n)$$

$$+s_n\alpha_n\leqslant\left(s_1\frac{\alpha_1}{1-\alpha_n}+\cdots+s_{n-1}\frac{\alpha_{n-1}}{1-\alpha_n}\right)(1-\alpha_n)+s_n\alpha_n$$

$$=s_1\alpha_1+\cdots+s_{n-1}\alpha_{n-1}+s_n\alpha_n.$$

This is (2).

Lemma 3.2. *If* $\alpha+\beta=1$, $\alpha>0$, $\beta>0$, *then for real* a_n *and* b_n $(1\le n\le r)$ *we always have*

$$\left|\sum_{n=1}^r a_n b_n\right|\leqslant\left(\sum_{n=1}^r|a_n|^{\frac{1}{\alpha}}\right)^\alpha\left(\sum_{n=1}^r|b_n|^{\frac{1}{\beta}}\right)^\beta.$$

(In the proofs below, this statement will be called Hölder's inequality, and the special case $\alpha=\beta=1/2$ will be called the Bunjakovski, Cauchy or Schwarz inequality.)

Proof. We know by Lemma 3.1 that

$$\frac{\sum_{n=1}^r|a_n b_n|}{\left(\sum_{n=1}^r|a_n|^{\frac{1}{\alpha}}\right)^\alpha\left(\sum_{n=1}^r|b_n|^{\frac{1}{\beta}}\right)^\beta}=\sum_{n=1}^r\left(\frac{|a_n|^{\frac{1}{\alpha}}}{\sum_{n=1}^r|a_n|^{\frac{1}{\alpha}}}\right)^\alpha\left(\frac{|b_n|^{\frac{1}{\beta}}}{\sum_{n=1}^r|b_n|^{\frac{1}{\beta}}}\right)^\beta$$

$$\leqslant\sum_{n=1}^r\left(\frac{\alpha|a_n|^{\frac{1}{\alpha}}}{\sum_{n=1}^r|a_n|^{\frac{1}{\alpha}}}+\frac{\beta|b_n|^{\frac{1}{\beta}}}{\sum_{n=1}^r|b_n|^{\frac{1}{\beta}}}\right)=\alpha+\beta=1.$$

Lemma 3.3. *Let*

$$\mathop{\Delta}_{y}Q(x)=\frac{1}{y}\left(Q(x+y)-Q(x)\right),\quad I=\sum_{x=1}^P e(f(x)),$$

and let the symbol Σ_x^P *denote a sum*[1] *which we split up into* $\leq c_2(k)$ *sections, in each of which the variable of summation* x *runs through* $\leq P$ *consecutive integers. Then when* $\mu = 1, 2, \cdots, k$ *we have the inequality*

$$|I|^{2^\mu} \leqslant c_3(\mu)\, P^{2^\mu-\mu-1} \sum_{y_1}^{P} \cdots \sum_{y_\mu}^{P} \sum_{x_{\mu+1}}^{P} e\,(y_1 \cdots y_\mu \underset{y_\mu}{\Delta} \cdots \underset{y_1}{\Delta} f(x_{\mu+1}))\,.$$

Proof. By the equality

$$|I|^2 = \sum_{x_1=1}^{P} \sum_{x_2=1}^{P} e\,(f(x_1) - f(x_2))$$

$$= \sum_{x_2}^{P} \sum_{y_1}^{P} e\,(f(x_2+y_1) - f(x_2))$$

$$= \sum_{y_1}^{P} \sum_{x_2}^{P} e\,(y_1 \underset{y_1}{\Delta} f(x_2))\,,$$

we know that the lemma is true when $\mu = 1$.

Now suppose that this lemma is true for $\mu - 1$. Using Cauchy's inequality, we obtain

$$|I|^{2^\mu} = (|I|^{2^{\mu-1}})^2$$

$$\leqslant (c_3(\mu-1))^2 P^{2(2^{\mu-1}-\mu)} \left| \sum_{y_1}^{P} \cdots \sum_{y_{\mu-1}}^{P} \sum_{x_\mu}^{P} e\,(y_1 \cdots y_{\mu-1} \underset{y_{\mu-1}}{\Delta} \cdots \underset{y_1}{\Delta} f(x_\mu)) \right|^2$$

$$\ll P^{2^\mu-2\mu} P^{\mu-1} \sum_{y_1}^{P} \cdots \sum_{y_{\mu-1}}^{P} \left| \sum_{x_\mu}^{P} e\,(y_1 \cdots y_{\mu-1} \underset{y_{\mu-1}}{\Delta} \cdots \underset{y_1}{\Delta} f(x_\mu)) \right|^2$$

$$\ll P^{2^\mu-\mu-1} \sum_{y_1}^{P} \cdots \sum_{y_\mu}^{P} \sum_{x_{\mu+1}}^{P} e\,(y_1 \cdots y_\mu \underset{y_\mu}{\Delta} \cdots \underset{y_1}{\Delta} f(x_{\mu+1}))\,.$$

Lemma 3.4. *If* $Q(x)$ *is a polynomial of the kth degree with leading coefficient* α, *then* $\Delta_y Q(x)$ *is a polynomial of the* $(k-1)$*th degree in* x *with* $k\alpha$ *as its leading coefficient. Hence we deduce that*

$$\underset{y_1}{\Delta} \cdots \underset{y_{k-1}}{\Delta} Q(x) = k!\,\alpha x + \beta,$$

$$\underset{y_1}{\Delta} \cdots \underset{y_k}{\Delta} Q(x) = k!\,\alpha.$$

The proof of the lemma is obvious.

---

1) In what follows this symbol will be used throughout.

§3. PROOF OF THE THEOREM

We can assume without loss of generality that $f(x)$ is a polynomial with integral coefficients. For suppose that q is the least common denominator of the coefficients of $f(x)$; then by Hölder's inequality (Lemma 3.2), we obtain

$$\int_0^1 |T(\alpha)|^\lambda d\alpha = \int_0^1 \left| \sum_{t=1}^{q} \sum_{x=0}^{[(P-t)/q]} e(f(qx+t)\alpha) \right|^\lambda d\alpha$$

$$\leqslant q^{\lambda-1} \sum_{t=1}^{q} \int_0^1 \left| \sum_{x=0}^{[(P-t)/q]} e((f(qx+t)-f(t))\alpha) \right|^\lambda d\alpha,$$

where $f(qx+t)-f(t)$ is a polynomial with integral coefficients. Also note that $q \le k!$.

The theorem is obvious when $\nu = 1$. By Lemma 3.3, we obtain

$$|T(\alpha)|^{2^\mu} \ll P^{2^\mu - 1} + P^{2^\mu - \mu - 1} \sum_{y_1}^{P} \cdots \sum_{y_\mu}^{P} \sum_{x_{\mu+1}}^{P}{}^{*} e(y_1 \cdots y_\mu \underset{y_\mu}{\Delta} \cdots \underset{y_1}{\Delta} f(x_{\mu+1})\alpha), \tag{1}$$

where the asterisk means that

$$y_1 \cdots y_\mu \underset{y_\mu}{\Delta} \cdots \underset{y_1}{\Delta} f(x_{\mu+1}) \neq 0.$$

Here, by the use of $y_1 \cdots y_\mu \Delta_{y_\mu} \cdots \Delta_{y_1} f(x_{\mu+1}) = 0$, we know that there is some ν such that $y_\nu = 0$ or $\Delta_{y_\mu} \cdots \Delta_{y_1} f(x_{\mu+1}) = 0$. Since the highest coefficient of $\Delta_{y_\mu} \cdots \Delta_{y_1} f(x_{\mu+1})$ is not zero, we therefore obtain the inequality (1).

Multiplying both members of the inequality by $|T(\alpha)|^{2^\mu}$ and integrating with respect to α from 0 to 1, we accordingly obtain

$$\left.\begin{aligned} &\int_0^1 |T(\alpha)|^{2^{\mu+1}} d\alpha \ll P^{2^\mu - 1} \int_0^1 |T(\alpha)|^{2^\mu} d\alpha \\ &+ P^{2^\mu-\mu-1} \int_0^1 \sum_{y_1}^{P} \cdots \sum_{y_\mu}^{P} \sum_{x_{\mu+1}}^{P}{}^{*} e(y_1 \cdots y_\mu \underset{y_\mu}{\Delta} \cdots \underset{y_1}{\Delta} f(x_{\mu+1})\alpha) |T(\alpha)|^{2^\mu} d\alpha. \end{aligned}\right\} \tag{2}$$

By the induction hypothesis we know that the first term of the right side of the form (2) is

$$O(P^{2^\mu-1} P^{2^\mu-\mu} (\log P)^{c_2(k,\mu)} (d(u))^{\mu-1})$$
$$= O(P^{2^{\mu+1}-\mu-1} (\log P)^{c_2(k,\mu)} (d(u))^{\mu-1}).$$

The second term of the right side of the form (2) is equal to

$$P^{2^\mu-\mu-1}\int_0^1 \sum_{y_1}^{P}\cdots\sum_{y_\mu}^{P}\sum_{x_{\mu+1}}^{P}{}^{*}\sum_{z_1}^{P}\cdots\sum_{z_{2^\mu}}^{P} e\big((y_1\cdots y_\mu \underset{y_\mu}{\Delta}\cdots\underset{y_1}{\Delta} f(x_{\mu+1})$$

$$-f(z_1)-\cdots-f(z_{2^{\mu-1}})+f(z_{2^{\mu-1}+1})+\cdots+f(z_{2^\mu}))\,\alpha\big)\,d\alpha$$

$$=P^{2^\mu-\mu-1}R,$$

where R is the number of solutions of the system

$$\left.\begin{aligned} &y_1\cdots y_\mu \underset{y_\mu}{\Delta}\cdots\underset{y_1}{\Delta} f(x_{\mu+1})=f(z_1)+\cdots+f(z_{2^{\mu-1}})-f(z_{2^{\mu-1}+1})-\cdots-f(z_{2^\mu}),\\ &\qquad y_1\cdots y_\mu \underset{y_\mu}{\Delta}\cdots\underset{y_1}{\Delta} f(x_{\mu+1})\neq 0,\quad z_\nu,\,y_\nu,\,x_{\nu+1}\ll P.\end{aligned}\right\}\quad(3)$$

For given $z_1,\cdots,z_{2\mu}$ the number of solutions of (3) is

$$\ll d^\mu\,(f(z_1)+\cdots+f(z_{2^{\mu-1}})-f(z_{2^{\mu-1}+1})-\cdots-f(z_{2^\mu})).$$

By Theorem 3, we know that

$$R\ll\sum_{z_1}^{P}\cdots\sum_{z_{2^\mu}}^{P}{}^{**}d^\mu\,(f(z_1)+\cdots-f(z_{2^\mu}))$$

$$\ll d^\mu(u)\,P^{2^\mu}\,(\log P)^{c_2(k,\mu)},$$

where the double asterisk means that $f(z_1)+\cdots-f(z_{2\mu})\neq 0$. Thus the theorem is proved.

§4. WEYL'S LEMMA

Lemma 3.5. *Let* $q>0$,

$$\left|\alpha-\frac{h}{q}\right|\leqslant\frac{1}{q^2},\qquad (h,q)=1,$$

and

$$Q=\sum_{x=f+1}^{f+q}\min\left(U,\frac{1}{2\{\alpha x\}}\right).$$

Then

$$Q<6U+q\log q.$$

Proof. Set $\alpha=h/q+\theta/q^2$, $|\theta|\le 1$. Letting $x=x_1+f$, we have $1\le x_1\le q$. Write αf in the form

$$\alpha f=\frac{b}{q}+\frac{\theta'}{q},\quad |\theta'|\leqslant 1,$$

where b is an integer.

Since $x_1 \le q$, we obtain

$$\{\alpha x\} = \{\alpha x_1 + \alpha f\} = \left\{\frac{h x_1}{q} + \frac{\theta x_1}{q^2} + \frac{b}{q} + \frac{\theta'}{q}\right\} = \left\{\frac{\rho + 2\theta''}{q}\right\}, \quad |\theta''| \leqslant 1,$$

where ρ denotes the residue of least absolute value obtained by dividing $hx_1 + b$ by q.

Since $(h, q) = 1$, if x_1 runs through a complete set of residues modulo q, then ρ runs through the values $0, 1, \cdots, [q/2]$, with each value occurring not more than twice.

We substitute U for the terms in Ω for which $\rho \le 2$; the other terms can be expressed in the form

$$\rho = 2 + s, \quad 0 < s \leqslant \frac{1}{2} q - 2.$$

Hence

$$\left\{\frac{\rho + 2\theta''}{q}\right\} > \frac{s}{q}.$$

Therefore

$$\Omega \leqslant 6U + 2 \sum_{s=1}^{[\frac{1}{2}q-2]} \frac{1}{\frac{2s}{q}} < 6U + q \log q.$$

Lemma 3.6 (Weyl). *If* $\alpha_k, \cdots, \alpha_0$ *are real,*

$$f(x) = \alpha_k x^k + \cdots + \alpha_1 x + \alpha_0,$$

$$\left|\alpha_k - \frac{h}{q}\right| \leqslant \frac{1}{q^2}, \quad (h, q) = 1,$$

then

$$S = \sum_{x=1}^{P} e(f(x)) \ll P^{1+\varepsilon} q^{\varepsilon} \left(\frac{1}{P} + \frac{1}{q} + \frac{q}{P^k}\right)^{2^{1-k}}.$$

Proof. By Lemmas 3.3 and 3.4, we obtain

$$|S|^{2^{k-1}} \ll P^{2^{k-1}-k} \sum_{y_1}^{P} \cdots \sum_{y_{k-1}}^{P} \sum_{x_k}^{P} e\left(\underset{y_{k-1}}{\Delta} \cdots \underset{y_1}{\Delta} f(x_k)\right)$$

$$\ll P^{2^{k-1}-k} \sum_{y_1}^{P} \cdots \sum_{y_{k-1}}^{P} \left| \sum_{x_k}^{P} e(k!\, y_1 \cdots y_{k-1} x_k \alpha_k) \right| \ll$$

$$\ll P^{2^{k-1}-1} + P^{2^{k-1}-k} \sum_{y_1}^{P} \cdots \sum_{y_{k-1}}^{P}{}^{*} \left| \sum_{x_k}^{P} e(k!\, y_1 \cdots y_{k-1} x_k \alpha_k) \right| ,$$

where the asterisk means $y_1 \cdots y_{k-1} \neq 0$. Since by Lemma 1.2 we know that the number of solutions of

$$k!\, y_1 \cdots y_{k-1} = Y , \qquad Y \ll P^{k-1} ,$$

is $\leq (d(Y))^{k-1} = O(P^{\epsilon})$, it follows that

$$|S|^{2^{k-1}} \ll P^{2^{k-1}-1} + P^{2^{k-1}-k+\varepsilon} \sum_{Y}^{P^{k-1}} \left| \sum_{x}^{P} e(Y x \alpha_k) \right| .$$

By Lemma 1.8, we know that

$$\sum_{x}^{P} e(Y x \alpha_k) \ll \min\left(P, \frac{1}{\{Y \alpha_k\}}\right).$$

Further, by Lemma 3.5, we obtain

$$\sum_{Y}^{P^{k-1}} \min\left(P, \frac{1}{\{Y \alpha_k\}}\right) \ll \left(\frac{P^{k-1}}{q} + 1\right) \max_{f} \left(\sum_{Y=f+1}^{f+q} \min\left(P, \frac{1}{\{Y \alpha_k\}}\right)\right)$$

$$\ll \left(\frac{P^{k-1}}{q} + 1\right)(P + q \log q) .$$

Hence we obtain

$$|S|^{2^{k-1}} \ll P^{2^{k-1}-1} + P^{2^{k-1}-k+\varepsilon}\left(\frac{P^{k-1}}{q} + 1\right)(P + q \log q)$$

$$\ll P^{\varepsilon} q^{\varepsilon} P^{2^{k-1}} \left(\frac{1}{P} + \frac{1}{q} + \frac{q}{P^{k}}\right).$$

CHAPTER IV

VINOGRADOV'S MEAN-VALUE THEOREM AND ITS COROLLARIES

§1. DESCRIPTION OF THE THEOREM

In this chapter we shall discuss Vinogradov's best known theorem and its corollaries. This theorem is a basic tool for the modern study of an analytic theory of numbers.

Theorem 5 (Vinogradov's mean-value theorem). *Let*

$$f(x) = \alpha_k x^k + \cdots + \alpha_1 x$$

and

$$C_k = C_k(P) = \sum_{x=1}^{P} e(f(x)) .$$

Let

$$t_1(k) = t_1 = \begin{cases} \frac{1}{4} k(k+1) + lk & \text{if } k \equiv 0, 3 \pmod 4, \\ \frac{1}{4}(k^2 + k + 2) + lk & \text{if } k \equiv 1, 2 \pmod 4 . \end{cases}$$

Then for $0 \le l \le c_1(k)$ *we have*

$$\int_0^1 \cdots \int_0^1 | C_k |^{2t_1} d\alpha_1 \cdots d\alpha_k \leqslant c_2(k)\, P^{2t_1 - \frac{1}{2}k(k+1) + \delta + \varepsilon},$$

where

$$\delta = \delta(k) = \frac{1}{2} k(k+1)(1-a)^l, \quad a = 1/k .$$

This theorem can be described in another form.

The value of the above integral obviously is equal to the number of sets of solutions $x_1, \cdots, x_{t_1}; y_1, \cdots, y_{t_1}$ of the equations

$$x_1^h + \cdots + x_{t_1}^h = y_1^h + \cdots + y_{t_1}^h, \quad 1 \leqslant h \leqslant k,$$

$$1 \leqslant x_i, y_i \leqslant P .$$

We shall prove that for an arbitrary integer T this integral is also equal to the number of sets of solutions of the equations

$$x_1^h + \cdots + x_{t_1}^h = y_1^h + \cdots + y_{t_1}^h, \quad 1 \leqslant h \leqslant k,$$
$$T < x_i, y_i \leqslant T + P.$$

Letting $X_i = x_i - T$ and $Y_i = y_i - T$, we obtain

$$\sum_{i=1}^{t_1} (X_i + T)^h = \sum_{i=1}^{t_1} (Y_i + T)^h, \quad 1 \leqslant h \leqslant k.$$

Expanding binomially we easily see that these equations and

$$\sum_{i=1}^{t_1} X_i^h = \sum_{i=1}^{t_1} Y_i^h, \quad 1 \leqslant h \leqslant k,$$

are identical.

Further, since $(0 \leq r \leq 2t_1)$

$$\int_0^1 \cdots \int_0^1 C_k^r \bar{C}_k^{2t_1 - r} e^{2\pi i (N_1 a_1 + \cdots + N_k a_k)} da_1 \cdots da_k$$
$$\leqslant \int_0^1 \cdots \int_0^1 | C_k |^{2t_1} da_1 \cdots da_k,$$

we know, by this theorem, that the number of integral solutions of the equations

$$\sum_{\nu=1}^{r} x_\nu^h - \sum_{\nu=r+1}^{2t_1} y_\nu^h = N_h, \quad 1 \leqslant h \leqslant k, \quad 1 \leqslant x, y \leqslant P,$$

is

$$\leqslant c_2(k) P^{2t_1 - \frac{1}{2}k(k+1) + \delta + \epsilon}.$$

The proof of this theorem is dependent upon Lemma 4.1, with some simplification and sharpening added by the author.

§2. LEMMAS

Lemma 4.1. *Let $Q = RH$, $R > 1$, $H > 1$ and*

$$1 \leqslant g_1 < g_2 < \cdots < g_k \leqslant H, \qquad g_\nu - g_{\nu-1} > 1,$$

where $g_1, \cdots, g_k$ are integers. Further, let x_ν vary over the interval

$$-\omega + (g_\nu - 1) R \leqslant x_\nu < -\omega + g_\nu R, \quad 0 \leqslant \omega \leqslant Q$$

Then the number of sets of integers $x_1, \cdots, x_k$ for which the expressions

$$x_1^h + \cdots + x_k^h, \quad 1 \leqslant h \leqslant k,$$

fall respectively within fixed intervals of length $\leq Q^{h-1}$ $(1 \leq h \leq k)$ *is*

$$\leqslant 2^k (2k H)^{\frac{1}{2}k(k-1)}.$$

Proof. When $k = 1$, this lemma is obviously true. Suppose that the lemma is true for $k - 1$. Let $x_1, \cdots, x_k$ and $y_1, \cdots, y_k$ be two sets of integers satisfying the conditions of the lemma. Let $s_h = \Sigma_{\nu=1}^{k} x_\nu^h$, and $s'_h = \Sigma_{\nu=1}^{k} y_\nu^h$, and let σ_h and σ'_h denote the elementary symmetric functions of the hth degree of $x_1, \cdots, x_k$ and $y_1, \cdots, y_k$, respectively. By the hypotheses of the lemma, we obtain

$$| s_h - s'_h | \leqslant Q^{h-1}, \quad 1 \leqslant h \leqslant k. \tag{1}$$

By (1) we can prove that

$$| \sigma_h - \sigma'_h | \leqslant \begin{cases} 1 , & h = 1; \\ \frac{3}{4}(2k\, Q)^{h-1}, & 2 \leqslant h \leqslant k. \end{cases} \tag{2}$$

In fact, the form (2) is obviously true when $h = 1$. Let us now assume that the form (2) is also true for $1, 2, \cdots, h - 1$. Introduce the well-known formulas for symmetric functions

$$s_h - \sigma_1 s_{h-1} + \sigma_2 s_{h-2} - \cdots - (-1)^h h\, \sigma_h = 0$$

and

$$s'_h - \sigma'_1 s'_{h-1} + \sigma'_2 s'_{h-2} - \cdots - (-1)^h h\, \sigma'_h = 0.$$

Since $|\sigma_\nu| \leq \binom{k}{\nu} Q^\nu$, $|s_\nu| \leq kQ^\nu$, it follows that when $1 \leq \nu < h$,

$$| \sigma_\nu s_{h-\nu} - \sigma'_\nu s'_{h-\nu} | \leqslant | \sigma_\nu - \sigma'_\nu | \, | s_{h-\nu} | + | \sigma'_\nu | \, | s_{h-\nu} - s'_{h-\nu} |$$

$$\leqslant \left((2k)^{\nu-1} k + \binom{k}{\nu} \right) Q^{h-1} \leqslant \left(1 + \frac{1}{\nu!} \right) (2k)^{\nu-1} k\, Q^{h-1}.$$

For $h \geq 2$ we obtain [1)]

---

1) When $h = 2$, the symbol $\Sigma_{\nu=2}^{1}$ denotes zero.

$$|\sigma_h - \sigma_h'| \leqslant \frac{1}{h}\left(1 + 2k + \frac{3}{2}k\sum_{\nu=2}^{h-1}(2k)^{\nu-1}\right)Q^{h-1}$$

$$\leqslant \frac{1}{2}\left(1 + \frac{1}{2}k + \frac{3}{2}k\,\frac{(2k)^{h-1}}{2k-1}\right)Q^{h-1} \leqslant \frac{3}{4}(2k)^{h-1}Q^{h-1}.$$

For X satisfying $|X| \leq Q$, we have

$$\Psi(X) = |(X - x_1)\cdots(X - x_k) - (X - y_1)\cdots(X - y_k)|$$

$$\leqslant \sum_{h=1}^{k}|\sigma_h - \sigma_h'|\,|X|^{k-h} \leqslant \left(1 + \frac{3}{4}\sum_{h=2}^{k}(2k)^{h-1}\right)Q^{k-1}$$

$$= \left(\frac{1}{4} + \frac{3}{4}\,\frac{(2k)^k}{2k-1}\right)Q^{k-1}.$$

Since $|y_k - x_\nu| \geq R$ $(\nu = 1, 2, \cdots, k-1)$, we obtain

$$R^{k-1}|y_k - x_k| \leqslant |(y_k - x_1)(y_k - x_2)\cdots(y_k - x_k)| = \Psi(y_k)$$

$$\leqslant \left(\frac{1}{4} + \frac{3}{4}\,\frac{(2k)^k}{2k-1}\right)Q^{k-1} \leqslant 2(2kQ)^{k-1}.$$

Hence we can see that the number of distinct values of x_k satisfying the conditions of the lemma is $\leq 2(2kH)^{k-1}$. For a fixed x_k the expressions

$$x_1^h + \cdots + x_{k-1}^h, \quad 1 \leqslant h \leqslant k-1,$$

fall respectively within intervals of length $\leq Q^{h-1}$ $(1 \leq h \leq k-1)$. By the induction hypothesis, the number of sets of $x_1, \cdots, x_{k-1}$ is

$$\leqslant 2^{k-1}(2(k-1)H)^{\frac{1}{2}(k-1)(k-2)}.$$

Since

$$(2(k-1)H)^{\frac{1}{2}(k-1)(k-2)}(2kH)^{k-1} \leqslant (2kH)^{\frac{1}{2}k(k-1)},$$

we accordingly obtain the lemma.

Lemma 4.2. *Let $c \geq 1$. By the hypotheses of Lemma 4.1, the number of sets of integers $x_1, \cdots, x_k$ for which the expressions*

$$x_1^h + \cdots + x_k^h \quad (1 \leqslant h \leqslant k)$$

fall respectively within intervals of length not exceeding $cQ^{(1-1/k)h}$ $(1 \leq h \leq k)$ does not exceed

$$(4c)^k(2kH)^{\frac{1}{2}k(k-1)}Q^{\frac{1}{2}(k-1)}.$$

Proof. Split the hth interval into

$$[cQ^{h(1-1/k)}/Q^{h-1}]+1$$

parts and apply Lemma 4.1 to each part. Since

$$\prod_{h=1}^{k}\left(\left[\frac{cQ^{h(1-1/k)}}{Q^{h-1}}\right]+1\right)\leqslant\prod_{h=1}^{k}(2c\,Q^{h(1-1/k)-(h-1)})=(2c)^k\,Q^{\frac{1}{2}(k-1)},$$

there are at most $(2c)^kQ^{\frac{1}{2}(k-1)}$ sets of subintervals such that each set satisfies Lemma 4.1. In each of these sets of subintervals there are at most $2^k(2kH)^{\frac{1}{2}k(k-1)}$ sets of solutions, and thus the lemma is proved.

Lemma 4.3. *A set of integers* $(g_1,\cdots,g_b)$, $1\le g_\nu\le H$, *is called a well-spaced set if there exist at least* k *sets, denoted by* $g_{j_1},\cdots,g_{j_k}$, *which satisfy*

$$g_{j_{\nu+1}}-g_{j_\nu}>1\quad(1\leqslant\nu\leqslant k-1).$$

The number of sets which are not well-spaced is at most

$$H^{k-1}(2(k-1))^b.$$

Proof. Let

$$\{g_1,\cdots,g_b\}$$

be such a set. Let G_1 be the least integer in the set; let G_2 be the least such integer greater than G_1+1; let G_3 be the least such integer greater than G_2+1; ... ; then we obtain a sequence of integers

$$G_1,\ G_2,\cdots,G_{n-1}.$$

It is easily seen that $n<k$, with any g necessarily equal to some G_i or G_i+1.

Since every G can take at most H values, we therefore have at most H^{k-1} integral sequences

$$G_1,\ G_2,\cdots,G_n.$$

Furthermore, when $G_1, G_2,\cdots,G_n$ are chosen, each g can take at most $2(k-1)$ values, and therefore the lemma is proved.

§3. PROOF OF THE THEOREM

Lemma 4.4 (Recursion formula). *Let* b *denote an integer* $\ge k(k+1)/4+k$ *and let*

$$\eta=\left[\frac{1}{k}\,\frac{\log Q}{\log 2}\right],\quad a=\frac{1}{k}.$$

Then

$$\int_0^1\cdots\int_0^1 |C_k(Q)|^{2b}\,d\alpha_1\cdots d\alpha_k \leqslant (5b)^{5b}\max(1,\eta^2)\,Q^{2k-\frac{1}{2}(k+1)+2(b-k)a}$$
$$\times\int_0^1\cdots\int_0^1 |C_k(Q^{1-a})|^{2(b-k)}\,d\alpha_1\cdots d\alpha_k.$$

Proof. 1) Suppose that $\eta \geq 2$, and let s denote an integer satisfying $1 \leq s \leq \eta - 1$. Split $C_k(Q)$ into 2^s parts, the length of each part being $R_s = Q2^{-s}$:

$$C_k(Q) = \sum_{g=1}^{2^s}\ \sum_{(g-1)R_s<x\leqslant gR_s} e^{2\pi i f(x)} = \sum_{g=1}^{2^s} Z_{sg}\quad\text{(definition)}.$$

Let $Z = (C_k(Q))^b$. Then

$$Z = \sum^{2^{sb}} Z_{sg_1}\cdots Z_{sg_b}, \tag{1}$$

where Σ^M denotes a sum, the number of terms being at most M (this type of summation will frequently occur hereafter). Further, simply write

$$Z_s = Z_{s;g_1,\cdots,g_b} = Z_{sg_1}\cdots Z_{sg_b}. \tag{2}$$

If $g_1,\cdots,g_b$ forms a well-spaced set, then $Z_{s;\,g_1,\cdots,g_b}$ is called a well-spaced sum and is denoted by Z'_s. By Lemma 4.3, the number of distinct sums which are not well-spaced does not exceed $(2(k-1))^b 2^{s(k-1)}$. Divide each of the factors in the sum Z_s which is not well-spaced into two parts. In this way, we obtain 2^b sums Z_{s+1} from the sum Z_s which is not well-spaced. The number of distinct well-spaced Z_{s+1} obtained from Z_s obviously does not exceed

$$(2(k-1))^b\,2^{s(k-1)}\cdot 2^b = (4(k-1))^b\,2^{s(k-1)}.$$

Let Z'_{s+1} denote the well-spaced Z_{s+1}. Divide up the sums which are not well-spaced by the foregoing method. We can make a beginning since Z_1 is definitely not well-spaced. Repeating this process for $s = 1, 2, \cdots$ up to $\eta - 1$, using Z'_η to denote all Z_η obtained from the $Z_{\eta-1}$ which are not well-spaced, we then obtain

$$Z = \sum_{s=1}^{\eta}\sum^{M_s} Z'_s, \tag{3}$$

where $M_s = (4(k-1))^b 2^{s(k-1)}$.

2) By the Schwarz inequality, we have

$$|C_k(Q)|^{2b} = |Z|^2 \leqslant \eta\sum_{s=1}^{\eta}\left|\sum^{M_s} Z'_s\right|^2 \leqslant \eta\sum_{s=1}^{\eta} M_s\sum^{M_s}|Z'_s|^2. \tag{4}$$

We can assume that $g_1, \cdots, g_k$ of $Z'_{s;\, g_1, \cdots, g_b}$ $(1 \le s \le \eta - 1)$ satisfy the conditions of Lemma 4.1. If not, it is necessary only to rearrange the indices. Since the geometric mean does not exceed the algebraic mean, therefore

$$| Z_{sg_{k+1}} \cdots Z_{sg_b} |^2 \leqslant \frac{1}{b-k} \sum_{i=k+1}^{b} | Z_{sg_i} |^{2(b-k)} . \tag{5}$$

Split Z_{sg_i} $(k+1 \le i \le b)$ into

$$[Q\, 2^{-s}/Q^{1-a}] + 1 \leqslant Q^a\, 2^{1-s}$$

(since $4 \le 2^\eta \le Q^a$) parts, each part being of the form

$$C^* = \sum_x e^{2\pi i f(x)} ,$$

where x runs through an interval of length $\le Q^{1-a}$; then there exists an integer ω such that

$$\omega < x \leqslant \omega + Q', \quad 0 < Q' \leqslant Q^{1-a}, \quad 0 \leqslant \omega \leqslant g_i R_s \leqslant Q .$$

Using Hölder's inequality, we know that

$$| Z_{sg_i} |^{2(b-k)} \leqslant \left(\sum^{Q^a 2^{1-s}} | C^* | \right)^{2(b-k)} \leqslant (Q^a\, 2^{1-s})^{2(b-k)-1} \sum^{Q^a 2^{1-s}} | C^* |^{2(b-k)} . \tag{6}$$

By (4), (5) and (6), we obtain

$$| Z |^2 \leqslant \frac{\eta}{b-k} \sum_{s=1}^{\eta} M_s (Q^a\, 2^{1-s})^{2(b-k)-1} \sum^{N_s}{}' | Z_{sg_1} |^2 \cdots | Z_{sg_k} |^2 | C^* |^{2(b-k)} , \tag{7}$$

where $N_s = M_s (b-k) Q^a 2^{1-s} = (4(k-1))^b \cdot 2^{s(k-1)} (b-k) Q^a 2^{1-s}$. Integrating over the k-dimensional unit cube $(0 \le \alpha_1 \le 1, \cdots, 0 \le \alpha_k \le 1)$, we obtain

$$\int_0^1 \cdots \int_0^1 | Z |^2 \, d\alpha_1 \cdots d\alpha_k \leqslant \frac{\eta}{b-k} \sum_{s=1}^{\eta} M_s (Q^a\, 2^{1-s})^{2(b-k)-1}$$

$$\times \sum^{N_s} \int_0^1 \cdots \int_0^1 | Z_{sg_1} |^2 \cdots | Z_{sg_k} |^2 | C^* |^{2(b-k)} \, d\alpha_1 \cdots d\alpha_k . \tag{8}$$

3) The integral

$$\int_0^1 \cdots \int_0^1 | Z_{sg_1} |^2 \cdots | Z_{sg_k} |^2 | C^* |^{2(b-k)} \, d\alpha_1 \cdots d\alpha_k \tag{9}$$

is equal to the number of solutions of the equations

$$x_1^h + \cdots + x_k^h + y_1^h + \cdots + y_{b-k}^h = x_1'^h + \cdots + x_k'^h + y_1'^h + \cdots + y_{b-k}'^h$$

$$(1 \leqslant h \leqslant k),$$

where the variables y and y' fall within an interval of the form

$$\omega < y, y' \leqslant \omega + Q' \quad (0 < Q' \leqslant Q^{1-a}, \quad 0 \leqslant \omega \leqslant Q)$$

and x and x' within the interval

$$(g_i - 1) R_s < x_i, x_i' \leqslant g_i R_s$$

with $s \leq \eta - 1$ and the integers $g_1, \cdots, g_k$ satisfying the conditions of Lemma 4.1.

Let $X + \omega$ and $Y + \omega$ replace x and y respectively. Then the form (9) is also the number of solutions of the equations

$$X_1^h + \cdots + X_k^h + Y_1^h + \cdots + Y_{b-k}^h = X_1'^h + \cdots + X_k'^h + Y_1'^h + \cdots + Y_{b-k}'^h$$
$$(1 \leqslant h \leqslant k), \qquad (10)$$

where the Y's fall within the interval $(0, Q')$, and X_i and X_i' within

$$-\omega + (g_i - 1) R_s < X_i, X_i' \leqslant -\omega + g_i R_s \quad (0 \leqslant \omega \leqslant Q) \qquad (11)$$

If we first fix X', then X satisfies the conditions in Lemma 4.2, in which $c = 2(b - k)$ and $H = 2^s$. Therefore the number of sets of X and X' does not exceed

$$R_s^k \{8(b-k)\}^k (2k2^s)^{\frac{1}{2}k(k-1)} Q^{\frac{1}{2}(k-1)}$$
$$= \{8(b-k)\}^k (2k)^{\frac{1}{2}k(k-1)} 2^{\frac{1}{2}sk(k-1)-sk} Q^{2k-\frac{1}{2}(k+1)}. \qquad (12)$$

Furthermore, for fixed X and X', the number of sets of Y and Y' does not exceed

$$\int_0^1 \cdots \int_0^1 | C_k(Q^{1-a}) |^{2(b-k)} d\alpha_1 \cdots d\alpha_k$$

(since $|\int_0^1 f(x) e^{ixy} dx| \leq \int_0^1 |f(x)| dx$). Therefore, when $1 \leq s \leq \eta - 1$,

$$\int_0^1 \cdots \int_0^1 | Z_{sg_1} \cdots Z_{sg_k} |^2 | C^* |^{2(b-k)} d\alpha_1 \cdots d\alpha_k$$
$$\leqslant (8(b-k))^k (2k)^{\frac{1}{2}k(k-1)} 2^{\frac{1}{2}sk(k+1)-2sk} Q^{2k-\frac{1}{2}(k+1)}$$
$$\times \int_0^1 \cdots \int_0^1 | C_k(Q^{1-a}) |^{2(b-k)} d\alpha_1 \cdots d\alpha_k. \qquad (13)$$

When $s = \eta$, we use the obvious inequality

$$\int_0^1 \cdots \int_0^1 | Z_{sg_1} \cdots Z_{sg_k} |^2 | C^* |^{2(b-k)} d\alpha_1 \cdots d\alpha_k$$
$$\leqslant R_\eta^{2k} \int_0^1 \cdots \int_0^1 | C_k(Q^{1-a}) |^{2(b-k)} d\alpha_1 \cdots d\alpha_k. \tag{14}$$

Since $\eta + 1 \geq \log Q/k \log 2$, it follows that $Q2^{-\eta k} \leq 2^k$. Further, since

$$R_\eta^{2k} = Q^{2k} 2^{-2k\eta} =$$
$$= 2^{-\eta[2k-\frac{1}{2}k(k+1)]} Q^{2k-\frac{1}{2}(k+1)} (Q2^{-\eta k})^{\frac{1}{2}(k+1)}$$
$$\leqslant 2^{-\eta[2k-\frac{1}{2}k(k+1)]} Q^{2k-\frac{1}{2}(k+1)} 2^{\frac{1}{2}k(k+1)},$$

we know that the form (13) is still true for $s = \eta$.

4) Combining (8) and (13) (when $s = 1, 2, \cdots, \eta$), we obtain

$$\int_0^1 \cdots \int_0^1 | C_k(Q) |^{2b} d\alpha_1 \cdots d\alpha_k \leqslant \frac{\eta}{b-k} \sum_{s=1}^{\eta} M_s(Q^a 2^{1-s})^{2(b-k)-1} N_s(8(b-k))^k$$
$$\times (2k)^{\frac{1}{2}k(k-1)} 2^{\frac{1}{2}sk(k+1)-2sk} Q^{2k-\frac{1}{2}(k+1)} \int_0^1 \cdots \int_0^1 | C_k(Q^{1-a}) |^{2(b-k)} d\alpha_1 \cdots d\alpha_k$$
$$\leqslant \eta c \sum_{s=1}^{\eta} 2^{-s(2b-\frac{1}{2}k(k+1)-2k)} Q^{2k-\frac{1}{2}(k+1)+2(b-k)a}$$
$$\times \int_0^1 \cdots \int_0^1 | C_k(Q^{1-a}) |^{2(b-k)} d\alpha_1 \cdots d\alpha_k$$
$$\leqslant \eta^2 c\, Q^{2k-\frac{1}{2}(k+1)+2(b-k)a} \int_0^1 \cdots \int_0^1 | C_k(Q^{1-a}) |^{2(b-k)} d\alpha_1 \cdots d\alpha_k, \tag{15}$$

where we have used the inequality $2b \geq k(k+1)/2 + 2k$, and

$$c = (4(k-1))^{2b} 2^{2(b-k)} (8b)^k (2k)^{\frac{1}{2}k(k-1)}.$$

Since

$$c < (4b)^{2b} 2^{2b} (8b)^b (2b)^{2b} \leqslant ((8b)^2 \cdot 8b \cdot (2b)^2)^b \leqslant (5b)^{5b},$$

this theorem is true when $\eta \geq 2$.

5) Suppose that $\eta < 2$. Then

$$\frac{1}{k} \log Q/\log 2 < 2, \text{ i.e., } Q < 4^k.$$

Split $C_k(Q)$ into four parts, each part being of the form

$$C^* = \sum_{\omega < x \leqslant \omega + Q'} e^{2\pi i f(x)} \quad \left(0 < Q' \leqslant \frac{1}{4} Q \leqslant Q^{1-a}\right).$$

By Hölder's inequality, we obtain

$$|C_k(Q)|^{2b} \leqslant 4^{2b-1}\sum^{4}|C^*|^{2b} \leqslant 4^{2b-1}Q^{2k(1-a)}\sum^{4}|C^*|^{2(b-k)}.$$

Integrating over the k-dimensional unit cube, we obtain

$$\begin{aligned}\int_0^1\cdots\int_0^1 |C_k(Q)|^{2b}\,d\alpha_1\cdots d\alpha_k &\leqslant 4^{2b-1}Q^{2k(1-a)}\sum^{4}\int_0^1\cdots\int_0^1 |C^*|^{2(b-k)}\,d\alpha_1\cdots d\alpha_k \\ &\leqslant 4^{2b}Q^{2k(1-a)}\int_0^1\cdots\int_0^1 |C_k(Q^{1-a})|^{2(b-k)}\,d\alpha_1\cdots d\alpha_k \\ &\leqslant 4^{2b}Q^{2k-\frac{1}{2}(k+1)+2(b-k)a}\int_0^1\cdots\int_0^1 |C_k(Q^{1-a})|^{2(b-k)}\,d\alpha_1\cdots d\alpha_k,\end{aligned}$$

where we have used $2b > k(k+1)/2$. Hence we obtain Lemma 4.4.

Theorem 5′. *As in the hypotheses of Theorem* 5, *if* $s \geq k(k+1)/4 + lk$, *then*

$$\int_0^1\cdots\int_0^1 |C_k(P)|^{2s}\,d\alpha_1\cdots d\alpha_k \leqslant (5s)^{5sl}(\log P)^{2l}P^{2s-\frac{1}{2}k(k+1)+\delta}.$$

This theorem is obviously a more precise form of Theorem 5.

Proof. If we let $P^{1-a} \leq 3$, then $P \leq 9$, and this theorem need not be proved. We assume that $P^{1-a} > 3$. Then $P > e$.

When $l = 0$, the theorem is obviously true. We now proceed by induction on l. Suppose that the conclusion is true for $l-1$. We know by Lemma 4.4 that

$$\begin{aligned}\int_0^1\cdots\int_0^1 |C_k(P)|^{2s}\,d\alpha_1\cdots d\alpha_k &\leqslant (5s)^{5s}P^{2k-\frac{1}{2}(k+1)+2(s-k)a} \\ &\times(\log P)^2\int_0^1\cdots\int_0^1 |C_k(P^{1-a})|^{2(s-k)}\,d\alpha_1\cdots d\alpha_k.\end{aligned} \tag{16}$$

By the hypothesis of induction and using $l-1$, $s-k$ and P^{1-a} to replace l, s and P, we know that when $P^{1-a} > 3 > 2$,

$$\begin{aligned}\int_0^1\cdots\int_0^1 |C_k(P^{1-a})|^{2(s-k)}\,d\alpha_1\cdots d\alpha_k &\leqslant (5s)^{5s(l-1)}(\log P)^{2(l-1)} \\ &\times P^{(1-a)(2s-2k-\frac{1}{2}k(k+1)+\frac{1}{2}k(k+1)(1-a)^{l-1})}.\end{aligned} \tag{17}$$

The theorem follows from (16) and (17).

§4. COROLLARY

Theorem 6. *Let* $P \geq 2$, $s \geq k(k+1)/4 + lk$. *Further, let* $f(x)$ *denote an integral-valued polynomial of the* k*th degree. Then*

$$\int_0^1 \left| \sum_{x=1}^{P} e(\alpha f(x)) \right|^{2s} d\alpha \ll (\log P)^{2l} P^{2s-k+\delta},$$

where

$$\delta = \frac{1}{2} k(k+1)(1-a)^l.$$

Proof. As in the proof of Theorem 4 in Chapter III, we can assume that $f(x)$ is a polynomial with integral coefficients

$$f(x) = A_k x^k + \cdots + A_1 x + A_0.$$

The number of sets of integral solutions of the equation

$$f(x_1) + \cdots + f(x_s) = f(y_1) + \cdots + f(y_s), \quad 1 \leqslant x, y \leqslant P,$$

is obviously equal to the number of solutions of the equations

$$x_1^h + \cdots + x_s^h - y_1^h - \cdots - y_s^h = N_h, \quad 1 \leqslant h \leqslant k, \tag{1}$$

where $N_1, \cdots, N_k$ satisfy

$$A_k N_k + \cdots + A_1 N_1 = 0, \quad N_h \ll P^h. \tag{2}$$

(Note that $x_1, \cdots, x_s, y_1, \cdots, y_s, N_1, \cdots, N_k$ are all treated as unknowns.)

Since $N_h \ll P^h$, we have

$$\ll P^{l+2+\cdots+k-1} \ll P^{\frac{1}{2}k(k-1)}$$

sets of $N_1, \cdots, N_k$ satisfying the condition (2), inasmuch as N_k is uniquely determined by $N_1, \cdots, N_{k-1}$.

For fixed $N_1, \cdots, N_{k-1}$ and N_k, the number of solutions of the form (1) is equal to

$$\int_0^1 \cdots \int_0^1 \left| \sum_{x=1}^{P} e(\alpha_k x^k + \cdots + \alpha_1 x) \right|^{2s} e(-(N_k \alpha_k + \cdots + N_1 \alpha_1))\, d\alpha_1 \cdots d\alpha_k.$$

By Theorem 5′, this integral is

$$\leqslant \int_0^1 \cdots \int_0^1 \left| \sum_{x=1}^{P} e(\alpha_k x^k + \cdots + \alpha_1 x) \right|^{2s} d\alpha_1 \cdots d\alpha_k$$

$$\leqslant (5s)^{5sl} (\log P)^{2l} P^{2s-\frac{1}{2}k(k+1)+\delta}.$$

§5. LEMMAS ON CONVEX FUNCTIONS

The real function $f(x)$ defined in the interval $a < x < b$ is called a convex function over (a, b) if for any three points $x_1 < x_2 < x_3$ within the interval we always have the inequality

$$f(x_2) \leqslant \frac{(x_3-x_2)\, f(x_1)+(x_2-x_1)\, f(x_3)}{x_3-x_1}.$$

Lemma 4.5. *Suppose that $x_1 < x_2 < x_3$ are three given points in the interval $a < x < b$, and $\alpha, \beta, 0 < \lambda \leq 1$ are three given numbers. Suppose further that $f(x)$ is a convex function on the interval (a, b) satisfying the conditions*

$$\begin{cases} f(x_1) \leqslant \alpha, \\ f(x_3) \leqslant \beta + \lambda f(x_2). \end{cases}$$

Then we have

$$f(x_2) \leqslant \frac{\alpha(x_3-x_2)+\beta(x_2-x_1)}{x_3-x_1-\lambda(x_2-x_1)}. \tag{1}$$

Proof. By the definition of a convex function and the hypotheses of the lemma, we obtain

$$f(x_2) \leqslant \frac{(x_3-x_2)\, f(x_1)+(x_2-x_1)\, f(x_3)}{x_3-x_1} \leqslant \frac{\alpha(x_3-x_2)+(\beta+\lambda f(x_2))\,(x_2-x_1)}{x_3-x_1}.$$

Changing terms and adjusting the above form, we at once obtain the inequality (1).

Lemma 4.6. *When $v \geq 0$, define $g(v)$ as the least upper bound of*

$$\log\left(\int_0^1 \cdots \int_0^1 |\, C_k(Q)\, |^{2v}\, d\alpha_1 \cdots d\alpha_k\right) \Big/ \log Q \tag{2}$$

where Q varies over the interval $Q_0 \leq Q < \infty$. Then $g(v)$ is a convex function of v on the interval $(0, \infty)$. Here Q_0 is a given positive constant.

Proof. Suppose that $v_2 > v_1 \geq 0$ are two arbitrary numbers. Then for $0 < t < 1$ the expression $v_1 t + v_2(1-t)$ denotes an arbitrary point in the interval $v_1 < v < v_2$. If we can prove that

$$g(v_1 t + v_2(1-t)) \leqslant t g(v_1) + (1-t)\, g(v_2), \tag{3}$$

the lemma is proved.

By Lemma 3.1 we know that

$$\frac{\int_0^1\cdots\int_0^1 |C_k|^{2(v_1t+v_2(1-t))}\,d\alpha_1\cdots d\alpha_k}{\left(\int_0^1\cdots\int_0^1 |C_k|^{2v_1}\,d\alpha_1\cdots d\alpha_k\right)^t\left(\int_0^1\cdots\int_0^1 |C_k|^{2v_2}\,d\alpha_1\cdots d\alpha_k\right)^{1-t}}$$

$$=\int_0^1\cdots\int_0^1\left(\frac{|C_k|^{2v_1}}{\int_0^1\cdots\int_0^1 |C_k|^{2v_1}\,d\alpha_1\cdots d\alpha_k}\right)^t\left(\frac{|C_k|^{2v_2}}{\int_0^1\cdots\int_0^1 |C_k|^{2v_2}\,d\alpha_1\cdots d\alpha_k}\right)^{1-t} d\alpha_1\cdots d\alpha_k$$

$$\leqslant\int_0^1\cdots\int_0^1\left(\frac{t\,|C_k|^{2v_1}}{\int_0^1\cdots\int_0^1 |C_k|^{2v_1}\,d\alpha_1\cdots d\alpha_k}+\frac{(1-t)\,|C_k|^{2v_2}}{\int_0^1\cdots\int_0^1 |C_k|^{2v_2}\,d\alpha_1\cdots d\alpha_k}\right)d\alpha_1\cdots d\alpha_k$$

$$=t+(1-t)=1\,.$$

But from this form we can at once obtain the inequality (3).

Lemma 4.7. *Suppose that $k\geq 2$, u_0 is a positive integer and Q_0' is a constant depending only on k. Suppose further that when $Q\geq Q_0'$,*

$$\int_0^1\cdots\int_0^1 |C_k(Q)|^{2u_0}\,d\alpha_1\cdots d\alpha_k\leqslant Q^{v_0}. \tag{4}$$

Then for some integer $u\geq\max(k(k+1)/4,\ u_0+1)$ and $\epsilon>0$, we have

$$\int_0^1\cdots\int_0^1 |C_k(Q)|^{2u}\,d\alpha_1\cdots d\alpha_k\leqslant b(k,u_0,v_0,u,\varepsilon)\,Q^{2u-\frac{1}{2}k(k+1)+\delta+\varepsilon}, \tag{5}$$

where

$$\delta=\frac{k^2(2v_0-4u_0+k^2+k)}{2(k^2+u-u_0)}\,. \tag{6}$$

Proof. We know by Lemma 4.4 that when $Q\geq Q_0''(k,u,\epsilon')$,

$$\int_0^1\cdots\int_0^1 |C_k(Q)|^{2(u+k)}\,d\alpha_1\cdots d\alpha_k\leqslant Q^{2k-\frac{1}{2}(k+1)+2ua+\varepsilon'}$$
$$\times\int_0^1\cdots\int_0^1 |C_k(Q^{1-a})|^{2u}\,d\alpha_1\cdots d\alpha_k\,.$$

We now take $Q_0=\max(Q_0',Q_0'')$ and let $g(v)$ be defined as in (2). Then we have $Q'\geq Q_0$ such that

$$g(u+k)\leqslant\log\left(\int_0^1\cdots\int_0^1 |C_k(Q')|^{2(u+k)}\,d\alpha_1\cdots d\alpha_k\right)\Big/\log Q'+\varepsilon'$$

$$\leqslant\left(2k-\frac{1}{2}(k+1)+2ua+2\varepsilon'\right)+\log\left(\int_0^1\cdots\int_0^1|C_k(Q'^{1-a})|^{2u}\,d\alpha_1\cdots d\alpha_k\right)\Big/\log Q'$$

$$\leqslant 2k-\frac{1}{2}(k+1)+2ua+2\varepsilon'+(1-a)\,g(u)\,.$$

Since $g(v)$ is a convex function and $u_0 < u < u + k$, we obtain by Lemma 4.5

$$g(u) \leqslant \frac{v_0(u+k-u) + \left(2k - \frac{1}{2}(k+1) + 2ua + 2\varepsilon'\right)(u-u_0)}{u+k-u_0-(1-a)(u-u_0)}$$

$$= \frac{2k^2 v_0 + (3k^2 - k + 4u)(u-u_0) + \varepsilon''}{2(k^2+u-u_0)}$$

$$\leqslant 2u - \frac{1}{2}k(k+1) + \frac{k^2(2v_0 - 4u_0 + k^2 + k)}{2(k^2+u-u_0)} + \varepsilon.$$

Hence the lemma is proved.

CHAPTER V

MEAN-VALUE THEOREMS FOR CERTAIN TRIGONOMETRIC SUMS (II)

§1. FORMULATION OF THEOREMS 7 AND 8

Theorem 7 (theorems B_k). *Suppose that for P a positive integer*

$$C_k = \sum_{x=1}^{P} e(\alpha_k x^k + \cdots + \alpha_1 x).$$

Then

$$\int_0^1 \cdots \int_0^1 | C_k |^\lambda \, d\alpha_1 \cdots d\alpha_k \leqslant C_1(k, \varepsilon) \, P^{\lambda - \frac{1}{2}k(k+1)+\varepsilon},$$

where the numerical value of $\lambda = \lambda(k)$ is defined according to the following table:

k	2	3	4	5	6	7	8	9	10
λ	6	16	46	110	240	414	672	1080	1770

When $k = 2$, we have a more precise result (theorem B_2'):

$$\int_0^1 \int_0^1 \left| \sum_{x=1}^{P} e(\alpha_2 x^2 + \alpha_1 x) \right|^6 d\alpha_1 \, d\alpha_2 \leqslant b_1 P^3 (\log P)^3.$$

The proof of this theorem is dependent on the following theorem.

Theorem 8 (theorems A_k). *Let*

$$f(x) = a_0 x^k + a_1 x^{k-1} + \cdots,$$

where a_0 represents an integer whose absolute value is $\leq b_2(k)$, and a_1 is an integer whose absolute value does not exceed $b_3(k) P$. Further, let

$$S_k = \sum_{x=1}^{P} e(\alpha_k f(x) + \alpha_{k-2} x^{k-2} + \cdots + \alpha_1 x).$$

Then

$$\int_0^1 \cdots \int_0^1 |S_k|^\lambda \, d\alpha_1 \cdots d\alpha_{k-2} \, d\alpha_k \leqslant c_2(k, \varepsilon) \, P^{\lambda - \frac{1}{2}(k^2-k+2)+\varepsilon},$$

where the numerical value of $\lambda = \lambda(k)$ *is defined according to the following table:*

k	3	4	5	6	7	8	9	10
λ	10	32	86	208	354	544	826	1258

The proofs of these two theorems are mutually dependent; that is to say, we use the theorems A_{l_1} $(l_1 \le k-1)$ and B_{l_2} $(l_2 \le k-1)$ to prove A_k, and then A_{l_1} $(l_1 \le k)$ and B_{l_2} $(l_2 \le k-1)$ to prove B_k. In the proofs for the different k's there is a slight change in method. Naturally we could have a uniform method if we used induction, but the results obtained would be less exact. Therefore, this method that varies at different stages is employed.

§2. REMARKS CONCERNING THEOREMS A_k (i.e., Theorem 8)

In theorems A_k we can take $f(x) = x^k$. The method of verification is as follows: The value of the integral

$$\int_0^1 \cdots \int_0^1 |S_k|^{2\mu} \, d\alpha_1 \cdots d\alpha_{k-2} \, d\alpha_k$$

is equal to the number of sets of integral solutions $x_1, \cdots, x_\mu, y_1, \cdots, y_\mu$ of the equations

$$f(x_1) + \cdots + f(x_\mu) = f(y_1) + \cdots + f(y_\mu),$$

$$x_1^h + \cdots + x_\mu^h = y_1^h + \cdots + y_\mu^h, \qquad 1 \leqslant h \leqslant k-2,$$

$$1 \leqslant x_\nu \leqslant P, \qquad 1 \leqslant y_\nu \leqslant P.$$

We may assume that $a_0 > 0$. Multiplying the above forms by $a_0^{k-1}k^k$ and $a_0^h k^h$ $(1 \le h \le k-2)$, we obtain

$$\sum_{\nu=1}^{\mu} \{(a_0 k x_\nu)^k + k a_1 (a_0 k x_\nu)^{k-1} + \cdots\} = \sum_{\nu=1}^{\mu} \{(a_0 k y_\nu)^k + k a_1 (a_0 k y_\nu)^{k-1} + \cdots\},$$

$$\sum_{\nu=1}^{\mu} (a_0 k x_\nu)^h = \sum_{\nu=1}^{\mu} (a_0 k y_\nu)^h, \qquad 1 \leqslant h \leqslant k-2.$$

Letting $x'_\nu = a_0 k x_\nu + a_1$ and $y'_\nu = a_0 k y_\nu + a_1$, we obtain the equations

$$x_1'^k + \cdots + x_\mu'^k = y_1'^k + \cdots + y_\mu'^k,$$

$$x_1'^h + \cdots + x_\mu'^h = y_1'^h + \cdots + y_\mu'^h, \qquad 1 \leqslant h \leqslant k-2, \tag{1}$$

in which, however,

$$k \mid (x'_\nu - a_1), \qquad k \mid (y'_\nu - a_1).$$

Hence we obtain

$$\int_0^1 \cdots \int_0^1 |S_k|^{2\mu}\, d\alpha_1 \cdots d\alpha_{k-2}\, d\alpha_k$$

$$\leqslant \int_0^1 \cdots \int_0^1 \left| \sum_{x=a_1}^{a_0 kP + a_1} e(\alpha_k x^k + \alpha_{k-2} x^{k-2} + \cdots + \alpha_1 x) \right|^{2\mu} d\alpha_1 \cdots d\alpha_{k-2}\, d\alpha_k$$

$$\leqslant 2^{2\mu-1} \Bigg(\int_0^1 \cdots \int_0^1 \left| \sum_{a_1 \leqslant x \leqslant -1} e(\alpha_k x^k + \alpha_{k-2} x^{k-2} + \cdots + \alpha_1 x) \right|^{2\mu} d\alpha_1 \cdots d\alpha_{k-2}\, d\alpha_k$$

$$+ \int_0^1 \cdots \int_0^1 \left| \sum_{x=0}^{a_0 kP + a_1} e(\alpha_k x^k + \alpha_{k-2} x^{k-2} + \cdots + \alpha_1 x) \right|^{2\mu} d\alpha_1 \cdots d\alpha_{k-2}\, d\alpha_k \Bigg)^{1)}$$

$$\ll \int_0^1 \cdots \int_0^1 \left| \sum_{x}^{P} e(\alpha_k x^k + \alpha_{k-2} x^{k-2} + \cdots + \alpha_1 x) \right|^{2\mu} d\alpha_1 \cdots d\alpha_{k-2}\, d\alpha_k + 1,$$

where we have used $a_0 \ll 1$ and $a_1 \ll P$. Therefore we need only examine the case $f(x) = x^k$.

§3. AN ESTIMATE OF TWO INTEGRALS BY MEANS OF SYMMETRIC FUNCTIONS

Our object now is to prove

$$\int_0^1 \cdots \int_0^1 |S_k|^{2k}\, d\alpha_1 \cdots d\alpha_{k-2}\, d\alpha_k \leqslant b_4(k)\, P^k L^{k(2^{k-1}-1)},$$

and

$$\int_0^1 \cdots \int_0^1 |C_k|^{2(k+1)}\, d\alpha_1 \cdots d\alpha_k \leqslant b_5(k)\, P^{k+1} L^{2^k-1},$$

where $L = \log P$.

1) If $a_1 > -1$, then the first integral vanishes and is denoted by 0. Further, if $a_0 kP + a_1 < 0$, then the second integral is to be set equal to 0.

Lemma 5.1. *Let*

$$s_\nu = x_1^\nu + \cdots + x_k^\nu, \qquad 1 \leqslant \nu \leqslant k.$$

The symmetric function

$$f = (s_1 - x_1) \cdots (s_1 - x_k)$$

can be expressed as a function depending on $s_1, \cdots, s_{k-2}$ *and* s_k *but not on* s_{k-1}.

Proof. Letting σ_i denote an elementary symmetric function of the ith degree in $x_1, \cdots, x_k$, we have

$$f = s_1^k - \sigma_1 s_1^{k-1} + \cdots + (-1)^{k-1} \sigma_{k-1} s_1 + (-1)^k \sigma_k.$$

From the well-known theorem on symmetric functions we obtain

$$f = (-1)^{k-1} \sigma_{k-1} s_1 + (-1)^k \sigma_k + f_1(s_1, \cdots, s_{k-2}). \tag{1}$$

By Newton's theorem on symmetric functions we know that

$$(-1)^k k \sigma_k = -s_k + \sigma_1 s_{k-1} + (-1)^k \sigma_{k-1} s_1 + f_2(s_1, \cdots, s_{k-2}),$$

and

$$(-1)^{k-1}(k-1)\sigma_{k-1} = -s_{k-1} + f_3(s_1, \cdots, s_{k-2}).$$

Hence we deduce that

$$\begin{aligned} &k((-1)^k \sigma_k + (-1)^{k-1} \sigma_{k-1} s_1) \\ &= -s_k + \sigma_1 s_{k-1} + (-1)^k \sigma_{k-1} s_1 + (-1)^{k-1} \sigma_{k-1} s_1 - s_1 s_{k-1} + f_4(s_1, \cdots, s_{k-2}) \\ &= -s_k + f_4(s_1, \cdots, s_{k-2}). \end{aligned} \tag{2}$$

From the equalities (1) and (2) we obtain the lemma.

Lemma 5.2.

$$\int_0^1 \cdots \int_0^1 |S_k|^{2k} \, d\alpha_1 \cdots d\alpha_{k-2} \, d\alpha_k \leqslant b_4(k) P^k L^{k(2^{k-1}-1)}.$$

Proof. Let $l = x_1 + \cdots + x_k$. Then by Lemma 5.1 we see that from the equalities

$$\left.\begin{aligned} &x_1^k + \cdots + x_k^k = y_1^k + \cdots + y_k^k, \\ &x_1^h + \cdots + x_k^h = y_1^h + \cdots + y_k^h, \qquad 1 \leqslant h \leqslant k-2 \end{aligned}\right\} \tag{3}$$

we obtain

$$(l - x_1) \cdots (l - x_k) = (l - y_1) \cdots (l - y_k). \tag{4}$$

For given $y_1, \cdots, y_k$ such that

$$(l-y_1)\cdots(l-y_k)\neq 0,$$

the number of sets of $x_1,\cdots,x_k$ is at most

$$d^{k-1}(|(l-y_1)(l-y_2)\cdots(l-y_k)|).$$

Hence the number of sets of solutions of the form (3) (by Lemma 2.5) is

$$\ll \sum_{y_1}^{P}\cdots\sum_{y_k}^{P} d^{k-1}(|(l-y_1)\cdots(l-y_k)|)$$

$$\leqslant \sum_{z_1}^{P}\cdots\sum_{z_k}^{P} d^{k-1}(z_1)\cdots d^{k-1}(z_k)$$

$$\leqslant \left(\sum_{z}^{P} d^{k-1}(z)\right)^k$$

$$\ll P^k L^{k(2^{k-1}-1)}.$$

Lemma 5.3. *From the equalities*

$$x_1^h+\cdots+x_{k+1}^h=y_1^h+\cdots+y_{k+1}^h,\qquad 1\leqslant h\leqslant k, \tag{5}$$

we can derive an equality of the form

$$(x_k-y_1)\cdots(x_k-y_k)=(x_{k+1}-y_{k+1})\,g(y_1,\cdots,y_k,x_k,y_{k+1},x_{k+1}),$$

where g is a homogeneous polynomial of the $(k-1)$th degree in which the homogeneous part containing x_{k+1}, y_{k+1} is not divisible by $x_{k+1}-y_{k+1}$, and the coefficient of x_{k+1}^{k-1} in g is a constant not equal to 0.

Proof. Let $s_\nu=\sum_{j=1}^{k-1}x_j^\nu$ and $t_\nu=\sum_{j=1}^{k-1}y_j^\nu$. Then (5) is equivalent to

$$s_h=t_h-(x_k^h-y_k^h)-(x_{k+1}^h-y_{k+1}^h),\qquad 1\leqslant h\leqslant k. \tag{6}$$

It is well known that

$$s_k-\sigma_1 s_{k-1}+\sigma_2 s_{k-2}+\cdots+(-1)^{k-1}\sigma_{k-1}s_1=0, \tag{7}$$

where $\sigma_i=\sigma_i(x_1,\cdots,x_{k-1})$ is an elementary symmetric function of the ith degree in $x_1,\cdots,x_{k-1}$. It is also known that $\sigma_1,\cdots,\sigma_{k-1}$ can be expressed in terms of $s_1,\cdots,s_{k-1}$. To be more specific, we have

$$s_k-s_1 s_{k-1}+\sigma_2(s_1,s_2)s_{k-2}+\cdots+(-1)^{k-1}\sigma_{k-1}(s_1,\cdots,s_{k-1})s_1=0. \tag{8}$$

By the same method, we obtain

$$t_k-t_1 t_{k-1}+\sigma_2(t_1,t_2)t_{k-2}+\cdots+(-1)^{k-1}\sigma_{k-1}(t_1,\cdots,t_{k-1})t_1=0. \tag{9}$$

Let the function obtained by substituting (6) in the left side of (8) be denoted by $T(y_1, \cdots, y_k, x_k, y_{k+1}, x_{k+1})$. Now we shall prove the formula

$$T(y_1, \cdots, y_k, x_k, x_{k+1}, x_{k+1}) = -k(x_k - y_1) \cdots (x_k - y_k).$$

When $x_k = y_k$, we know by (9) that the left side of the above formula is zero, and therefore $T(y_1, \cdots, y_k, x_k, x_{k+1}, x_{k+1})$ contains the factor $x_k - y_k$. If we let $t_\nu = \sum_{\substack{j=1 \\ j \neq i}}^k y_j^\nu$, then by the same argument, we know that it contains the factor $x_k - y_i$ $(1 \le i \le k-1)$. Now $T(y_1, \cdots, y_k, x_k, x_{k+1}, x_{k+1})$ is a polynomial of the kth degree in the x_k, and by comparison of the coefficients of $y_1, \cdots, y_k$ on the two sides of the above formula the equality is obviously established.

Hence we know that the value of the polynomial

$$T(y_1, \cdots, y_k, x_k, y_{k+1}, x_{k+1}) + k(x_k - y_1) \cdots (x_k - y_k)$$

is zero when $x_{k+1} = y_{k+1}$. Hence

$$k^{-1} T(y_1, \cdots, y_k, x_k, y_{k+1}, x_{k+1})$$
$$= -(x_k - y_1) \cdots (x_k - y_k) + (x_{k+1} - y_{k+1}) g(y_1, \cdots, y_k, x_k, y_{k+1}, x_{k+1}).$$

Finally, after the substitution of (6) in the left side of (8), the homogeneous polynomial of the kth degree in x_{k+1}, y_{k+1} which is contained in the first term of (8) will be divisible by $x_{k+1} - y_{k+1}$ but not by $(x_{k+1} - y_{k+1})^2$. The other terms are all multiples of $(x_{k+1} - y_{k+1})^2$. Also, the coefficient of x_{k+1}^k in $T(y_1, \cdots, y_k, x_k, y_{k+1}, x_{k+1})$ is obviously $-k$, and therefore, the coefficient of x_{k+1}^{k-1} in g is -1. Hence the lemma.

Lemma 5.4.

$$\int_0^1 \cdots \int_0^1 |C_k|^{2(k+1)} \, d\alpha_1 \cdots d\alpha_k \leqslant b_5(k) P^{k+1} L^{2k-1}.$$

Proof. The left member of the inequality in the lemma is equal to the number of solutions of the equations

$$\sum_{\nu=1}^{k+1} x_\nu^h = \sum_{\nu=1}^{k+1} y_\nu^h, \qquad 1 \leqslant h \leqslant k, \qquad 1 \leqslant x, y \leqslant P. \tag{10}$$

By Lemma 5.3, we obtain

$$(x_k - y_1) \cdots (x_k - y_k) = (x_{k+1} - y_{k+1}) g(y_1, \cdots, y_k, x_k, y_{k+1}, x_{k+1}). \tag{11}$$

If $(x_k - y_1) \cdots (x_k - y_k) = 0$, then $x_1, \cdots, x_{k+1}$ is obtained as a permutation of $y_1, \cdots, y_{k+1}$. The equation has $O(P^{k+1})$ solutions.

Let n denote an integer $\neq 0$. Also, $n = \lambda_1 \cdots \lambda_k = \mu_1\mu_2$. We now examine the number of solutions of the equations

$$x_k - y_\nu = \lambda_\nu \qquad (1 \leqslant \nu \leqslant k), \tag{12}$$

$$x_{k+1} - y_{k+1} = \mu_1 \tag{13}$$

and

$$g(y_1, \cdots, y_k, x_k, y_{k+1}, x_{k+1}) = \mu_2. \tag{14}$$

If $\lambda_1, \cdots, \lambda_k, \mu_1, \mu_2$ and x_k are given, then the unknowns $y_1, \cdots, y_k$ are uniquely determined by (12). Moreover, by (13) and (14) and the property of g, we know that there are at most k pairs of x_{k+1}, y_{k+1} satisfying (13) and (14).

But for a known n the number of sets of integers $\lambda_1, \cdots, \lambda_k, \mu_1, \mu_2$ is $\leq d^k(n)$. And for the known $\lambda_1, \cdots, \lambda_k, \mu_1, \mu_2$ and x_k, the number of solutions of (10) is $O(1)$. Hence the number of solutions of (10) is

$$\ll \sum_{x_k=1}^{P} \sum_{n}^{P^k} d^k(n) \ll P^{k+1} L^{2^k-1}.$$

Here we have used Lemma 2.5.

Lemma 5.5.

$$\int_0^1 \cdots \int_0^1 |S_k|^{2u} d\alpha_1 \cdots d\alpha_{k-2}\, d\alpha_k \leqslant (2u+1)\, P^{k-1} \int_0^1 \cdots \int_0^1 |C_k|^{2u} d\alpha_1 \cdots d\alpha_k.$$

Proof. Obviously we have

$$\int_0^1 \cdots \int_0^1 |S_k|^{2u} d\alpha_1 \cdots d\alpha_{k-2}\, d\alpha_k \leqslant \sum_{|N| \leqslant uP^{k-1}} \int_0^1 \cdots \int_0^1 |C_k|^{2u} e^{-2\pi i \alpha_{k-1} N} d\alpha_1 \cdots d\alpha_k$$

$$\leqslant (2u+1)\, P^{k-1} \int_0^1 \cdots \int_0^1 |C_k|^{2u} d\alpha_1 \cdots d\alpha_k.$$

§4. A FURTHER LEMMA

Lemma 5.6. *Let $g_\nu(x)$ be a polynomial in x with integral coefficients, and let*

$$g(x) = g_1(x)\,\alpha_1 + \cdots + g_s(x)\,\alpha_s$$

be a polynomial of the kth degree. Let

$$F=\sum_{x=1}^{P} e^{2\pi i g(x)}.$$

Then, letting Δ^{μ} *denote* $\Delta_{y_\mu}\cdots\Delta_{y_1}$, *for* $\mu=1,2,\cdots,k-1$

$$F^{2^\mu}\ll P^{2^\mu-1}+P^{2^\mu-\mu-1}\sum_{y_1}^{P}\cdots\sum_{y_\mu}^{P}\sum_{x_{\mu+1}}^{P}{}^{*}\, e(y_1\cdots y_\mu\,\Delta^\mu g(x_{\mu+1})),$$

where the asterisk means that either (i)

$$y_1\cdots y_\mu\,\Delta^\mu g_i(X)$$

is identically equal to zero or (ii)

$$y_1\cdots y_\mu\,\Delta^\mu g_i(x_{\mu+1})\neq 0\,.$$

Proof. This lemma can be deduced from Lemma 3.3. For if $y_1\cdots y_\mu\Delta^\mu g_i(X)$ is not identically equal to zero, then the number of solutions of

$$y_1\cdots y_\mu\,\Delta^\mu g_i(x_{\mu+1})=0$$

is $\ll P^\mu$.

§5. PROOF OF THE THEOREMS

B_2 and B_2' are immediate consequences of Lemma 5.4.

Proof of A_3. By Lemma 5.6, we obtain

$$|S_3|^4\ll P^3+P\sum_{y_1}^{P}\sum_{y_2}^{P}\sum_{x_3}^{P}{}^{*}\,e(y_1 y_2\,\Delta^2(\alpha_3 x_3^3+\alpha_1 x_3)).$$

Multiplying both members of this form by $|S_3|^6$ and integrating separately over α_1 and α_3 from 0 to 1, we obtain

$$\int_0^1\int_0^1 |S_3|^{10}\,d\alpha_1\,d\alpha_3\ll P^3\int_0^1\int_0^1 |S_3|^6\,d\alpha_1\,d\alpha_3+PR, \tag{1}$$

where R is the number of solutions of the equations

$$y_1 y_2\,\Delta^2 x_3^3=z_1^3+z_2^3+z_3^3-z_4^3-z_5^3-z_6^3,$$
$$0=z_1+z_2+z_3-z_4-z_5-z_6,\qquad z\ll P.$$

By Lemma 1.2 we know that

$$R\ll\sum_{z_1}^{P}\cdots\sum_{z_5}^{P} d^3(z_1^3+\cdots-z_5^3-(z_1+\cdots-z_5)^3)\ll P^{5+\varepsilon}.$$

By Lemma 5.2 and (1) we know that

$$\int_0^1\int_0^1 |S_3|^{10}\, d\alpha_1\, d\alpha_3 \ll P^{6+\varepsilon}. \tag{2}$$

Proof of B_3. By Lemma 5.6,

$$|C_3|^4 \ll P^3 + P \sum_{y_1}^{P}\sum_{y_2}^{P}\sum_{x_3}^{P}{}^{*} e(y_1 y_2 \Delta^2 (x_3^3\alpha_3 + x_3^2\alpha_2 + x_3\alpha_1)). \tag{3}$$

Multiplying by $|C_3|^8$ and integrating separately over α_1, α_2, α_3 from 0 to 1, we obtain, by Lemma 5.4,

$$\int_0^1\int_0^1\int_0^1 |C_3|^{12}\, d\alpha_1\, d\alpha_2\, d\alpha_3 \ll P^{7+\varepsilon} + PR,$$

where R is the number of solutions of the equations

$$\begin{aligned} y_1 y_2 w &= z_1^3 + \cdots - z_8^3, \\ 2 y_1 y_2 &= z_1^2 + \cdots - z_8^2, \\ 0 &= z_1 + \cdots - z_8, \qquad z_\nu \ll P, \end{aligned}$$

in which $w = \Delta^2 x_3^3 \ll P$.

By Lemma 5.2 the number of solutions of the equations

$$\begin{gathered} 2z_1^3 - w z_1^2 + \cdots - (2z_8^3 - w z_8^2) = 0, \\ z_1 + \cdots - z_8 = 0 \end{gathered}$$

for fixed w is $\ll P^{5+\epsilon}$. But for fixed $z_1, \cdots, z_8$, the number of values of y_1 and y_2 is $\le d(z_1^2 + \cdots - z_8^2) = O(P^{\epsilon})$. Therefore

$$R \ll \sum_w P^{5+\varepsilon} \ll P^{6+\varepsilon}.$$

Hence we obtain

$$\int_0^1\int_0^1\int_0^1 |C_3|^{12}\, d\alpha_1\, d\alpha_2\, d\alpha_3 \ll P^{7+\varepsilon}. \tag{4}$$

Multiplying (3) by $|C_3|^{12}$ and integrating, we find by (2) and (4) that

$$\int_0^1\int_0^1\int_0^1 |C_3|^{16}\, d\alpha_1\, d\alpha_2\, d\alpha_3 \ll P^{10+\varepsilon}.$$

Proof of A_4. By Lemma 5.6,

$$|S_4|^8 \ll P^7 + P^4 \sum_{y_1}^{P}\sum_{y_2}^{P}\sum_{y_3}^{P}\sum_{x_4}^{P}{}^{*} e(y_1 y_2 y_3 \Delta^3 (x_4^4\alpha_4 + x_4^2\alpha_2 + x_4\alpha_1)).$$

Multiplying by $|S_4|^8$ and integrating, we see from Lemma 5.2 that

$$\int_0^1\int_0^1\int_0^1 |S_4|^{16}\,d\alpha_1\,d\alpha_2\,d\alpha_4 \ll P^{11+\varepsilon} + P^4 R,$$

where R is the number of solutions of the equations

$$y_1 y_2 y_3 \Delta^3 x_4^4 = z_1^4 + \cdots - z_8^4,$$
$$0 = z_1^2 + \cdots - z_8^2,$$
$$0 = z_1 + \cdots - z_8, \qquad z \ll P.$$

According to theorem B_2, the number of sets of $z_1, \cdots, z_8$ that satisfy the last two equations is $\ll P^{8-3+\epsilon}$, and for fixed $z_1, \cdots, z_8$ we know from the first equation that the number of sets of y_1, y_2, y_3, x_4 is $\leq d^3(z_1^4 + \cdots - z_8^4) = O(P^\epsilon)$. Thus $R \ll P^{8-3+\epsilon} = P^{5+\epsilon}$ and therefore

$$\int_0^1\int_0^1\int_0^1 |S_4|^{16}\,d\alpha_1\,d\alpha_2\,d\alpha_4 \ll P^{11+\varepsilon}. \tag{5}$$

Repeating this process, we obtain

$$\int_0^1\int_0^1\int_0^1 |S_4|^{24}\,d\alpha_1\,d\alpha_2\,d\alpha_4 \ll P^{18+\varepsilon} \tag{6}$$

and

$$\int_0^1\int_0^1\int_0^1 |S_4|^{32}\,d\alpha_1\,d\alpha_2\,d\alpha_4 \ll P^{25+\varepsilon}. \tag{7}$$

Proof of B_4. By Lemma 5.4 we obviously have

$$\int_0^1\int_0^1\int_0^1\int_0^1 |C_4|^{10}\,d\alpha_1\,d\alpha_2\,d\alpha_3\,d\alpha_4 \ll P^{5+\varepsilon}.$$

By Lemma 5.6,

$$|C_4|^4 \ll P^3 + P \sum_{y_1}^{P}\sum_{y_2}^{P}\sum_{x_3}^{P}{}^{*} e(y_1 y_2 \Delta^2 (x_3^4\alpha_4 + x_3^3\alpha_3 + x_3^2\alpha_2 + x_3\alpha_1)).$$

Multiplying by $|C_4|^{10}$ and integrating, we obtain

$$\int_0^1\int_0^1\int_0^1\int_0^1 |C_4|^{14}\,d\alpha_1\,d\alpha_2\,d\alpha_3\,d\alpha_4 \ll P^{8+\varepsilon} + PR,$$

where R is the number of solutions of the equations

$$y_1 y_2 \Delta^2 x_3^4 = z_1^4 + \cdots - z_{10}^4,$$
$$y_1 y_2 \Delta^2 x_3^3 = z_1^3 + \cdots - z_{10}^3,$$
$$2 y_1 y_2 = z_1^2 + \cdots - z_{10}^2,$$
$$0 = z_1 + \cdots - z_{10}.$$

Let $\Delta^2 x_3^3 = 2w$ (obviously w is linear in y_1, y_2 and x_3, with integral coefficients). For fixed w, we know by (2) that the number of solutions of the equations

$$0 = z_1^3 - w z_1^2 + \cdots - (x_{10}^3 - w z_{10}),$$
$$0 = z_1 + \cdots - z_{10}$$

is $\ll P^{6+\epsilon}$. Hence we obtain $R \ll P^{7+\epsilon}$. Therefore

$$\int_0^1\int_0^1\int_0^1\int_0^1 |C_4|^{14}\, d\alpha_1\, d\alpha_2\, d\alpha_3\, d\alpha_4 \ll P^{8+\varepsilon}. \tag{8}$$

By Lemma 5.6, we obtain

$$|C_4|^8 \ll P^7 + P^4 \sum_{y_1}^{P}\sum_{y_2}^{P}\sum_{y_3}^{P}\sum_{x_4}^{P}{}^{*} e(y_1 y_2 y_3 \Delta^3 (x_4^4 \alpha_4 + x_4^3 \alpha_3 + x_4^2 \alpha_2 + x_4 \alpha_1)). \tag{9}$$

Multiplying by $|C_4|^{14}$ and integrating, we obtain

$$\int_0^1\int_0^1\int_0^1\int_0^1 |C_4|^{22}\, d\alpha_1\, d\alpha_2\, d\alpha_3\, d\alpha_4 \ll P^{15+\varepsilon} + P^4 R,$$

where R is the number of solutions of the equations

$$6 y_1 y_2 y_3 w = z_1^4 + \cdots - z_{14}^4,$$
$$6 y_1 y_2 y_3 = z_1^3 + \cdots - z_{14}^3,$$
$$0 = z_1^2 + \cdots - z_{14}^2,$$
$$0 = z_1 + \cdots - z_{14}$$

where $w = \Delta^3 x_4^4/6$ is linear in y_1, y_2, y_3 and x_4, with integral coefficients. Obviously, R does not exceed $\ll P^{1+\epsilon}$ times the number of solutions of the equations

$$z_1^4 - w z_1^3 + \cdots - (z_{14}^4 - w z_{14}^3) = 0,$$
$$z_1^2 + \cdots - z_{14}^2 = 0,$$
$$z_1 + \cdots - z_{14} = 0.$$

By Lemma 5.2 we know that

$$R \ll P^{1+\varepsilon} P^{14-4+\varepsilon} \ll P^{11+\varepsilon}$$

and

$$\int_0^1\int_0^1\int_0^1\int_0^1 |C_4|^{22}\, d\alpha_1 \cdots d\alpha_4 \ll P^{15+\varepsilon}. \tag{10}$$

Continuing the same process but substituting (5) and (6) for Lemma 5.2, we obtain

$$\int_0^1\int_0^1\int_0^1\int_0^1 |C_4|^{22+8\lambda}\, d\alpha_1 \cdots d\alpha_4 \ll P^{15+7\lambda+\varepsilon}, \qquad \lambda = 1, 2, 3. \tag{11}$$

We shall use below the abridged notation

$$\int f\, dx$$

for

$$\int_0^1\int_0^1 \cdots \int_0^1 f(x_1, \cdots, x_n)\, dx_1\, dx_2 \cdots dx_n.$$

Proof of A_5. By Lemma 5.6,

$$|S_5|^4 \ll P^3 + P \sum_{y_1}^{P} \sum_{y_2}^{P} \sum_{x_3}^{P} e(y_1 y_2 \Delta^2 g(x_3)),$$

where $g(x_3) = x_3^5\alpha_5 + x_3^3\alpha_3 + x_3^2\alpha_2 + x_3\alpha_1$. Multiplying by $|S_5|^{10}$ and integrating, we obtain

$$\int |S_5|^{14}\, d\alpha \ll P^{8+\varepsilon} + PR,$$

where R is the number of solutions of the equations[1)]

$$y_1 y_2 \Delta^2 x_3^5 = z_1^5 + \cdots - z_{10}^5,$$
$$2 y_1 y_2 w = z_1^3 + \cdots - z_{10}^3,$$
$$2 y_1 y_2 = z_1^2 + \cdots - z_{10}^2,$$
$$0 = z_1 + \cdots - z_{10}.$$

For fixed w, we know by A_3 that the number of solutions of

$$z_1^3 - w z_1^2 + \cdots - (z_{10}^3 - w z_{10}^2) = 0,$$
$$z_1 + \cdots - z_{10} = 0$$

is $\ll P^{6+\epsilon}$. Consequently, $R \ll P^{7+\epsilon}$. In this manner we get

$$\int |S_5|^{14}\, d\alpha \ll P^{8+\varepsilon}. \tag{12}$$

By Lemma 5.6

---

1) Here and below we will not repeat the definitions of w.

$$|S_5|^8 \ll P^7 + P^4 \sum_{y_1}^{P} \sum_{y_2}^{P} \sum_{y_3}^{P} \sum_{x_4}^{P}{}^{*} e(y_1 y_2 y_3 \Delta^3 g(x_4)).$$

Multiplying by $|S_5|^{14}$ and integrating, we obtain

$$\int |S_5|^{22}\, d\alpha \ll P^{15+\varepsilon} + P^4 R,$$

where R is the number of solutions of the equations

$$\begin{aligned} y_1 y_2 y_3 \Delta^3 x_3^5 &= z_1^5 + \cdots - z_{14}^5, \\ 6\, y_1 y_2 y_3 &= z_1^3 + \cdots - z_{14}^3, \\ 0 &= z_1^2 + \cdots - z_{14}^2, \\ 0 &= z_1 + \cdots - z_{14} \end{aligned}$$

Therefore by B_2 we know that $R \ll P^{14-3+\epsilon}$. Hence we obtain

$$\int |S_5|^{22}\, d\alpha \ll P^{15+\varepsilon}.$$

By Lemma 5.6,

$$|S_5|^{16} \ll P^{15} + P^{11} \sum_{y_1}^{P} \sum_{y_2}^{P} \sum_{y_3}^{P} \sum_{y_4}^{P} \sum_{x_5}^{P}{}^{*} e(y_1 y_2 y_3 y_4 \Delta^4 g(x_5)).$$

Multiplying by $|S_5|^{22}$ and integrating, we obtain by B_3

$$\int |S_5|^{38}\, d\alpha \ll P^{30+\varepsilon}. \tag{13}$$

Repeating this process we obtain

$$\int |S_5|^{38+16\lambda}\, d\alpha \ll P^{30+15\lambda+\varepsilon}, \qquad \lambda = 1, 2, 3. \tag{14}$$

§6. PROOF OF THE THEOREMS (continued)

When $k \geq 5$, let $l \geq 1$, $a = 1/k$ and

$$u = \tfrac{1}{4} k(k+1) + \begin{cases} 0 & \text{if } k \equiv 0, 3 \pmod 4, \\ \tfrac{1}{2} & \text{if } k \equiv 1, 2 \pmod 4. \end{cases} \tag{1}$$

In Lemma 4.7 take $u_0 = k + 1$. By Lemma 5.4 we know that for some $\epsilon > 0$ the hypothesis of this lemma is true when $v_0 = k + 1 + \epsilon$. Hence we obtain

$$\int |C_k(P)|^{2u}\, d\alpha \leqslant b(k,\varepsilon)\, P^{2u-\frac{1}{2}k(k+1)+\delta+\varepsilon}, \tag{2}$$

where

$$\delta = \frac{k^2(k^2-k-2)}{2(u+k^2-k-1)}. \tag{3}$$

By l-fold application of Lemma 4.4 we obtain

$$\int |C_k(P)|^{2(u+lk)}\, d\alpha \ll P^{2kl-\frac{1}{2}k(k+1)+\frac{1}{2}k(k+1)(1-a)^l+2u(1-(1-a)^l)+\varepsilon}$$

$$\times \int |C_k(P^{(1-a)^l})|^{2u}\, d\alpha \ll P^{2(u+lk)-\frac{1}{2}k(k+1)+\delta(1-a)^l+\varepsilon}. \tag{4}$$

Now when $5 \le k \le 10$ we obtain the values of l given in the following table and calculate the corresponding values of $\delta(1-a)^l$ and $2(u+lk)$:

k	5	6	7	8	9	10
u	8	11	14	18	23	28
l	5	10	16	23	29	34
$\delta(1-a)^l <$	2.74	2.04	1.52	1.098	0.991	1.046
$2(u+lk)$	66	142	252	404	568	736

Proof of B_5. By (4) and the above table, we obtain

$$\int |C_5|^{66}\, d\alpha \ll P^{66-15+2.74+\varepsilon}. \tag{5}$$

By Lemma 5.6,

$$|C_5|^{16} \ll P^{15} + P^{11} \sum_{y_1}^{P} \sum_{y_2}^{P} \sum_{y_3}^{P} \sum_{y_4}^{P} \sum_{x_5}^{P}{}^{*}\, e(y_1 y_2 y_3 y_4 \Delta^4 g(x_5)). \tag{6}$$

Thus, multiplying both members of this inequality by $|C_5|^{66}$ and integrating, we obtain

$$\int |C_5|^{82}\, d\alpha \ll P^{82-15+1.74+\varepsilon} + P^{12+\varepsilon} \int |S_5|^{66}\, d\alpha. \tag{7}$$

By B_5 and the properties of a convex function, we see at once that

$$\int |S_5|^{66}\, d\alpha \ll P^{45+12\times\frac{15}{16}+\varepsilon} = P^{56.25+\varepsilon}.$$

So by (7) we have

$$\int |C_5|^{82}\, d\alpha \ll P^{82-15+1.74+\varepsilon}. \tag{8}$$

By (5) and (8), we obtain

$$\int |C_5|^{78}\, d\alpha \ll P^{78-15+1.99+\varepsilon}. \tag{9}$$

Repeating the above process, we obtain

$$\int |C_5|^{110}\, d\alpha \ll P^{95+\varepsilon}. \tag{10}$$

Proof of A_6 and B_6. By (4) and the above table, we obtain

$$\int |C_6|^{142}\, d\alpha \ll P^{142-21+2.04+\varepsilon}. \tag{11}$$

By Lemma 5.5, we obtain

$$\int |S_6|^{142}\, d\alpha \ll P^{142-16+2.04+\varepsilon}. \tag{12}$$

Applying the case $\mu = 5$ in Lemma 5.6 and using B_4 we obtain

$$\int |S_6|^{142+32\lambda}\, d\alpha \ll P^{142+32\lambda-16+(2.04-2\lambda)+\varepsilon}, \qquad \lambda = 1, 2. \tag{13}$$

By (13) we obtain

$$\int |S_6|^{176}\, d\alpha \ll P^{176-16+0.98+\varepsilon}. \tag{14}$$

Again applying the case $\mu = 5$ in Lemma 5.6 and using B_4, we accordingly obtain

$$\int |S_6|^{208}\, d\alpha \ll P^{208-16+\varepsilon}. \tag{15}$$

By (11) we directly obtain

$$\int |C_6|^{174}\, d\alpha \ll P^{155.04+\varepsilon}. \tag{16}$$

Again using the above inequality and applying the case $\mu = 5$ in Lemma 5.6 and (13), we obtain

$$\int |C_6|^{206}\, d\alpha \ll P^{186.04+\varepsilon}. \tag{17}$$

By (16) and (17), we obtain

$$\int |C_6|^{176}\, d\alpha \ll P^{156.98}. \tag{18}$$

Again, repeating the above process, we obtain

$$\int |C_6|^{208}\, d\alpha \ll P^{187.98+\varepsilon}. \tag{19}$$

$$\int |C_6|^{240}\, d\alpha \ll P^{219+\varepsilon}. \tag{20}$$

Proof of A_7 and B_7. By (4) and the listed table, we obtain

$$\int |C_7|^{252}\, d\alpha \ll P^{224+1.52+\varepsilon}. \tag{21}$$

By Lemma 5.5,

$$\int |S_7|^{252}\, d\alpha \ll P^{230+1.52+\varepsilon}. \tag{22}$$

Applying the case $\mu = 6$ in Lemma 5.6 and using B_5, we obtain

$$\int |S_7|^{316}\, d\alpha \ll P^{294+0.52+\varepsilon}. \tag{23}$$

By (22) and (23), we obtain

$$\int |S_7|^{286}\, d\alpha \ll P^{264+0.99+\varepsilon}. \tag{24}$$

Again applying the case $\mu = 6$ in Lemma 5.6 and using B_5, we accordingly obtain

$$\int |S_7|^{350}\, d\alpha \ll P^{328+\varepsilon}. \tag{25}$$

By (21), we directly obtain

$$\int |C_7|^{316}\, d\alpha \ll P^{288+1.52+\varepsilon}. \tag{26}$$

Applying the case $\mu = 6$ in Lemma 5.6 and (23), we obtain

$$\int |C_7|^{380}\, d\alpha \ll P^{352+0.52+\varepsilon}. \tag{27}$$

By (26) and (27), we obtain

$$\int |C_7|^{350}\, d\alpha \ll P^{322+0.99+\varepsilon}. \tag{28}$$

Applying the case $\mu = 6$ in Lemma 5.6 and using B_7, we accordingly obtain

$$\int |C_7|^{414}\, d\alpha \ll P^{386+\varepsilon}. \tag{29}$$

Proof of A_8 **and** B_8**.** By (4) and the above table, we obtain

$$\int |C_8|^{404}\, d\alpha \ll P^{368+1.098+\varepsilon}, \tag{30}$$

$$\int |C_8|^{420}\, d\alpha \ll P^{384+1.098\times\frac{7}{8}+\varepsilon} = P^{384+0.962+\varepsilon}. \tag{31}$$

From these two inequalities we obtain

$$\int |C_8|^{416}\, d\alpha \ll P^{380+0.996+\varepsilon}. \tag{32}$$

As in the proof for A_7 and B_7, we obtain, by (32),

$$\int |S_8|^{544}\, d\alpha \ll P^{515+\varepsilon}. \tag{33}$$

$$\int |C_8|^{672}\, d\alpha \ll P^{636+\varepsilon}. \tag{34}$$

In exactly the same way as for A_8 and B_8, we obtain the following results:

A_9 :
$$\int |S_9|^{824}\, d\alpha \ll P^{787+\varepsilon}. \tag{35}$$

B_9 :
$$\int |C_9|^{1080}\, d\alpha \ll P^{1035+\varepsilon}. \tag{36}$$

A_{10} :
$$\int |S_{10}|^{1258}\, d\alpha \ll P^{1212+\varepsilon}. \tag{37}$$

B_{10} :
$$\int |C_{10}|^{1770}\, d\alpha \ll P^{1715+\varepsilon}. \tag{38}$$

§7. THE RELATION BETWEEN A SINGLE SUM AND THE MEAN VALUE

Lemma 5.7. *Let* $\tau \geq 1$ *and*

$$\left|\alpha - \frac{h}{q}\right| \leqslant \frac{\tau}{q^2}, \qquad (h, q) = 1.$$

Then the number of distinct integers y *satisfying the inequality*

$$\{\alpha y\} \leqslant \frac{V}{q}, \qquad f \leqslant y \leqslant f + N,$$

is

$$\leqslant 2(V+2\tau)\left(\frac{N}{q}+1\right).$$

Proof. If we can prove that the number of distinct integers y satisfying

$$\{\alpha y\} \leqslant \frac{V}{q}, \qquad f \leqslant y \leqslant f+q, \tag{1}$$

is $\leq 2(V+2\tau)$, then the lemma is proved. Now write

$$y=f+z, \qquad \alpha=\frac{h}{q}+\frac{\tau\vartheta}{q^2}, \qquad |\vartheta| \leqslant 1.$$

Then

$$\alpha y=\frac{hz}{q}+\frac{\tau\vartheta z}{q^2}+\frac{hf}{q}+\frac{\tau\vartheta f}{q^2}$$

$$=\frac{hz+[c]+(c-[c])+\tau\vartheta z/q}{q}, \qquad \left|\frac{\tau\vartheta z}{q}\right| \leqslant \tau,$$

where $c = hf + \tau\vartheta f/q$.

If $q \leq 2(V + 2\tau)$, the theorem is obviously true. When z runs through a complete set of residues $\bmod q$, then $w = hz + [c]$ does likewise. Therefore

$$\alpha y=\frac{w+\sigma(w)}{q},$$

where

$$-\tau \leqslant c-[c]-\tau \leqslant \sigma(w) \leqslant c-[c]+\tau<1+\tau.$$

The w satisfying the inequality

$$V+\tau \leqslant w<q-\tau-V-1 \tag{2}$$

obviously also satisfies the inequality

$$\frac{V}{q} \leqslant \frac{w+\sigma(w)}{q}<1-\frac{V}{q}.$$

But it does not satisfy (1). The number of distinct integers w satisfying (2) is $\geq q - 2V - 2\tau - 2$, and therefore the number of distinct integers satisfying (1) is

$$\leqslant q-(q-2V-2\tau-2)=2V+2\tau+2 \leqslant 2(V+2\tau).$$

Lemma 5.8. *Let $Y \geq 1$. Further, let $A_0, A_1, \cdots, A_{k-1}$ be integers satisfying*

$$A_0=1, \qquad |A_r| \leqslant (r+1)\, Y^r.$$

Then from the equations

$$v_r = \sum_{s=r}^{k} \binom{s+1}{r} A_{s-r}\, u_s \tag{3}$$

we see that $(k+1)k\cdots(r+1)u_r$ *is linear in* $v_1, \cdots, v_r$. *ts coefficients are all integers, i.e.,*

$$(k+1)\, k \cdots (r+1)\, u_r = \sum_{s=r}^{k} a_{rs}\, v_s\,, \tag{4}$$

and

$$a_{rs} = O(Y^{s-r})\,.$$

Proof. If $r = k$, then this lemma is obviously true. Suppose that it is also true for $k, k-1, \cdots, r+1$. By (3), we know that

$$(k+1)\cdots(r+1)\, u_r = (k+1)\cdots(r+2)\left(v_r - \sum_{s=r+1}^{k} \binom{s+1}{r} A_{s-r}\, u_s\right)$$

$$= (k+1)\cdots(r+2)\, v_r - \sum_{s=r+1}^{k} \binom{s+1}{r} A_{s-r} \frac{s\,!}{(r+1)!}\,(k+1)\cdots(s+1)\, u_s$$

$$= (k+1)\cdots(r+2)\, v_r - \sum_{s=r+1}^{k} \binom{s+1}{r} A_{s-r} \frac{s\,!}{(r+1)!} \sum_{s\leqslant u\leqslant k} a_{su}\, v_u\,.$$

If $k \geq u > r$, then

$$a_{ru} = \sum_{r+1\leqslant s\leqslant u} \binom{s+1}{r} A_{s-r} \frac{s\,!}{(r+1)!}\, a_{su}$$

is obviously an integer, and

$$a_{ru} = O\Big(\sum_{r+1\leqslant s\leqslant u} |A_{s-r}|\, |a_{su}|\Big)$$

$$= O(Y^{s-r} \cdot Y^{u-s}) = O(Y^{u-r})\,.$$

If $u = r$, then obviously

$$a_{rr} = O(1)\,.$$

Lemma 5.9. *Let* $\xi_1, \cdots, \xi_n$ *be real. Then, for integers* $l_1, \cdots, l_n$, *we have the inequality*

$$\left\{\sum_{i=1}^{n} l_i\, \xi_i\right\} \leqslant \sum_{i=1}^{n} |\, l_i\,|\, \{\xi_i\}.$$

This lemma is a corollary of the inequality

$$\{\xi_1 \pm \xi_2\} \leqslant \{\xi_1\} + \{\xi_2\}.$$

Lemma 5.10. *Let $\alpha_k, \cdots, \alpha_1$ be real and*

$$f(x) = \alpha_k x^k + \cdots + \alpha_1 x.$$

Suppose, given $0 < \delta_1 < 1$ and T an arbitrary integer, that

$$\int_0^1 \cdots \int_0^1 \left| \sum_{x=T+1}^{T+P} e(f(x)) \right|^{2t_1} d\alpha_1 \cdots d\alpha_k = O(P^{2t_1 - \frac{1}{2}k(k+1)+\delta_1}), \tag{5}$$

where the constants included in the symbol O are dependent on t_1, δ_1 and k (though, as used below, t_1 and δ_1 will both be functions of k). On this assumption, we have:

Let $\beta_{k+1}, \cdots, \beta_1$ be real and

$$F(x) = \beta_{k+1} x^{k+1} + \cdots + \beta_1 x.$$

Further, let r be an integer satisfying $2 \leq r \leq k+1$. Supposing that

$$\left| \beta_r - \frac{h}{q} \right| \leqslant \frac{1}{q^2}, \qquad (h, q) = 1, \qquad 1 \leqslant q \leqslant P^r, \tag{6}$$

then, for some $T = O(P)$, we have

$$S = \sum_{x=T+1}^{T+P} e(F(x)) = O \begin{cases} P^{1-\rho} \left(\dfrac{P}{q} \right)^{\frac{1}{2t_1+k+1}} & \text{if } 1 \leqslant q \leqslant P, \\ P^{1-\rho} & \text{if } P \leqslant q \leqslant P^{r-1}, \\ P^{1-\rho} \left(\dfrac{q}{P^{r-1}} \right)^{\frac{1}{2t_1+k+1}} & \text{if } P^{r-1} \leqslant q \leqslant P^r, \end{cases}$$

where

$$\rho = \frac{1-\delta_1}{2t_1+k+1}.$$

Proof. (This important technique was invented by Vinogradov.) When $0 < y \leq Y < P$, let

$$S_0 = \sum_{x=T+1}^{T+P} e(F(x+y) - F(y)) = \sum_{x=T+1}^{T+P} e(\phi(x)),$$

where

$$\phi(x) = Y_1 x + \cdots + Y_{k+1} x^{k+1},$$

$$Y_j = Y_j(y) = \frac{1}{j!} \frac{d^j}{dy^j} F(y)$$

$$= \binom{k+1}{j} \beta_{k+1} y^{k+1-j} + \cdots + \binom{j+1}{j} \beta_{j+1} y + \beta_j. \qquad (7)$$

Obviously we have

$$|S_0| = |S| + 2\vartheta y, \qquad |\vartheta| \leqslant 1.$$

Hence

$$|S| = O\left(Y^{-1} \sum_{y=1}^{Y} |S_0| + Y\right).$$

Using Hölder's inequality twice, we have

$$|S|^{2t_1} = O\left(\left(Y^{-1} \sum_{y=1}^{Y} |S_0|\right)^{2t_1} + Y^{2t_1}\right) = O\left(Y^{-1} \sum_{y=1}^{Y} |S_0|^{2t_1} + Y^{2t_1}\right). \qquad (8)$$

Let

$$S_1 = \sum_{x=T+1}^{T+P} e(\alpha_1 x + \cdots + \alpha_k x^k + \beta_{k+1} x^{k+1}).$$

For a fixed y, the numbers $Y_1, \cdots, Y_k$ are also fixed. Now let us discuss the set of real numbers $\alpha_1, \cdots, \alpha_k$ satisfying

$$\{\alpha_1 - Y_1\} \leqslant \frac{1}{2} P^{-2} Y, \cdots, \{\alpha_k - Y_k\} \leqslant \frac{1}{2} P^{-k-1} Y, \qquad 0 \leqslant \alpha_i < 1,$$

Use $\Omega(y)$ to denote the domain determined by these $(\alpha_1, \cdots, \alpha_k)$. If $(\alpha_1, \cdots, \alpha_k)$ is in $\Omega(y)$, then

$$S_0 = S_1 + O(Y),$$

and we accordingly obtain

$$|S_0|^{2t_1} = O(|S_1|^{2t_1}) + O(Y^{2t_1}).$$

Integrating over both members of the equality, where the integration is taken over $\Omega(y)$, we obtain

$$|S_0|^{2t_1} = O\left(P^{\frac{1}{2}k(k+1)+k} Y^{-k} \int \cdots \int_{\Omega(y)} |S_1|^{2t_1} d\alpha_1 \cdots d\alpha_k\right) + O(Y^{2t_1}), \qquad (9)$$

where we have used

$$\int_{\Omega(y)} \cdots \int d\alpha_1 \cdots d\alpha_k \gg \prod_{i=1}^{k} (P^{-(i+1)} Y) = P^{-\frac{1}{2}k(k+1)-k} Y^k .$$

Combining (8) and (9), we see that

$$|S|^{2t_1} = O\left(P^{\frac{1}{2}k(k+1)+k} Y^{-k-1} \sum_{y=1}^{Y} \int_{\Omega(y)} \cdots \int |S_1|^{2t_1} d\alpha_1 \cdots d\alpha_k\right) + O(Y^{2t_1}) . \qquad (10)$$

We shall now find the number of distinct y's such that $\Omega(y)$ also includes a fixed point. If $\Omega(y)$ and $\Omega(y_0)$ have a common point, then

$$\{Y_r(y) - Y_r(y_0)\} \leqslant P^{-r-1} Y , \qquad 1 \leqslant r \leqslant k .$$

Let $v_r = Y_r(y) - Y_r(y_0)$, $u_s = \beta_{s+1}(y - y_0)$ and

$$A_{s-r} = \frac{y^{s-r+1} - y_0^{s-r+1}}{y - y_0} .$$

By (7) we know that

$$v_r = \sum_{r \leqslant s \leqslant k} \binom{s+1}{r} \beta_{s+1} (y^{s-r+1} - y_0^{s-r+1})$$

$$= \sum_{r \leqslant s \leqslant k} \binom{s+1}{r} A_{s-r} u_s .$$

By Lemmas 5.8 and 5.9 we know that when $1 \le r < k$,

$$\left\{\frac{(k+1)!}{r!} u_r\right\} \leqslant \sum_{r \leqslant s \leqslant k} |a_{rs}| \{v_s\}$$

$$= O\left(\sum_{r \leqslant s \leqslant k} Y^{s-r} P^{-s-1} Y\right)$$

$$= O(Y P^{-r-1}) .$$

If we substitute r for $r - 1$, then when $2 \le r < k + 1$, we obtain

$$\left\{\frac{(k+1)!}{(r-1)!} \beta_r (y - y_0)\right\} = O(Y P^{-r}) , \qquad (11)$$

where

$$1 \leqslant y \leqslant Y . \qquad (12)$$

By Lemma 5.7, we know that the number of distinct y's satisfying (11) and (12) is

$$O\left(\left(\frac{Yq}{P^r}+1\right)\left(1+\frac{Y}{q}\right)\right)=O\left(1+\frac{Y}{q}+\frac{Yq}{P^r}\right)$$

(since $Y^2 \le P^2 \le P^r$).

Therefore, each point $(\alpha_1, \cdots, \alpha_k)$ in the k-dimensional unit cube

$$0 \le \alpha_1 \le 1, \cdots, 0 \le \alpha_k \le 1$$

is covered by at most $O(1 + Y/q + Yq/P^r)$ of the $\Omega(y)$ $(y = 1, \cdots, Y)$. Hence by (10) we know that

$$|S|^{2t_1} = O\left(P^{\frac{1}{2}k(k+1)+k}\, Y^{-k-1}\left(1+\frac{Y}{q}+\frac{Yq}{P^r}\right)\int_0^1\cdots\int_0^1 |S_1|^{2t_1}\, d\alpha_1 \cdots d\alpha_k\right)$$
$$+\, O(Y^{2t_1}).$$

By

$$\int_0^1\cdots\int_0^1 |S_1|^{2t_1}\, d\alpha_1\cdots d\alpha_k \leqslant \int_0^1\cdots\int_0^1 \left|\sum_{x=T+1}^{T+P} e(f(x))\right|^{2t_1} d\alpha_1\cdots d\alpha_k$$

and (5) we know that

$$|S|^{2t_1} = O\left(P^{\frac{1}{2}k(k+1)+k}\, Y^{-k-1}\left(1+\frac{Y}{q}+\frac{Yq}{P^r}\right)P^{2t_1-\frac{1}{2}k(k+1)+\delta_1}\right)+O(Y^{2t_1})$$
$$= O\left(P^{2t_1+k+\delta_1}\, Y^{-k-1}\left(1+\frac{Y}{q}+\frac{Yq}{P^r}\right)\right)+O(Y^{2t_1}).$$

Taking

$$Y = \begin{cases} \left[P^{1-\rho}\left(\dfrac{P}{q}\right)^{\frac{1}{2t_1+k+1}}\right]+1 & \text{if } P^{\delta_1} \leqslant q \leqslant P, \\ [P^{1-\rho}]+1 & \text{if } P \leqslant q \leqslant P^{r-1}, \\ \left[P^{1-\rho}\left(\dfrac{q}{P^{r-1}}\right)^{\frac{1}{2t_1+k+1}}\right]+1 & \text{if } P^{r-1} \leqslant q \leqslant P^{r-\delta_1}, \end{cases}$$

we obtain the lemma.

§8. ESTIMATES FOR TRIGONOMETRIC SUMS

Theorem 9. *We suppose that the numerical values of* σ_k *are given by the following table:*

k	2	3	4	5	6	7	8	9	10	11	$\geqslant 12$
σ_k	4	9	20	51	116	247	422	681	1090	1781	$2k^2(2\log k+\log\log k+3)$

Let $2 \le r \le k$, *and*

$$\left|\alpha_r - \frac{h}{q}\right| \leqslant \frac{1}{q^2}, \qquad (h, q) = 1, \qquad 1 \leqslant q \leqslant P^r; \tag{1}$$

further, let

$$f(x) = \alpha_k x^k + \cdots + \alpha_1 x.$$

Then, when $P \le q \le P^{r-1}$,

$$\sum_{x=1}^{P} e(f(x)) = O\left(P^{1-\frac{1}{\sigma_k}+\varepsilon}\right). \tag{2}$$

Proof. When $k \le 11$, this result can be deduced directly from Lemma 5.10 (in which $\delta_1 = \epsilon$, $\sigma_k = 2t_1 + k$) and Theorem 7.

When $k > 11$, we take, in Theorem 5,

$$l = \left[\frac{2\log k + \log\log k}{-\log\left(1-\frac{1}{k}\right)}\right] + 1,$$

and then

$$t_1 = \tfrac{1}{4}k(k-1) + l(k-1) + \begin{cases} 0 & \text{if } k \equiv 0, 3 \pmod 4, \\ \tfrac{1}{2} & \text{if } k \equiv 1, 2 \pmod 4, \end{cases}$$

$$\delta_1 = \frac{1}{2}k(k-1)\left(1-\frac{1}{k-1}\right)^l.$$

Since

$$k-1 \leqslant \frac{1}{-\log\left(1-\frac{1}{k}\right)} = \left(\frac{1}{k} + \frac{1}{2k^2} + \frac{1}{3k^3} + \cdots\right)^{-1} \leqslant k,$$

we obviously obtain

$$\frac{1}{2}(k+1) < l < k(2\log k + \log\log k) + 1,$$

$$\delta_1 < \frac{1}{2}k^2\left(1-\frac{1}{k}\right)^l \leqslant \frac{1}{2\log k} < \frac{1}{2}.$$

Since for x satisfying $0 \le x \le 1/2$ we always have

$$(1-x)^{-1} \leqslant 1 + 2x,$$

it follows that

$$\frac{1}{\rho} = \frac{2t_1+k}{1-\delta_1} \leqslant \left(\frac{1}{2} k^2 + 2l(k-1) + k + 1\right)(1+2\delta_1)$$

$$\leqslant \left\{\frac{1}{2} k^2 + 2k(2k \log k + k \log \log k + 1)\right\}\left(1 + \frac{1}{\log k}\right)$$

$$\leqslant 2k^2\left(2 \log k + \log \log k + 2 + \frac{1}{4} + \frac{\log \log k}{\log k} + \frac{1}{4 \log k} + \frac{1}{k} + \frac{1}{k \log k}\right)$$

$$\leqslant 2k^2(2 \log k + \log \log k + 3). \tag{3}$$

Hence, by Theorem 5 and Lemma 5.10, we obtain the theorem.

Another corollary of Theorem 7 and Lemma 5.10 is as follows:

Lemma 5.11. *Supposing that* $k \le 11$, *then by the conditions of Theorem 9 we have*

$$\sum_{x=1}^{P} e^{2\pi i f(x)} \ll \begin{cases} P^{1-\frac{1}{\sigma_k}+\varepsilon}\left(\dfrac{P}{q}\right)^{\frac{1}{\sigma_k}} & \text{if } 1 \leqslant q \leqslant P, \\ P^{1-\frac{1}{\sigma_k}+\varepsilon}\left(\dfrac{q}{P^{r-1}}\right)^{\frac{1}{\sigma_k}} & \text{if } P^{r-1} \leqslant q \leqslant P^r. \end{cases}$$

When $k \ge 12$, we can not obtain such a precise result. However, for the applications below, we first provide a preliminary result as follows:

Lemma 5.12. *If* $k \ge 12$, *then by the conditions of Theorem 9, when* $P^{1/(4k)} \le q \le P$ *and* $P^{r-1} \le q \le P^{r-1/(4k)}$, *we have*

$$\sum_{x=1}^{P} e^{2\pi i f(x)} \ll P^{1-\frac{1}{\rho'}}, \qquad \rho' = 50 k^3 \log k.$$

Proof. By Lemma 5.10 we know that

$$\sum_{x=1}^{P} e^{2\pi i f(x)} \ll P^{1-\rho} \left\{\begin{matrix} P^{\frac{1}{2t_1+k} - \frac{1}{4k(2t_1+k)}} \\ P^{\frac{1-r}{2t_1+k} + \frac{r-1/4k}{2t_1+k}} \end{matrix}\right\} \ll P^{1-\frac{1/4k-\delta_1}{2t_1+k}}.$$

Here

$$\delta_1 = \frac{1}{2} k(k-1)\left(1 - \frac{1}{k-1}\right)^l.$$

Taking

$$l = \left[\frac{4 \log k}{-\log(1 - 1/k)}\right] + 1,$$

then

$$\frac{1}{2}(k+1) \leqslant l \leqslant 4k \log k + 1$$

and

$$\delta_1 \leqslant k^2\left(1 - \frac{1}{k}\right)^l \leqslant \frac{1}{k^2}.$$

As in the case (3), we obtain

$$\begin{aligned}
&(2t_1 + k + 1) \Big/ \left(\frac{1}{4k} - \delta_1\right) \\
&\leqslant \left(\frac{1}{2} k^2 + 2lk\right) \Big/ \left(\frac{1}{4k} - \frac{1}{k^2}\right) \\
&\leqslant \left(\frac{1}{2} k^2 + 8k^2 \log k + 2k\right) 4k \left(1 - \frac{4}{k}\right)^{-1} \\
&\leqslant 4k^3 \log k \left(8 + \frac{1}{2 \log k} + \frac{2}{k \log k}\right)\left(1 - \frac{4}{k}\right)^{-1} \\
&\leqslant 4k^3 \log k \left(8 + \frac{2}{3 \log 12}\right)\left(\frac{3}{2}\right) \\
&< 50\, k^3 \log k.
\end{aligned}$$

Remark. A more complete result than Lemma 5.12 is as follows: *If* $k \leq 9$ *and* $P^{r-1} \leq q \leq P^r$, *then*

$$\sum_{x=1}^{P} e^{2\pi i f(x)} \ll P^{1-1/\sigma'}\left(\frac{q}{P^{r-1}}\right)^{1/\sigma'},$$

where

$$\sigma' = k^3(3 \log k + \log \log k + 5).$$

This result can be deduced from Theorem 16 below.

CHAPTER VI

TRIGONOMETRIC SUMS DEPENDING ON PRIME NUMBERS

§1. FORMULATION OF THEOREM 10

The object of this chapter is to prove Theorem 10, a basic tool for developing the additive theory of prime numbers. Theorem 10 is essentially due to I. M. Vinogradov [1)] and is presented here in a form adapted to the particular problems discussed in this book. We frequently use L to represent $\log P$.

Theorem 10. *Let* $0 < Q \leq c_1(k) L^{\sigma_1}$ *and*

$$S = \sum_{\substack{p \leqslant P \\ p \equiv t \pmod{Q}}} e(f(p)),$$

in which

$$f(x) = \frac{h}{q} x^k + \alpha_1 x^{k-1} + \cdots + \alpha_k, \qquad (h, q) = 1,$$

the numbers α *being real. Suppose that* $L^{\sigma} < q \leq P^k L^{-\sigma}$. *For arbitrary* $\sigma_0 > 0$, *when* $\sigma \geq 2^{6k}(\sigma_0 + \sigma_1 + 1)$, *we always have*

$$|S| \leqslant c_2(k) P L^{-\sigma_0} Q^{-1}.$$

§2. CERTAIN ESSENTIAL LEMMAS

Lemma 6.1. *When* $\sigma_2 \geq 2^{3t} - 1$,

$$\sum_{0 < z \leqslant M}' (d(z))^t = O(M(\log M)^{-\sigma_2}),$$

where Σ' *denotes a sum in which* z *satisfies the inequality*

$$(\log M)^{\sigma_2} \leqslant c_3(d(z))^t.$$

---

1) Trudy Mat. Inst. Tbilisi III (1937), 1–34, 35–61.

Proof. By Lemma 2.5, we obtain

$$(\log M)^{2\sigma_2} \sum_{0<z\leqslant M}' (d(z))^t \ll \sum_{0<z\leqslant M} (d(z))^{3t}$$
$$\ll M(\log M)^{2^{3t}-1} \ll M(\log M)^{\sigma_2}.$$

Hence we obtain the present lemma.

Lemma 6.2. *Let l be a positive integer ($\leq L^{\sigma_3}$), let Q be a positive integer $\ll L^{\sigma_4}$, and let*

$$f(x) = \frac{h}{q}x^k + \alpha_1 x^{k-1} + \cdots + \alpha_k, \qquad (h,q)=1,$$

where the α are real. Suppose that $L^{\sigma} < q \leq P^k L^{-\sigma}$. Then, when

$$\sigma \geqslant 2^k(\sigma_0+\sigma_3) + 2k\,\sigma_4 + 2^{3(k-2)}$$

we have

$$S = \sum_{\substack{lx\leqslant P \\ lx\equiv t \pmod Q}} e(f(lx)) = O(P_1 L^{-\sigma_0}),$$

where $P_1 = P/Ql$.

Proof. If the congruence $lx \equiv t \pmod Q$ has no solution, then the lemma is clear without proof. If we let t' be the least positive solution of this congruence, the other solutions can be expressed in the form $x = t' + Qy/(l, Q)$, with $0 \leq y \leq P_2 = P(Q, l)/Ql$. Hence S can be written as

$$S = \sum_{y\leqslant P_2} e(f(l'Qy+lt')), \qquad l' = l/(Q,l).$$

If $k = 1$, we obtain by Lemma 1.8

$$|S| = \left| \sum_{x\leqslant P_2} e\left(\frac{h}{q}\, l'Qx+lt'\right)\right| \leqslant q \leqslant PL^{-\sigma} \ll P_1 L^{-\sigma_0}.$$

Suppose that $k > 1$. By Lemmas 3.3, 3.4 and 1.8, we know that

$$|S|^{2^{k-1}} \ll P_2^{2^{k-1}-1} + P_2^{2^{k-1}-k} \sum_{\xi_1=1}^{P_2} \cdots \sum_{\xi_{k-1}=1}^{P_2} \min\left(P_2, \frac{1}{2\left\{l'^k Q^k k! \frac{h}{q}\xi_1\cdots\xi_{k-1}\right\}}\right), \tag{1}$$

or

$$|S|^{2^{k-1}} \ll P_2^{2^{k-1}-1} + P_2^{2^{k-1}-k} \sum,$$

where Σ denotes the sum on the right side of the preceding inequality.

Letting

$$z = l'^k Q^k k! \xi_1 \cdots \xi_{k-1}, \tag{2}$$

we obtain $z \le l'^k Q^k k! P_2^{k-1} = M$.

For a fixed z, the number of solutions of the form (2) is $\le d^{k-2}(z)$. By Lemma 6.1, when $\sigma_2 \ge 2^{3(k-2)} - 1$,

$$\Sigma \ll P_2 \sum_{z=1}^{M}{}' d^{k-2}(z) + L^{\sigma_2} \sum_{z=1}^{M} \min\left(P_2, \frac{1}{2\{hz/q\}}\right)$$

$$\ll M L^{-\sigma_2} P_2 + L^{\sigma_2} \sum_{z=1}^{M} \min\left(P_2, \frac{1}{2\{hz/q\}}\right).$$

(This is because $\log M \gg \log P$.) By Lemma 3.5 and $MP_2 \ll l'^k Q^k P_2^k = P^k \ll P_1^k L^{k(\sigma_3+\sigma_4)}$, we obtain

$$\Sigma \ll M L^{-\sigma_2} P_2 + L^{\sigma_2}\left(\frac{M}{q} + 1\right)(P_2 + q \log q)$$

$$\ll P_1^k (L^{k(\sigma_3+\sigma_4)-\sigma_2} + L^{\sigma_2+k(\sigma_3+\sigma_4)-\sigma+1}).$$

If we take

$$\sigma_2 = 2^{k-1}(\sigma_0+\sigma_3) + k\sigma_4 + 2^{3(k-2)} - 1,$$

then, since $\sigma \ge 2^k(\sigma_0 + \sigma_3) + 2k\sigma_4 + 2^{3(k-2)}$, we have

$$\Sigma \ll P_1^k L^{-2^{k-1}\sigma_0 - (2^{k-1}-k)\sigma_3}.$$

Therefore from (1) we obtain

$$|S|^{2^{k-1}} \ll P_2^{2^{k-1}-k} P_1^k L^{-2^{k-1}\sigma_0 - (2^{k-1}-k)\sigma_3} \ll P_1^{2^{k-1}} L^{-2^{k-1}\sigma_0},$$

i.e.,

$$S \ll P_1 L^{-\sigma_0}.$$

Lemma 6.3. *Let l be a positive integer ($\le L^{\sigma_3}$), and*

$$\Omega = \sum_d \sum_m e(f(ldm)), \qquad f(x) = \frac{h}{q} x^k + \alpha_1 x^{k-1} + \cdots + \alpha_k,$$

where $(h, q) = 1$, all α being real, and $L^\sigma < q \le P^k L^{-\sigma}$. The index d in Ω runs through a set of positive integers satisfying the conditions

$$D < d \leqslant D', \qquad 1 < D < \frac{P}{l} = P_1, \qquad D' \leqslant 2D.$$

Further, for a fixed d, the index m runs through a set of positive integers *satisfying the inequality*

$$P'/d < m \leqslant P_1/d,$$

where P' *is a positive number. Hence, for* $L^{\sigma_5} < D < PL^{-\sigma_6}$, *subject to the conditions*

$$\sigma_5 \geqslant 2^{2k}\sigma_0, \qquad \sigma_6 \geqslant (2k+1)\sigma_3 + 2^{2k+1}\sigma_0 + 2^{3(2k-1)}$$

and

$$\sigma \geqslant 2k\sigma_3 + 2^{2k+1}\sigma_0 + 2^{3(2k-1)}$$

we have

$$\Omega \ll P_1 L^{-\sigma_0}.$$

Proof. 1) For brevity, let $P_0 = [P_1/D]$. By Cauchy's inequality, we know that

$$|\Omega|^2 \leqslant D \sum_d \Big| \sum_m e(f(ldm)) \Big|^2$$
$$\leqslant D \sum_x \sum_m \sum_{m_1} e\Big(\frac{h}{q} l^k x^k (m^k - m_1^k) + \cdots\Big), \tag{1}$$

where x runs through all integers satisfying $D < x \leq D'$. For a fixed x, the indices m and m_1 run through a certain set of integers satisfying the inequalities

$$\frac{P'}{x} < m \leqslant \frac{P_1}{x}, \qquad \frac{P'}{x} < m_1 \leqslant \frac{P_1}{x}.$$

Rearranging the signs of summation in (1), we obtain

$$|\Omega|^2 \leqslant D \sum_{m_1} \sum_m \sum_x e\Big(\frac{h}{q} l^k x^k (m^k - m_1^k) + \cdots\Big), \tag{2}$$

where m and m_1 run through a certain set of integers satisfying

$$0 < m \leqslant P_0, \qquad 0 < m_1 \leqslant P_0$$

and for fixed m and m_1, the index x runs through all integers satisfying

$$\max\Big(D, \frac{P'}{m}, \frac{P'}{m_1}\Big) < x \leqslant \min\Big(D', \frac{P_1}{m}, \frac{P_1}{m_1}\Big).$$

2) We have

$$\Big| \sum_m \sum_x e\Big(\frac{h}{q} l^k x^k (m^k - m_1^k) + \cdots\Big) \Big| \leqslant \sum_{y=1}^{P_0} S_y, \tag{3}$$

where

$$S_y = \left| \sum_x e\left(\frac{h}{q}\, l^k x^k (y^k - m_1^k) + \cdots\right) \right|,$$

in which x runs through all integers contained in the interval

$$\max\left(D'', \frac{P'}{y}\right) < x \leqslant \min\left(D''', \frac{P_1}{y}\right),$$

with

$$D'' = \max\left(D, \frac{P'}{m_1}\right), \qquad D''' = \min\left(D', \frac{P_1}{m_1}\right).$$

Applying Lemmas 3.3 and 3.4, we obtain

$$|S_y|^{2k} = \left| \sum_x e\left(\frac{h}{q}\, l^k x^k (y^k - m_1^k) + \cdots\right) \right|^{2k}$$

$$\ll D^{2k-k-1} \sum_{\xi_1}^{D} \cdots \sum_{\xi_k}^{D} \sum_x^{D} e\left(\frac{h}{q}\, l^k (y^k - m_1^k)\, k!\, \xi_1 \cdots \xi_k\right).$$

Summing over y and rearranging the signs of summation, we obtain

$$\sum_{y=1}^{P_0} |S_y|^{2k} \ll D^{2k-k} \sum_{\xi_1}^{D} \cdots \sum_{\xi_k}^{D} \left| \sum_{y=1}^{P_0} e\left(\frac{h}{q}\, l^k (y^k - m_1^k)\, k!\, \xi_1 \cdots \xi_k\right) \right|. \qquad (4)$$

3) If $k = 1$, then

$$\sum_{y=1}^{P_0} |S_y|^2 \ll D \sum_{\xi_1}^{D} \left| \sum_{y=1}^{P_0} e\left(\frac{h}{q}\, l\, y\, \xi_1\right) \right|$$

$$\ll D \sum_{\xi_1}^{D} \min\left(P_0, \frac{1}{\{h l \xi_1 / q\}}\right) \ll D \sum_{\xi}^{Dl} \min\left(P_0, \frac{1}{\{h \xi / q\}}\right)$$

$$\ll D\left(\frac{Dl}{q} + 1\right)(P_0 + q \log q).$$

By (2) and (3) and Cauchy's inequality,

$$|Q|^2 \leqslant D P_0 \max_{m_1} \sum_{y=1}^{P_0} |S_y| \ll D P_0 \max_{m_1} \sqrt{P_0 \sum_{y=1}^{P_0} |S_y|^2}$$

$$\leqslant D^2 P_0^2 \left(\left(\frac{l}{q} + \frac{1}{D}\right)\left(1 + \frac{q \log q}{P_0}\right)\right)^{\frac{1}{2}},$$

and we obtain

$$\Omega \ll D P_0\left(\frac{l}{q}+\frac{1}{D}+\frac{l \log q}{P_0}+\frac{q \log q}{D P_0}\right)^{\frac{1}{4}}$$

$$\ll P_1(L^{\sigma_3-\sigma}+L^{-\sigma_5}+L^{2\sigma_3-\sigma_6+1}+L^{\sigma_3-\sigma+1})^{\frac{1}{4}} \ll P_1 L^{-\sigma_0}.$$

Here we have used

$$\sigma \geqslant \sigma_3+1+4\sigma_0, \qquad \sigma_5 \geqslant 4\sigma_0, \qquad \sigma_6 \geqslant 2\sigma_3+1+4\sigma_0.$$

4) Suppose that $k>1$. By Hölder's inequality, we obtain

$$\left(\sum_{\xi_1}^{D} \cdots \sum_{\xi_k}^{D}\left|\sum_{y=1}^{P_0} e\left(\frac{h}{q} l^k y^k k!\, \xi_1 \cdots \xi_k\right)\right|\right)^{2^{k-1}}$$

$$\ll D^{k(2^{k-1}-1)} \sum_{\xi_1}^{D} \cdots \sum_{\xi_k}^{D}\left|\sum_{y=1}^{P_0} e\left(\frac{h}{q} l^k y^k k!\, \xi_1 \cdots \xi_k\right)\right|^{2^{k-1}}. \tag{5}$$

By Lemmas 3.3, 3.4 and 1.8, we know that

$$\left|\sum_{y=1}^{P_0} e\left(\frac{h}{q} l^k y^k k!\, \xi_1 \cdots \xi_k\right)\right|^{2^{k-1}}$$

$$\ll P_0^{2^{k-1}-k} \sum_{\eta_1}^{P_0} \cdots \sum_{\eta_{k-1}}^{P_0} \min\left(P_0, \frac{1}{2\left\{\frac{h}{q} l^k k!^2 \xi_1 \cdots \xi_k \eta_1 \cdots \eta_{k-1}\right\}}\right), \tag{6}$$

and hence, by (5) and (6), we obtain

$$\left(\sum_{\xi_1} \cdots \sum_{\xi_k}\left|\sum_{y=1}^{P_0} e\left(\frac{h}{q} l^k y^k k!\, \xi_1 \cdots \xi_k\right)\right|\right)^{2^{k-1}} \ll D^{k(2^{k-1}-1)} P_0^{2^{k-1}-k}$$

$$\times \sum_{\xi_1}^{D} \cdots \sum_{\xi_k}^{D} \sum_{\eta_1}^{P_0} \cdots \sum_{\eta_{k-1}}^{P_0} \min\left(P_0, \frac{1}{2\left\{\frac{h}{q} l^k (k!)^2 \xi_1 \cdots \xi_k \eta_1 \cdots \eta_{k-1}\right\}}\right). \tag{7}$$

5) The sum of the terms in this sum satisfying

$$\xi_1 \cdots \xi_k \eta_1 \cdots \eta_{k-1}=0$$

is

$$\ll D^{k 2^{k-1}} P_0^{2^{k-1}}\left(\frac{1}{D}+\frac{1}{P_0}\right) \ll D^{k 2^{k-1}} P_0^{2^{k-1}}(L^{-\sigma_5}+L^{\sigma_3-\sigma_6}). \tag{8}$$

Further, the number of terms satisfying

$$z=l^k k!^2 \xi_1 \cdots \xi_k \eta_1 \cdots \eta_{k-1}$$

is $\le (d(z))^{2k-1}$, and $|z| \ll l^k k!^2 D^k P_0^{k-1}$. Define $l^k k!^2 D^k P_0^{k-1} = M$; by (7), (8) and Lemma 6.1, if $\sigma_2 > 2^{3(2k-1)} - 1$, then

$$\left(\sum_{\xi_1} \cdots \sum_{\xi_k} \left| \sum_{y=1}^{P_0} e\left(\frac{h}{q} l^k y^k k! \xi_1 \cdots \xi_k\right)\right|\right)^{2k-1} \ll D^{k 2^{k-1}} P_0^{2k-1} (L^{-\sigma_5} + L^{\sigma_3-\sigma_6})$$

$$+ D^{k 2^{k-1}-k} P_0^{2k-1-k}\left(M L^{-\sigma_2} P_0 + L^{\sigma_2} \sum_{0<z\ll M} \min\left(P_0, \frac{1}{2\{hz/q\}}\right)\right). \quad (9)$$

By Lemma 3.5 and $M \ll L^{k\sigma_3} D^k P_0^{k-1}$, we obtain

$$\sum_{0<z\ll M} \min\left(P_0, \frac{1}{2\{hz/q\}}\right) \ll \left(\frac{M}{q} + 1\right)(P_0 + q \log q)$$

$$\ll D^k P_0^k (L^{1+k\sigma_3-\sigma} + L^{(k+1)\sigma_3-\sigma_6+1}).$$

Thus from (9) we at once obtain

$$\left(\sum_{\xi_1} \cdots \sum_{\xi_k} \left| \sum_{y=1}^{P_0} e\left(\frac{h}{q} l^k k! \xi_1 \cdots \xi_k (y^k - m_1^k)\right)\right|\right)^{2k-1}$$

$$\ll D^{k 2^{k-1}} P_0^{2k-1} (L^{-\sigma_5} + L^{\sigma_3-\sigma_6} + L^{\sigma_2+1+k\sigma_3-\sigma} + L^{\sigma_2+(k+1)\sigma_3-\sigma_6+1}).$$

6) Take

$$\sigma_2 = k\sigma_3 + 2^{2k}\sigma_0 + 2^{3(2k-1)} - 1.$$

Since

$$\sigma_5 \geqslant 2^{2k}\sigma_0, \sigma_6 \geqslant (2k+1)\sigma_3 + 2^{2k+1}\sigma_0 + 2^{3(2k-1)}$$

and

$$\sigma > 2k\sigma_3 + 2^{2k+1}\sigma_0 + 2^{3(2k-1)},$$

we obtain

$$\sum_{\xi_1} \cdots \sum_{\xi_k} \left| \sum_{y=1}^{P_0} e\left(\frac{h}{q} l^k k! \xi_1 \cdots \xi_k (y^k - m_1^k)\right)\right| \ll D^k P_0 L^{-2^{k+1}\sigma_0}.$$

By (4), we obtain

$$\sum_{y=1}^{P_0} |S_y|^{2k} \ll D^{2k} P_0 L^{-2^{k+1}\sigma_0}.$$

Using Hölder's inequality, we obtain

$$\sum_{y=1}^{P_0} |S_y| \leqslant P_0^{1-2^{-k}} \left(\sum_{y=1}^{P_0} |S_y|^{2k}\right)^{2^{-k}} \ll D P_0 L^{-2\sigma_0}.$$

Further, by (2) we obtain

$$|\Omega|^2 \leqslant D P_0 D P_0 L^{-2\sigma_0}$$

and

$$\Omega \ll D P_0 L^{-\sigma_0} \ll P_1 L^{-\sigma_0}.$$

§3. PROOF OF THE THEOREM

1) Let H represent the product of all primes not greater than $\sqrt{P}$. Let (d) represent the sequence of numbers formed by the divisors of H. Applying a well-known method of proof, we have the result that

$$S = \sum_{(d) \leqslant P} \mu(d) S_d + O(\sqrt{P}),$$

where $\mu(d)$ is the Möbius function, and

$$S_d = \sum_{\substack{dm \leqslant P \\ dm \equiv t \pmod{Q}}} e(f(dm)).$$

2) Now let us first estimate the value of

$$S_0 = \sum_{(d) \leqslant L^{\lambda_1}} \mu(d) S_d, \qquad \lambda_1 = 2^{2k}(\sigma_0 + \sigma_1 + 1).$$

Taking $l = d$, $\sigma_3 = \lambda_1$, $\sigma_4 = \sigma_1$ in Lemma 6.2 and substituting $\sigma_0 + 1$ for σ_0, we obtain

$$|S_d| \ll \frac{P}{Q d} L^{-\sigma_0 - 1}.$$

(Here we have used $\sigma \geq 2k\sigma_1 + 2^k(\sigma_0 + 1 + \lambda_1) + 2^{3(k-2)}$.) Therefore

$$S_0 \ll \sum_{l \leqslant L^{\lambda_1}} \frac{P}{Q d} L^{-\sigma_0 - 1} \ll P Q^{-1} L^{-\sigma_0}.$$

3) Let (d_0) denote the subset of (d) formed by numbers with an even number of prime factors, and let (d_1) denote the remaining part of (d). Let

$$S' = \sum_{L^{\lambda_1} < (d) \leqslant P} \mu(d) S_d = T_0 - T_1,$$

where

$$T_0 = \sum_{L^{\lambda_1} < (d_0) \leqslant P} S_{d_0}, \qquad T_1 = \sum_{L^{\lambda_1} < (d_1) \leqslant P} S_{d_1}.$$

Now we shall confine ourselves to the study of T_0, since the same method can be applied to T_1.

4) Let us consider the following partial sum of the sum T_0:

$$T_0' = \sum_{L^{\lambda_1}<(d_0)\leqslant PL^{-\lambda_2}} S_{d_0}, \qquad \lambda_2 = 2^{2k+1}(\sigma_0+\sigma_1+1)+2^{3(2k-1)}.$$

We split this sum into $O(L)$ parts, each taken over an interval of the form

$$D<d\leqslant D', \qquad D'\leqslant 2D.$$

Let Ω express one of the parts. Then

$$\Omega = \sum_d \sum_m e(f(dm)),$$

where d runs through a numerical sequence satisfying

$$D<d\leqslant D', \qquad D'\leqslant 2D, \qquad L^{\lambda_1}<D\leqslant PL^{-\lambda_2}.$$

For fixed d the index m runs through a numerical sequence satisfying

$$0<m\leqslant \frac{P}{d}, \qquad md\equiv t \pmod{Q}.$$

Taking $l=1$, $\sigma_3=0$, $\sigma_5=\lambda_1$, $\sigma_6=\lambda_2$ in Lemma 6.3 and substituting $\sigma_0+\sigma_1+1$ for σ_0, and noting that $\sigma\geq 2^{2k+1}(\sigma_0+\sigma_1+1)+2^{3(2k-1)}$, we obtain

$$\Omega \ll PL^{-\sigma_0-1-\sigma_1}.$$

Hence

$$T_0' \ll L|\Omega| \ll \frac{P}{Q}L^{-\sigma_0}.$$

5) The part of the sum which remains to be considered can be written as

$$T_0'' = \sum_d \sum_m e(f(dm)),$$

where d runs through the integers in (d_0) satisfying

$$PL^{-\lambda_2}<d\leqslant P$$

and, for a fixed d, the index m runs through the integers satisfying

$$0<m\leqslant P/d, \qquad md\equiv t \pmod{Q}.$$

Interchanging the signs of summation, we obtain

$$T_0'' = \sum_m T(m), \qquad T(m) = \sum_d e(f(dm)),$$

where m runs through the integers

$$m = 1, 2, \cdots, [L^{\lambda_2}],$$

and, for a fixed m, the index d runs through a set of integers satisfying

$$PL^{-\lambda_2} < d \leqslant \frac{P}{m}.$$

6) Let (d_0') denote the subset of (d_0) consisting of the integers which have prime factors $\geq L^{\lambda_3}$ $(\lambda_3 = \sigma_0 + \lambda_2 + \sigma_1)$, and let (d_0'') denote the remaining part of (d_0). Then

$$T(m) = T'(m) + T''(m), \qquad T'(m) = \sum_{(d_0')}, \qquad T''(m) = \sum_{(d_0'')}.$$

The number of elements of (d_0'') satisfying the inequality $PL^{-\lambda_2} < d \leq P/m$ is smaller that the number F of integers l satisfying the following conditions: (i) l is square-free, (ii) l satisfies the inequality

$$P^{\frac{1}{2}} < l < P,$$

and (iii) no prime factor of l is greatet than L^{λ_3}. Let us assume that l has s prime factors; then

$$D < d \leqslant D', \qquad D' \leqslant 2D, \qquad L^{\lambda_1} < D \leqslant PL^{-\lambda_2}.$$

Hence we obtain $s \geq L/(2\lambda_3 \log L)$. It follows that

$$0 < m \leqslant \frac{P}{d}, \qquad md \equiv t \pmod{Q}.$$

By Lemma 2.5,

$$FL^{\lambda_3+1} \leqslant \sum_{l=1}^{P} d(l) \ll PL,$$

and accordingly

$$F \ll PL^{-\lambda_3}.$$

Therefore, we obtain

$$T(m) = T'(m) + O(PL^{-\lambda_3}) = T'(m) + O\left(\frac{P}{Q} L^{-\sigma_0-\lambda_2}\right).$$

(Here we have used $\lambda_3 = \sigma_0 + \lambda_2 + \sigma_1$.)

7) Let $T_s(m)$ denote the sum extended over the subset of (d_0') whose elements contain exactly s prime factors $\geq L^{\lambda_3}$. Since

$$L^{\lambda_3 s} \leqslant P, \qquad s \leqslant \frac{L}{\lambda_3 \log L} < L,$$

we obtain

$$T'(m) = \sum_{s<L} T_s(m),$$

with

$$T_s(m) = \sum_d e(f(md)),$$

where the summation is taken over all d satisfying the inequality

$$P L^{-\lambda_2} < d \leqslant P_1 = \frac{P}{m}, \qquad md \equiv t \pmod{Q},$$

such that d is a member of (d'_0) and therefore has exactly s prime factors $\geq L^{\lambda_3}$.

8) In order to estimate $T_s(m)$ we introduce the general sum

$$T_{s0}(m) = \sum_u \sum_v e(f(m\,u\,v)),$$

where u runs through all primes $\geq L^{\lambda_3}$ which are in (d), and, for given u, the index v runs through all integers satisfying the inequality

$$\frac{PL^{-\lambda_2}}{u} < v \leqslant \frac{P_1}{u}, \qquad m\,u\,v \equiv t \pmod{Q}$$

and such that v is in (d_1); that is, v has exactly $s-1$ prime factors $\geq L^{\lambda_3}$.

Each term $e(f(md))$ in $T_s(m)$ occurs s times in $T_{s0}(m)$. The terms in $T_{s0}(m)$ which do not occur in $T_s(m)$ are of the form

$$e(f(m\,p^2\,v_1)), \qquad \frac{PL^{-\lambda_2}}{p^2} < v_1 \leqslant \frac{P_1}{p^2},$$

where $p \geq L^{\lambda_3}$, and v_1 runs through the elements in (d_0) which have exactly $s-2$ prime factors $\geq L^{\lambda_3}$. (When $s = 1$, this type of term does not exist.) Such terms occur once and only once in $T_{s0}(m)$ (because v_1 contains no square factors). For a given p the total number of terms is $\ll P_1/p^2$. Therefore

$$T_{s0}(m) = s\,T_s(m) + O\Bigl(\sum_{p \geqslant L^{\lambda_3}} \frac{P_1}{p^2}\Bigr) = s\,T_s(m) + O\Bigl(\frac{P}{m} L^{-\lambda_3}\Bigr).$$

Hence

$$T_s(m) = \frac{1}{s} T_{s0}(m) + O\Bigl(\frac{P}{m\,s} L^{-\lambda_3}\Bigr).$$

9) Apply Lemma 6.3 to $T_{s0}(m)$. In the sum

$$T_{s0}(m) = \sum_u \sum_v e(f(m\,u\,v))$$

u runs through all primes in $L^{\lambda_3} \le u \le \sqrt{P}$. For a fixed u, the index v runs through all elements in (d_1) satisfying the following conditions:

(i) v possesses exactly $s - 1$ prime factors $\ge L^{\lambda_3}$;

(ii) $PL^{-\lambda_2}/u < v \le P_1/u$;

(iii) $muv \equiv t \pmod{Q}$.

Split $L^{\lambda_3} \le u \le \sqrt{P}$ into $O(L)$ parts, so that Lemma 6.3 can be applied to each part. Now in Lemma 6.3 take $l = m$, $\sigma_3 = \lambda_2$, $\sigma_5 = \lambda_3$, and take σ_6 to be an arbitrarily large integer. Also, substitute $\sigma_1 + \sigma_0 + 2$ for σ_0. Then from

$$\lambda_3 \geqslant 2^{2k}(\sigma_1+\sigma_0+2), \qquad \sigma \geqslant 2k\,\lambda_2 + 2^{2k+1}(\sigma_1+\sigma_0+2) + 2^{3(2k-1)}$$

we obtain

$$T_{s0}(m) \ll \frac{P}{m} L^{-\sigma_0-\sigma_1-2} L = \frac{P}{m} L^{-\sigma_0-\sigma_1-1}.$$

Hence we obtain

$$T_s(m) \ll \frac{P}{sm} L^{-\sigma_0-\sigma_1-1} + \frac{P}{sm} L^{-\lambda_3} \ll \frac{P}{sm} L^{-\sigma_0-\sigma_1-1}.$$

Here we have used $\lambda_3 \ge \sigma_0 + \sigma_1 + 1$.

Consequently

$$\begin{aligned} T_0 = T_0' + T_0'' = T_0' + \sum_m T(m) &\ll T_0' + \sum_m T'(m) + \sum_m \frac{P}{Q} L^{-\sigma_0-\lambda_2} \\ &\ll \frac{P}{Q} L^{-\sigma_0} + \sum_m \sum_{s<L} T_s(m) \ll \frac{P}{Q} L^{-\sigma_0} + \sum_m \sum_{s<L} \frac{P}{Qsm} L^{-\sigma_0-1} \\ &\ll \frac{P}{Q} L^{-\sigma_0}. \end{aligned}$$

Hence we obtain

$$S \ll \frac{P}{Q} L^{-\sigma_0}.$$

CHAPTER VII

AN ASYMPTOTIC FORMULA FOR THE NUMBER OF SOLUTIONS OF THE WARING-GOLDBACH PROBLEM

§1. FORMULATION OF THEOREM 11

Let $f(x)$ denote an integral-valued polynomial of the kth degree with positive leading coefficient A. Further, suppose that there exists no integer q (> 1) such that $f(x) \equiv f(0) \pmod q$ for all x. Let $I_s(N)$ denote the number of solutions of the equation

$$f(p_1) + \cdots + f(p_s) = N$$

in which $p_1, \cdots, p_s$ are primes. (For brevity, this problem is called the Waring-Goldbach problem.) The object of this chapter is to prove the following theorem:

Theorem 11. *If*

$$s \geqslant \begin{cases} 2^k + 1 & \text{when } 1 \leqslant k \leqslant 10, \\ 2k^2(2\log k + \log\log k + 2.5) & \text{when } k > 10, \end{cases}$$

then

$$\left| I_s(N) - A^{-sa}\mathfrak{S}(N)\frac{\Gamma^s(a)}{\Gamma(sa)}\frac{N^{sa-1}}{(\log N)^s} \right| \leqslant \frac{c(k,s,f)\,N^{sa-1}}{(\log N)^{s+1}}\log\log N,$$

where

$$\mathfrak{S}(N) = \sum_{q=1}^{\infty} B_s(N,q),$$

$$B_s(N,q) = \sum_{\substack{h=1 \\ (h,q)=1}} \left(\frac{W_{h,q}}{\varphi(\bar{q})}\right)^s e_q(-hN),$$

$$W_{h,q} = \sum_{\substack{l=1 \\ (l,q)=1}} e_q(hf(l)),$$

with $\bar{q} = q\prod_{p|q,\ p^t\|d} p^t$, *in which* d *is the least common denominator of the coefficients of* $f(x)$.

In proving Theorem 11 it is necessary to have an important lemma: *let* $r_{2t}(P)$ *denote the number of sets of integral solutions* $x_1, \cdots, x_t, y_1, \cdots, y_t$ *of the equation*

$$f(x_1) + \cdots + f(x_t) = f(y_1) + \cdots + f(y_t), \quad 0 \leqslant x, y \leqslant P.$$

Then when $k \geq 11$ *and*

$$2t > k^2 (2 \log k + \log \log k + 2.5) - 2$$

we have

$$r_{2t} = \int_0^1 |T(\alpha)|^{2t} d\alpha \ll P^{2t-k}, \quad T(\alpha) = \sum_{x=1}^{P} e(f(x)\alpha).$$

§2. CERTAIN LEMMAS

Lemma 7.1. *Let* $\tau \geq 1$. *For any real* α *there exist two integers* h *and* q *such that*

$$\left|\alpha - \frac{h}{q}\right| \leqslant \frac{1}{q\tau}, \quad 0 < q < \tau, \quad (h, q) = 1.$$

Proof. We can assume without loss of generality that $\alpha > 0$. Expand α into a continued fraction and let

$$\frac{P_1}{Q_1} = \frac{[\alpha]}{1}, \quad \frac{P_2}{Q_2}, \quad \frac{P_3}{Q_3}, \cdots$$

denote its successive convergents. The numerical sequence Q_ν either has only finitely many terms or else increases beyond all bounds with increasing ν. If it ends at P_s/Q_s, $Q_s \leq \tau$, then $\alpha = P_s/Q_s$, and the lemma is obviously true. If there exists an m such that

$$Q_m < \tau \leqslant Q_{m+1},$$

then

$$\left|\alpha - \frac{P_m}{Q_m}\right| \leqslant \left|\frac{P_{m+1}}{Q_{m+1}} - \frac{P_m}{Q_m}\right| = \frac{1}{Q_m Q_{m+1}} \leqslant \frac{1}{Q_m \tau},$$

and we obtain our lemma with $h = P_m$, $q = Q_m$.

Lemma 7.2 (the Euler sum formula). *Let*

$$b_1(x) = x - [x] - \frac{1}{2}.$$

Define the following functions by induction:

$$b_l(x+1) = b_l(x), \tag{1}$$

$$\int_0^x b_l(y)\,dy = b_{l+1}(x) - b_{l+1}(0). \tag{2}$$

Let $b > a$. *Suppose in the interval* $a \le x \le b$ *that the function* $g(x)$ *is continuous together with all its derivatives that occur below. Then for all* t

$$\sum_{\substack{m \\ a \leqslant m+t < b}} g(m+t) = \int_a^b g(x)\,dx$$

$$+ \sum_{r=0}^{l-1} \left(g^{(r)}(b)\, b_{r+1}(t-b) - g^{(r)}(a)\, b_{r+1}(t-a)\right) - \int_a^b g^{(l)}(x)\, b_l(t-x)\,dx. \tag{3}$$

Proof. 1) Simplification of the lemma.

1.1) We may assume that $t = 0$. Since we take $a - t = A$, $b - t = B$, $g(x+t) = G(x)$, we then have

$$\sum_{A \leqslant m < B} G(m) = \int_A^B G(x)\,dx$$

$$+ \sum_{r=0}^{l-1} \left(G^{(r)}(B)\, b_{r+1}(-B) - G^{(r)}(A)\, b_{r+1}(-A)\right) - \int_A^B G^{(l)}(x)\, b_l(-x)\,dx.$$

1.2) Since each side of this equality is additive, we need only prove the case

$$w \leqslant A < B \leqslant w+1$$

in which w is an integer.

1.3) As in 1.1) we can assume without loss of generality that $w = 0$.

2) When $l = 1$, the lemma is true, since

$$G(0) = \int_0^B G(x)\,dx + G(B)\, b_1(-B) - G(0)\, b_1(0)$$

$$- \int_0^B G(x)\, b_1(-x)\,dx \quad \text{when } A = 0, \tag{4}$$

and

$$0 = \int_A^B G(x)\,dx + G(B)\, b_1(-B) - G(A)\, b_1(-A)$$

$$- \int_A^B G'(x)\, b_1(-x)\,dx \quad \text{when } 0 < A < B \leqslant 1. \tag{5}$$

The proof of these two equalities is as follows:

$$\int_A^B G'(x)\, b_1(-x)\, dx = \int_A^B G'(x)\left(-x-[-1]-\frac{1}{2}\right)dx$$

$$=\left[\left(-x+\frac{1}{2}\right)G(x)\right]_A^B+\int_A^B G(x)\, dx$$

$$=\int_A^B G(x)\, dx+\left(-B+\frac{1}{2}\right)G(B)-\left(-A+\frac{1}{2}\right)G(A)$$

$$=\int_A^B G(x)\, dx + b_1(-B)\, G(B)$$

$$-\, b_1(-A)\, G(A) - \begin{cases} 0 & \text{if } A \neq 0, \\ G(A) & \text{if } A = 0, \end{cases}$$

since $1/2 = -1/2 + 1 = b_1(0) + 1$.

3) Induction. By integration by parts we obtain

$$-\int_A^B G^{(l)}(x)\, b_l(-x)\, dx = G^{(l)}(B)\, b_{l+1}(-B) - G^{(l)}(A)\, b_{l+1}(-A)$$

$$-\int_A^B G^{(l+1)}(x)\, b_{l+1}(-x)\, dx.$$

The lemma is proved.

Lemma 7.3. *In any bounded interval $b_l(x)$ is a function of bounded variation.*

Proof. When $l = 1$, the lemma is obvious since $b_1(x)$ in $(0, 1)$ is the difference of two monotonic functions, and is therefore a function of bounded variation. In general, the lemma can be derived from the fact that $b_l(x)$ is an integral of $b_{l-1}(x)$.

Lemma 7.4. *If $x \neq [x]$, then*

$$b_1(x) = x - [x] - \frac{1}{2} = -\frac{1}{\pi}\sum_{n=1}^{\infty}\frac{\sin 2\pi n x}{n}.$$

Proof. We shall confine ourselves to the discussion of the case where $0 < x < 1$. Since

$$\log(1-z) = -\left(z+\frac{z^2}{2}+\cdots+\frac{z^n}{n}+\cdots\right),$$

it follows that the real part of the expansion of $(\pi i)^{-1}\log(1 - e^{2\pi i x})$ is equal to the right side of the equality in the lemma, the real part of $(\pi i)^{-1}\log(1 - e^{2\pi i x})$ being equal to

$$-\frac{1}{\pi}\operatorname{arc\,tg}\frac{\sin 2\pi x}{1-\cos 2\pi x}=x-\frac{1}{2}.$$

Thus the lemma is proved.

Lemma 7.5. *Let $b>a$. Suppose that $\phi(x)$ and $f'(x)$ are continuous real functions on the interval (a, b), in which they have only a bounded number*[1] *of maximum and minimum values. Then*

$$1)\qquad \int_a^b \varphi(x)\, e(x)\, dx \ll \max_{0\leqslant\xi\leqslant 1}\ \max_{a\leqslant v\leqslant b-\xi}\int_v^{v+\xi}|\varphi(x)|\, dx. \tag{6}$$

2) *Suppose that $f(x)$ is differentiable and satisfies $|f'(x)|\leq 1/2$. Then*

$$\sum_{a\leqslant x\leqslant b} e^{2\pi i f(x)}-\int_a^b e^{2\pi i f(x)}\, dx \ll 1. \tag{7}$$

Proof. 1) When $b-a\leq 1$, statement 1) of the lemma is obviously true. Now suppose that $a<b-1$. If we can prove that

$$\int_a^b \varphi(x)\, e(x)\, dx \ll \max_{a\leqslant v\leqslant b-1}\int_v^{v+1}|\varphi(x)|\, dx, \tag{8}$$

then the lemma is proved. We can also assume without loss of generality that $\phi(x)$ is monotonic. If it is not, we can split the interval into a finite number of sections in each of which $\phi(x)$ is monotonic. Since the methods are the same, we shall discuss only the case when $\phi(x)$ is monotonically decreasing. Since

$$\left|\int_a^b \varphi(x)\, e(x)\, dx\right|\leqslant\int_a^{[a]+1}|\varphi(x)|\, dx+\left|\int_{[a]+1}^{[b]}\varphi(x)\, e(x)\, dx\right|+\int_{[b]}^b|\varphi(x)|\, dx,$$

we need only prove (8) when a and b are integers.

We now have

$$\begin{aligned}\int_a^b \varphi(x)\sin 2\pi x\, dx &= \int_a^{a+\frac12}\varphi(x)\sin 2\pi x\, dx+\int_{a+\frac12}^{a+1}\varphi(x)\sin 2\pi x\, dx+\cdots\\ &=\int_0^{\frac12}\Big(\varphi(x+a)-\varphi\big(x+a+\frac{1}{2}\big)+\varphi(x+a+1)-\cdots\\ &\qquad\cdots-\varphi\big(x+b-\frac{1}{2}\big)\Big)\sin 2\pi x\, dx.\end{aligned}$$

1) By a bounded number of maximum and minimum values we here mean a number not exceeding a number which depends only on k.

Because $\phi(x)$ is a monotonically decreasing function, it follows that

$$0\leqslant \varphi(x+a)-\varphi\left(x+a+\frac{1}{2}\right)+\varphi(x+a+1)-\cdots-\varphi\left(x+b-\frac{1}{2}\right)\leqslant \varphi(x+a).$$

Hence we at once obtain

$$0\leqslant\int_a^b \varphi(x)\sin 2\pi x\,dx\leqslant\int_0^{\frac{1}{2}}\varphi(x+a)\sin 2\pi x\,dx$$
$$\leqslant\int_0^{\frac{1}{2}}|\varphi(x+a)|\,dx\leqslant\int_a^{a+\frac{1}{2}}|\varphi(x)|\,dx.$$

Using the same method to discuss

$$\int_a^b \varphi(x)\cos 2\pi x\,dx,$$

and combining the results thus acquired, we obtain statement 1) of the lemma.

2) As in the proof of 1), we again assume that $f'(x)$ is monotonic. Now we estimate the integral

$$\int_a^b f'(x)\,e^{2\pi i(f(x)\pm mx)}\,dx, \qquad m \text{ an integer.}$$

If we let $f(x)\pm mx=y$, this integral is equal to

$$\int \frac{f'(x)}{f'(x)\pm m}\,e^{2\pi iy}\,dy.$$

By 1), we find that

$$\left|\int_a^b f'(x)\,e^{2\pi i(f(x)\pm mx)}\,dx\right|\leqslant\int\left|\frac{f'(x)}{m\pm f'(x)}\right|dy\ll\frac{1}{m}.$$

It follows at once that

$$\int_a^b e^{2\pi i f(x)}f'(x)\sin 2\pi mx\,dx=O\left(\frac{1}{m}\right).$$

By Lemma 7.4 we obtain

$$\left|\int_a^b e^{2\pi i f(x)}f'(x)\,b_1(-x)\,dx\right|=\frac{1}{\pi}\left|\int_a^b e^{2\pi i f(x)}f'(x)\sum_{m=1}^{\infty}\frac{\sin 2\pi mx}{m}\,dx\right|$$
$$=\frac{1}{\pi}\left|\sum_{m=1}^{\infty}\frac{1}{m}\int_a^b e^{2\pi i f(x)}f'(x)\sin 2\pi mx\,dx\right|$$
$$=O\left(\sum_{m=1}^{\infty}\frac{1}{m^2}\right)=O(1).$$

(The termwise integration is valid, since the series for $b_1(-x)$ is convergent to a finite limit.)

Finally, by the Euler sum formula, we obtain our lemma.

Lemma 7.6. *Let* $\Psi_1(x) = e^{ix^k}$. *Then*

$$\Psi_1^{(r)}(x) = e^{ix^k} F_r(x),$$

where $F_r(x)$ *is a polynomial of the* $(k-1)r$*th degree.*

By induction, we can obtain the proof of this lemma without difficulty.

Lemma 7.7. *Let* $\Psi(x) = e(\beta A(qx)^k)$. *If* $q \le c_1(k) P^{1-\epsilon}$, $|\beta| \le c_2(k) q^{-1} P^{-k+1-\epsilon}$ *and* $0 \le x \le P/q$, *then*

$$|\Psi^{(r)}(x)| \leqslant c_3(A, \epsilon, r, k) P^{-r\epsilon}.$$

Proof. Since

$$\begin{aligned} |\beta|^a q &\leqslant (c_2(k))^a q^{1-a} P^{-1+a-\epsilon a} \\ &\leqslant (c_2(k))^a (c_1(k))^{1-a} P^{(1-\epsilon)(1-a)-1+a-\epsilon a} \end{aligned}$$

and

$$(|\beta|^a q)^k x^{k-1} \leqslant |\beta| q^k \left(\frac{P}{q}\right)^{k-1} \leqslant c_2(k) P^{-\epsilon},$$

we know by Lemma 7.6 that

$$\begin{aligned} |\Psi^{(r)}(x)| &= |\Psi(x) F_r((2\pi\beta A)^a q x)((2\pi i \beta A)^a q)^r| \\ &\leqslant c_4(A, \epsilon, r, k)(1 + (|\beta|^a q x)^{(k-1)r})(|\beta|^a q)^r \\ &\leqslant c_3(A, \epsilon, r, k) P^{-r\epsilon}. \end{aligned}$$

Lemma 7.8. *Let* $f(x) = A_k x^k + \cdots + A_1 x + A_0$,

$$\Phi(x) = e(\beta f(qx)).$$

Then subject to the conditions of Lemma 7.7,

$$|\Phi^{(r)}(x)| \leqslant c_5(A_k, \cdots, A_0, \epsilon, r, k) P^{-r\epsilon}.$$

Proof. The lemma is obviously true for $k = 1$. Let

$$\Phi(x) = \Psi(x)\Phi_1(x), \qquad \Phi_1(x) = e(\beta f(qx) - \beta A_k (qx)^k).$$

Suppose that the lemma is true for $k-1$. Then for $|\beta| \ll q^{-1} P^{-k+2-\epsilon}$ we have

$$|\Phi_1^{(r)}(x)| \leqslant c_6(A_{k-1}, \cdots, A_0, \epsilon, r, k) P^{-r\epsilon}.$$

Since $q^{-1}P^{-k+2-\epsilon} > q^{-1}P^{-k+1-\epsilon}$, it follows for $|\beta| \leq c_2(k)q^{-1}P^{-k+1-\epsilon}$ that

$$|\Phi_1^{(r)}(x)| \leqslant c_6 P^{-r\epsilon}.$$

Hence for

$$\Phi^{(r)}(x) = \Psi^{(r)}(x)\Phi_1(x) + \binom{r}{1}\Psi^{(r-1)}(x)\Phi_1'(x) + \cdots + \Psi(x)\Phi_1^{(r)}(x)$$

we obtain

$$|\Phi^{(r)}(x)| \leqslant c_5 P^{-r\epsilon}.$$

§3. FAREY'S DISSECTION

Let $k > 2$. We know by Lemma 7.1 that for any number α in the interval $-1/\tau \leq \alpha \leq 1 - 1/\tau$ there is a pair of integers h and q such that

$$\left|\alpha - \frac{h}{q}\right| \leqslant \frac{1}{q\tau}, \quad 0 < q < \tau, \quad (h, q) = 1,$$

where $\tau = P^{k-1+\epsilon}$.

In the interval $(-1/\tau, 1 - 1/\tau)$ make a subinterval

$$\left|\alpha - \frac{h}{q}\right| \leqslant \frac{1}{q\tau}$$

in the vicinity of any rational point h/q. Use $\mathfrak{M}(h, q)$ to denote the subintervals of $q \leq P^{1-\epsilon}$. Let E denote the points in the interval $(-1/\tau, 1 - 1/\tau)$ which are not in any of the subintervals $\mathfrak{M}(h, q)$.

We now prove that any two $\mathfrak{M}(h, q)$ have no common point. For otherwise, if

$$\alpha = \frac{h}{q} + \beta, \quad \alpha = \frac{h_1}{q_1} + \beta_1, \quad |\beta| \leqslant \frac{1}{q\tau}, \quad |\beta_1| \leqslant \frac{1}{q_1\tau},$$

then

$$\left|\frac{h_1}{q_1} - \frac{h}{q}\right| = |\beta_1 - \beta|, \text{ i.e., } \frac{1}{qq_1} \leqslant \frac{1}{q\tau} + \frac{1}{q_1\tau}, \quad 1 \leqslant \frac{q_1+q}{\tau}.$$

Since $q + q_1 \leq 2P^{1-\epsilon}$, this is an impossibility.

Hence if we let

$$T(\alpha) = \sum_{x=1}^{P} e(f(x)\alpha),$$

then when P is sufficiently large, we have

$$r_{2t}(P) = \int_0^1 |T(\alpha)|^{2t}\,d\alpha = \int_{-\frac{1}{\tau}}^{1-\frac{1}{\tau}} |T(\alpha)|^{2t}\,d\alpha$$

$$= \int_E |T(\alpha)|^{2t}\,d\alpha + \sum_{q \leqslant P^{1-\epsilon}} \sum_{\substack{h=1 \\ (h,q)=1}}^{q} \int_{\mathfrak{M}(h,q)} |T(\alpha)|^{2t}\,d\alpha .$$

§4. AN ESTIMATE OF THE ABSOLUTE VALUE OF AN INTEGRAL TAKEN OVER E

Lemma 7.9. *When* $k \geq 12$ *and* $t > k^2(2\log k + \log\log k + 2.5) - 2$, *we have*

$$\int_E |T(\alpha)|^{2t}\,d\alpha \ll P^{2t-k}.$$

Proof. Letting $t = t_1 + t_2$, we obtain, by Theorems 6 and 9,

$$\int_E |T(\alpha)|^{2t}\,d\alpha \ll P^{2(1-1/\sigma_k)t_2+2t_1-k+\delta+\varepsilon}$$

$$\ll P^{2t-k+\delta-2t_2/\sigma_k+\varepsilon}.$$

Now take $t_2 = 2k^2$ and

$$l = \left[\frac{\log\left(\frac{1}{2}k(k+1)\log k^2\right)}{-\log(1-a)} + 1\right].$$

Then

$$\delta = \frac{1}{2}k(k+1)(1-a)^l < \frac{1}{2\log k},$$

and

$$\frac{2t_2}{\sigma_k} = \frac{4k^2}{2k^2(2\log k + \log\log k + 3)} > \frac{1}{2\log k}.$$

Hence if we could prove

$$\frac{1}{4}(k^2+k+2) + lk + 2k^2 \leqslant k^2(2\log k + \log\log k + 2.5) - 2,$$

we would at once obtain the lemma.

Since

$$l \leqslant \frac{\log\left(\frac{1}{2}k(k+1)\log k^2\right)}{-\log(1-a)} + 1 \leqslant \left(1 - \frac{a}{2}\right)k\log(k^2\log k) + 2$$

$$\leqslant k\log(k^2\log k) - \log k - \frac{1}{2}\log\log k + 2,$$

we know that

$$\frac{1}{4}(k^2+k+2)+lk+2k^2 \leq k^2(2\log k+\log\log k+2.5)-2.$$

Hence the proof of the lemma is complete.

§5. LEMMAS CONCERNING $\mathfrak{M}(h, q)$

Let

$$T^*(\alpha, h, q) = \bar{q}^{-1} S_{h,q} \int_0^P e(f(y)\beta)\,dy,$$

where

$$S_{h,q} = \sum_{v=1}^{\bar{q}} e_q(hf(v)),\quad \bar{q} = q \prod_{p|q,\, p^t \| d} p^t.$$

Here d is the least common denominator of the coefficients of $f(x)$.

Lemma 7.10.

$$T^*(\alpha, h, q) \ll q^{-a+\epsilon} \min(P, |\beta|^{-a}).$$

Proof. By Theorem 1 (Corollary 1.2) we know that

$$S_{h,q} \ll q^{1-a+\epsilon}.$$

Further, since $\int_0^P e(\beta f(y))\,dy = O(P)$, we can prove the following conclusion: When $|\beta|^{-a} \leq P$,

$$\int_0^P e(\beta f(y))\,dy \ll |\beta|^{-a}.$$

There exists a constant c such that

$$f(y+c) = g(y)$$

is a polynomial with positive coefficients. Hence

$$\int_c^P e(\beta f(y))\,dy = \int_{|\beta|^{-a}}^{P-c} e(\beta g(y))\,dy + O(|\beta|^{-a}).$$

Let $w = |\beta|\, g(y)$. Then y is seen to be a monotonically increasing function of w. Let $w_0 = |\beta|\, g(|\beta|^{-a})$. Then by the second mean-value theorem, we know that

$$\int_{w_0} \frac{e^{\pm 2\pi i w}}{|\beta|\, g'(y)}\,dw \ll \left(\frac{1}{|\beta|\, g'(y)}\right)_{w=w_0} \ll \frac{1}{|\beta|^a}.$$

Lemma 7.11. *Let* $\alpha = h/q + \beta$. *If* $q \leq P^{1-\epsilon}$ *and* $|\beta| \leq q^{-1}P^{-k+1-\epsilon}$, *then*

$$T(\alpha) - T^*(\alpha, h, q) \ll q^{1-a+\varepsilon}.$$

Proof. We have

$$T(\alpha) = \sum_{x=1}^{P} e(f(x)\alpha)$$
$$= \sum_{v=1}^{\bar{q}} \sum_{\substack{0<r\leqslant P \\ r\equiv v \pmod{\bar{q}}}} e\left(\frac{h}{q} f(r)\right) e(\beta f(r))$$
$$= \sum_{v=1}^{\bar{q}} e\left(\frac{h}{q} f(v)\right) \Lambda_v,$$

where

$$\Lambda_v = \sum_{\substack{j \\ 0<\bar{q}j+v\leqslant P}} e(\beta f(\bar{q}j+v)) = \sum_{\substack{j \\ 0<j+\frac{v}{\bar{q}}\leqslant\frac{P}{\bar{q}}}} \Phi\left(j+\frac{v}{\bar{q}}\right),$$

and

$$\Phi(x) = e(\beta f(\bar{q}x)).$$

Using Lemma 7.2, we obtain

$$\Lambda_v = \int_0^{P/\bar{q}} \Phi(x)\, dx + \sum_{r=1}^{l-1} \left(\Phi^{(r)}\left(\frac{P}{\bar{q}}\right) b_{r+1}\left(\frac{v}{\bar{q}} - \frac{P}{\bar{q}}\right) - \Phi^{(r)}(0)\, b_{r+1}\left(\frac{v}{\bar{q}}\right)\right)$$
$$- \int_0^{P/\bar{q}} \Phi^{(l)}(x)\, b_l\left(\frac{v}{\bar{q}} - x\right) dx.$$

From

$$\int_0^{P/\bar{q}} \Phi(x)\, dx = \int_0^{P/\bar{q}} e(\beta f(\bar{q}x))\, dx = \frac{1}{\bar{q}} \int_0^{P} e(\beta f(y))\, dy,$$

it follows that

$$T(\alpha) = T^*(\alpha, h, q) + \sum_{r=1}^{l-1} \left(\Phi^{(r)}\left(\frac{P}{\bar{q}}\right) a_{r+1}\left(\frac{P}{\bar{q}}\right) - \Phi^{(r)}(0)\, a_{r+1}(0)\right) - R,$$

where

$$a_{r+1}(t) = \sum_{v=1}^{\bar{q}} e_q(hf(v))\, b_{r+1}\left(\frac{v}{\bar{q}} - t\right)$$

and

$$R = \sum_{v=1}^{\bar{q}} e_q(hf(v)) \int_0^{P/\bar{q}} \Phi^{(l)}(x)\, b_l\left(\frac{v}{\bar{q}} - x\right) dx.$$

Now if we take $l = [1/\epsilon] + 1$, we know by Lemma 7.8 that

$$\Phi^{(l)}(x) \ll P^{-1},$$

and

$$R \ll \bar{q} \int_0^{P/\bar{q}} P^{-1}\, dx \ll 1.$$

Let

$$s_v = \sum_{x=1}^{v} e_q(h f(x)).$$

Then

$$\begin{aligned} a_{r+1}(t) &= s_1 b_{r+1}\left(\frac{1}{\bar{q}} - t\right) + \sum_{v=2} (s_v - s_{v-1})\, b_{r+1}\left(\frac{v}{\bar{q}} - t\right) \\ &= \sum_{m=1}^{\bar{q}-1} s_m \left(b_{r+1}\left(\frac{m}{\bar{q}} - t\right) - b_{r+1}\left(\frac{m+1}{\bar{q}} - t\right)\right) + s_{\bar{q}}\, b_{r+1}(1 - t). \end{aligned}$$

By Theorem 2

$$s_v = O(q^{1-a+\varepsilon}).$$

Since $b_{r+1}(x)$ is a bounded function, we obtain

$$\begin{aligned} |a_{r+1}(t)| &\ll q^{1-a+\varepsilon}\left(\sum_{m=1}^{\bar{q}-1} \left| b_{r+1}\left(\frac{m}{q} - t\right) - b_{r+1}\left(\frac{m+1}{\bar{q}} - t\right)\right| + 1\right) \\ &\ll q^{1-a+\varepsilon}. \end{aligned}$$

Furthermore, by Lemma 7.8, we obtain

$$\begin{aligned} T(\alpha) - T^*(\alpha, h, q) &\ll \left(\sum_{r=1}^{l-1} P^{-r\varepsilon} + 1\right) q^{1-a+\varepsilon} \\ &\ll q^{1-a+\varepsilon}. \end{aligned}$$

§6. AN ESTIMATE OF THE ABSOLUTE VALUE OF AN INTEGRAL TAKEN OVER $\mathfrak{M}(h, q)$

Lemma 7.12. *For* $2t > 2k + 1$ *we have*

$$\sum_{\mathfrak{M}} \int_{\mathfrak{M}} |T(\alpha)|^{2t}\, d\alpha \ll P^{2t-k}.$$

Proof. By Lemmas 7.10 and 7.11 we know that on $\mathfrak{M}(h, q)$

$$T(\alpha) \ll q^{-a+\varepsilon} \min(P, |\beta|^{-a}) + q^{1-a+\varepsilon}$$
$$\ll q^{-a+\varepsilon} \min(P, |\beta|^{-a}).$$

The sum mentioned in the lemma does not exceed

$$\ll \sum_{\mathfrak{M}} \int_{\mathfrak{M}} q^{-2ta+\varepsilon} \min(P^{2t}, |\beta|^{-2ta})\, d\beta$$

$$\ll \sum_{q \leqslant P^{1-\epsilon}} \sum_{h=1}^{q} q^{-2ta+\varepsilon} \left(\int_0^{P^{-k}} P^{2t}\, d\beta + \int_{P^{-k}} \beta^{-2ta}\, d\beta \right)$$

$$\ll P^{2t-k} \sum_{q \leqslant P^{1-\epsilon}} q^{1-2ta+\varepsilon} \ll P^{2t-k}$$

(because of the convergence of Σq^{1-2ta}).

Lemma 7.13. *When* $k \geq 12$ *and*

$$t > k^2 (2 \log k + \log\log k + 2.5) - 2$$

we have

$$r_{2t}(P) \ll P^{2t-k}.$$

This result is derived directly from Lemmas 7.9 and 7.12.

§7. LEMMAS ESSENTIAL FOR THE PROOF OF THE THEOREM

Let $N = f(P)$, and

$$\mathfrak{T}(\alpha) = \sum_{p \leqslant P} e(f(p)\alpha),$$

$$\mathfrak{T}^*(\alpha, h, q) = \frac{1}{A^a} \frac{W_{h,q}}{\varphi(\bar{q})} \sum_{2 \leqslant n \leqslant N} \frac{e(n\beta)}{n^{1-a} \log \frac{n}{A}},$$

where A is the coefficient of the highest power of $f(x)$ and $W_{h,q}$ is defined at the beginning of this chapter.

We shall dissect the interval $-1/\tau \leq \alpha \leq 1 - 1/\tau$ in the same way as in §3 but we shall use $q \leq \tau = NL^{-\sigma}$, where σ is so chosen that σ_0 in Theorem 10 is greater than $c_2(k, k)$ in Theorem 4 plus a certain integer s_1.

Let $\mathfrak{M}(h, q)$ denote the interval

$$\left| \alpha - \frac{h}{q} \right| \leqslant \frac{1}{q\tau}, \qquad q \leqslant L^{\sigma}.$$

Use E to denote all points in the interval $(-1/\tau, 1-1/\tau)$ not falling within $\mathfrak{M}(h, q)$. It is easy to prove (as before) that no two $\mathfrak{M}(h, q)$ have a common point.

Lemma 7.14 (Siegel-Walfisz).[1] *Suppose that* $q \leq L^{\sigma}$, $(l, q) = 1$, *and* $n \leq P$. *Let* $\pi(n; l, q)$ *denote the number of distinct primes not greater than* n *in the arithmetic progression* $l + qx$. *Then*

$$\pi(n; l, q) = \frac{1}{\varphi(q)} \operatorname{li} n + O(P e^{-c_1\sqrt{L}}),$$

where $\operatorname{li} x = \int_2^x \frac{dt}{\log t}$, *and the constants included in the symbol* O *are independent of* q.

Lemma 7.15. *On* $\mathfrak{M}(h, q)$ *we have*

$$\mathfrak{T}(\alpha) - \mathfrak{T}^*(\alpha, h, q) = O(P e^{-c_2\sqrt{L}}).$$

Proof. Let $\alpha = h/q + \beta$. Further, let

$$S_n = \sum_{f(p) \leqslant n} e_q(hf(p)), \quad n \leqslant N.$$

Then

$$S_n = \sum_{\substack{l=1 \\ (l, \bar{q})=1}}^{\bar{q}} e_q(hf(l))\, \pi(n'; l, \bar{q}) + O(q^{\varepsilon}),$$

where n' is the greatest positive root of the equation $f(x) = n$. (When n is sufficiently large, n' exists and is unique.) Let us now prove

$$n' - \left(\frac{n}{A}\right)^a \ll 1.$$

This inequality follows from

$$n' - \left(\frac{n}{A}\right)^a = n' - \left(\frac{f(n')}{A}\right)^a = n' - (n'^k + O(n'^{k-1}))^a$$
$$= n'(1 - (1 + O(n'^{-1}))^a) = O(1).$$

By Lemma 7.14, we have, for sufficiently large n,

---

1) Math. Z. 40 (1936), 592–601, Hilfsatz 3. For a complete proof, see: N. G. Čudakov, *Introduction to the theory of Dirichlet's L-functions*, OGIZ, Moscow, 1947, or T. Estermann, *Introduction to modern prime number theory*, Cambridge Tracts in Mathematics and Mathematical Physics, no. 41, Cambridge at the University Press, 1952.

$$\pi(n'; l, \bar{q}) = \frac{1}{\varphi(\bar{q})} \operatorname{li} n' + O(P e^{-c_1\sqrt{L}})$$
$$= \frac{1}{\varphi(\bar{q})} \operatorname{li}\left(\frac{n}{A}\right)^a + O(P e^{-c_1\sqrt{L}}).$$

The last equality is true for all n' not greater than P. Consequently,

$$S_n = \sum_{\substack{l=1\\(l,\bar{q})=1}}^{\bar{q}} e_q(h f(l)) \left(\frac{1}{\varphi(\bar{q})} \operatorname{li}\left(\frac{n}{A}\right)^a + O(P e^{-c_1\sqrt{L}})\right) + O(q^\varepsilon)$$
$$= \sum_{\substack{l=1\\(l,\bar{q})=1}}^{\bar{q}} \frac{e_q(h f(l))}{\varphi(\bar{q})} \operatorname{li}\left(\frac{n}{A}\right)^a + O(P e^{-c_3\sqrt{L}})$$
$$= \frac{W_{h,q}}{\varphi(\bar{q})} \operatorname{li}\left(\frac{n}{A}\right)^a + O(P e^{-c_3\sqrt{L}}).$$

Therefore

$$\mathfrak{T}(\alpha) = \sum_{n=2}^{N} (S_n - S_{n-1}) e(n\beta) + O(1)$$
$$= \sum_{n=2}^{N} S_n (e(n\beta) - e((n+1)\beta)) + S_N e((N+1)\beta) + O(1)$$
$$= \frac{W_{h,q}}{\varphi(\bar{q})} \left(\sum_{n=2}^{N} \operatorname{li}\left(\frac{n}{A}\right)^a (e(n\beta) - e((n+1)\beta)) + \operatorname{li}\left(\frac{N}{A}\right)^a e((N+1)\beta)\right)$$
$$+ O(P e^{-c_4\sqrt{L}}).$$

Since

$$\operatorname{li}\left(\frac{n}{A}\right)^a - \operatorname{li}\left(\frac{n-1}{A}\right)^a = \int_{((n-1)/A)^a}^{(n/A)^a} \frac{dt}{\log t}$$
$$= A^{-a} \int_{(n-1)^a}^{n^a} \frac{dy}{\log(y A^{-a})} = \frac{1}{A^a n^{1-a} \log \frac{n}{A}} + O\left(\frac{1}{n^{2-a} \log n}\right),$$

we obtain the desired result.

Lemma 7.16. *When* $|\beta| \le 1/2$,

$$\mathfrak{T}^*(\alpha, h, q) \ll q^{-a+\varepsilon} \min(P, |\beta|^{-a}).$$

An analogous result exists for $\mathfrak{T}(\alpha)$ *over* $\mathfrak{M}(h, q)$.

Proof. By Theorem 1, Corollary 1.3, we obtain

$$\mathfrak{T}^*(\alpha, h, q) \ll q^{-a+\varepsilon} \sum_{n \leqslant f(P)} \frac{1}{n^{1-a}}$$
$$\ll q^{-a+\varepsilon} P.$$

(Here, we have used $\phi(q) \geq q/d(q) \gg q^{1-\epsilon}$.) Further,

$$\sum_{n \leqslant N} \frac{e(n\beta)}{n^{1-a} \log \frac{n}{A}} = \sum_{n \leqslant |\beta|^{-1}} \frac{e(n\beta)}{n^{1-a} \log \frac{n}{A}} + \sum_{N \geqslant n > |\beta|^{-1}} \frac{e(n\beta)}{n^{1-a} \log \frac{n}{A}}.$$

Let Σ_1 and Σ_2 denote these two sums respectively. Obviously we have

$$\left| \Sigma_1 \right| \ll \sum_{n \leqslant |\beta|^{-1}} \frac{1}{n^{1-a} \log n} = O(|\beta|^{-a}).$$

Letting $S_n = \Sigma_{|\beta|^{-1} < m < n} e(m\beta)$ and summing by parts, we obtain

$$\left| \Sigma_2 \right| = \left| \sum_{N \geqslant n > |\beta|^{-1}} \frac{e(n\beta)}{n^{1-a} \log \frac{n}{A}} \right| = \left| \sum_{N \geqslant n > |\beta|^{-1}} \frac{S_n - S_{n-1}}{n^{1-a} \log \frac{n}{A}} \right|.$$

$$\leqslant \sum_{N \geqslant n > |\beta|^{-1}} |S_n| \left(\frac{1}{n^{1-a} \log \frac{n}{A}} - \frac{1}{(n+1)^{1-a} \log \left(\frac{n+1}{A} \right)} \right)$$

$$+ \frac{|S_N|}{(N+1)^{1-a} \log \frac{N+1}{A}}.$$

Since $|S_n| \leq 1/|\beta|$, we know that

$$\left| \Sigma_2 \right| \leqslant \sum_{N \geqslant n > |\beta|^{-1}} \frac{1}{|\beta|} \left(\frac{1}{n^{1-a} \log \frac{n}{A}} - \frac{1}{(n+1)^{1-a} \log \left(\frac{n+1}{A} \right)} \right)$$

$$+ \frac{1}{|\beta|} \frac{1}{(N+1)^{1-a} \log \frac{N+1}{A}} \ll |\beta|^{-a}.$$

This completes the proof for the first conclusion of the lemma.

By Lemma 7.15 we know that

$$\mathfrak{T}(\alpha) = \mathfrak{T}^*(\alpha, h, q) + O(P e^{-c_2\sqrt{L}}).$$

Since $Pe^{-c2\sqrt{L}} \ll Pq^{-a}$ and $Pe^{-c2\sqrt{L}} \ll |\beta|^{-a} q^{-a}$, we obtain

$$\mathfrak{T}(\alpha) \ll q^{-a+\varepsilon} \min(P, |\beta|^{-a}).$$

§8. PROOF OF THE THEOREM

We shall first prove a theorem which is slightly different from Theorem 11.

Theorem 11′. *Suppose that*

$$s \geqslant \begin{cases} 2^k + 1 & \text{if } 1 \leqslant k \leqslant 11, \\ 2k^2(2\log k + \log\log k + 2.5) & \text{if } k > 11. \end{cases}$$

Then for any given integer s_1 *we always have*

$$\left| I_s(N) - A^{-sa}\mathfrak{S}(N)\Psi(N) \right| \leqslant \frac{c(k; s_1, f(x))\, N^{sa-1}}{(\log N)^{s_1}},$$

where

$$\Psi(N) = \sum_{\substack{n_1+\cdots+n_s=N \\ n_\nu \geqslant 2}} \frac{1}{n_1^{1-a}\log\frac{n_1}{A}\cdots n_s^{1-a}\log\frac{n_s}{A}}.$$

Proof. 1) We have

$$I_s(N) = \int_0^1 \mathfrak{T}^s(\alpha)\, e(-N\alpha)\, d\alpha = \int_{-\frac{1}{\tau}}^{1-\frac{1}{\tau}} \mathfrak{T}^s(\alpha)\, e(-N\alpha)\, d\alpha$$

$$= \int_E \mathfrak{T}^s(\alpha)\, e(-N\alpha)\, d\alpha + \sum_{\mathfrak{M}(h,q)} \int_{\mathfrak{M}(h,q)} \mathfrak{T}^s(\alpha)\, e(-N\alpha)\, d\alpha.$$

2) For $k > 11$, since $s > 2k^2(2\log k + \log\log k + 2.5)$, we can select an integer t such that

$$s - 2t \geqslant 1, \quad t > k^2(2\log k + \log\log k + 2.5) - 2.$$

By Theorem 10 and Lemma 7.13, we obtain

$$\int_E \mathfrak{T}^s(\alpha)\, e(-N\alpha)\, d\alpha \ll (PL^{-\sigma_0})^{s-2t} \int_0^1 |\mathfrak{T}(\alpha)|^{2t}\, d\alpha$$

$$\ll P^{s-2t} L^{-s_1} \int_0^1 |T(\alpha)|^{2t}\, d\alpha$$

$$\ll P^{s-k} L^{-s_1}.$$

For $1 \leq k \leq 11$ we obtain by Theorem 4

$$\int_E (\mathfrak{T}(\alpha))^{2^k+1}\, e(-N\alpha)\, d\alpha \ll PL^{-s_1-c_2(k,k)} \int_0^1 |T(\alpha)|^{2^k}\, d\alpha$$

$$\ll P^{2^k-k+1} L^{-s_1}$$

(because of the selection of σ).

3) By Lemmas 7.15 and 7.16 and the simplified equality

$$|\xi^s - \eta^s| \leqslant s\, |\xi - \eta| \max(|\xi|^{s-1}, |\eta|^{s-1}),$$

we have, on $\mathfrak{M}(h, q)$, the following result:

$$|\mathfrak{T}^s(\alpha) - \mathfrak{T}^{*s}(\alpha, h, q)| \leqslant s|\mathfrak{T}(\alpha) - \mathfrak{T}^*(\alpha, h, q)| \max(|\mathfrak{T}(\alpha)|^{s-1}, |\mathfrak{T}^*(\alpha, h, q)|^{s-1})$$
$$\ll P e^{-c_2\sqrt{L}} (q^{-a+\varepsilon})^{s-1} \min(P, |\beta|^{-a})^{s-1}.$$

Integrating over $\mathfrak{M}(h, q)$, we accordingly obtain

$$\int_{\mathfrak{M}(h, q)} \mathfrak{T}^s(\alpha)\, e(-N\alpha)\, d\alpha - \int_{\mathfrak{M}(h, q)} \mathfrak{T}^{*s}(\alpha, h, q)\, e(-N\alpha)\, d\alpha$$
$$\ll P e^{-c_2\sqrt{L}} q^{-a(s-1)+\varepsilon}\left(\int_0^{P^{-k}} P^{s-1}\, d\beta + \int_{P^{-k}} \beta^{-a(s-1)}\, d\beta\right)$$
$$\ll q^{-a(s-1)+\varepsilon} P^{s-k} e^{-c_2\sqrt{L}}.$$

Summing up all $\mathfrak{M}(h, q)$, we obtain

$$\sum_{\mathfrak{M}} \int_{\mathfrak{M}} \mathfrak{T}^s(\alpha)\, e(-N\alpha)\, d\alpha - \sum_{\mathfrak{M}} \int_{\mathfrak{M}} \mathfrak{T}^{*s}(\alpha, h, q)\, e(-N\alpha)\, d\alpha$$
$$\ll P^{s-k} e^{-c_2\sqrt{L}} \sum_{q \leqslant L^\sigma} q^{1-a(s-1)+\varepsilon}$$
$$\ll P^{s-k} e^{-c_5\sqrt{L}}.$$

4) By Lemma 7.16, we have

$$\int_{\mathfrak{M}(h, q)} \mathfrak{T}^{*s}(\alpha, h, q)\, e(-N\alpha)\, d\alpha - \int_{-\frac{1}{2}}^{\frac{1}{2}} \mathfrak{T}^{*s}(\alpha, h, q)\, e(-N\alpha)\, d\beta$$
$$\ll q^{-as+\varepsilon} \int_{q^{-1}\tau^{-1}}^{\infty} \beta^{-as}\, d\beta$$
$$\ll q^{-1+\varepsilon} P^{s-k} L^{-\sigma(sa-1)}.$$

Therefore

$$\sum_{\mathfrak{M}} \int_{\mathfrak{M}} \mathfrak{T}^{*s}(\alpha, h, q)\, e(-N\alpha)\, d\alpha - \sum_{\mathfrak{M}} \int_{-\frac{1}{2}}^{\frac{1}{2}} \mathfrak{T}^{*s}(\alpha, h, q)\, e(-N\alpha)\, d\beta$$
$$\ll P^{s-k} L^{-\sigma(sa-1)} \sum_{q \leqslant L^\sigma} q^\varepsilon$$
$$\ll P^{s-k} L^{-\sigma(sa-2)+\varepsilon} \ll P^{s-k} L^{-s_1}$$

(since $2s_1 < \sigma$ and $sa - 2 \geq 1/2$).

5) We have

$$\sum_{\mathfrak{M}} \int_{-\frac{1}{2}}^{\frac{1}{2}} \mathfrak{T}^{*s}(\alpha, h, q)\, e(-N\alpha)\, d\beta$$

$$= A^{-sa} \sum_{\mathfrak{M}} \left(\frac{W_{h,q}}{\varphi(\bar{q})}\right)^s e\left(-\frac{Nh}{q}\right) \int_{-\frac{1}{2}}^{\frac{1}{2}} \left(\sum_{2 \leqslant n \leqslant N} \frac{e(n\beta)}{n^{1-a} \log \frac{n}{A}}\right)^s e(-N\beta)\, d\beta$$

$$= A^{-sa} \sum_{q \leqslant L^\sigma} \sum_{\substack{h=1 \\ (h,q)=1}}^{q} \left(\frac{W_{h,q}}{\varphi(\bar{q})}\right)^s e\left(-\frac{Nh}{q}\right) \Psi(N),$$

where $\Psi(N)$ is defined in Theorem 11′.

6) We have

$$\left|\sum_{q > L^\sigma} \sum_{\substack{h=1 \\ (h,q)=1}}^{\bar{q}} \left(\frac{W_{h,q}}{\varphi(\bar{q})}\right)^s e\left(-\frac{Nh}{q}\right)\right| \ll \sum_{q > L^\sigma} q \cdot q^{-sa+\varepsilon} \ll L^{(2-sa)\sigma+\varepsilon} \ll L^{-s_1}.$$

Therefore

$$\sum_{q \leqslant L^\sigma} \sum_{\substack{h=1 \\ (h,q)=1}} \left(\frac{W_{h,q}}{\varphi(\bar{q})}\right)^s e\left(-\frac{Nh}{q}\right) = \mathfrak{S}(N) + O(L^{-s_1}).$$

7) Summing up the results of 3), 4), 5) and 6), we obtain

$$\sum_{\mathfrak{M}(h,q)} \int_{\mathfrak{M}(h,q)} \mathfrak{T}^s(\alpha)\, e(-N\alpha)\, d\alpha = \mathfrak{S}(N)\, A^{-sa}\, \Psi(N) + O(N^{sa-1} L^{-s_1}).$$

Again by the results of 1) and 2) we know that

$$I_s(N) = \mathfrak{S}(N)\, A^{-sa}\, \Psi(N) + O(N^{sa-1} L^{-s_1}).$$

§9. PROOF OF THE THEOREM (conclusion)

Lemma 7.17. *When* $0 < \lambda_1 < 1$ *and* $\lambda_2 \geq \lambda_1$,

$$\sum_{n=1}^{N-1} \frac{1}{n^{1-\lambda_1}(N-n)^{1-\lambda_2}} = \frac{\Gamma(\lambda_1)\Gamma(\lambda_2)}{\Gamma(\lambda_1+\lambda_2)} N^{\lambda_1+\lambda_2-1}(1 + O(N^{-\lambda_1})).$$

Proof. Write

$$\sum_{n=1}^{N-1} \frac{1}{n^{1-\lambda_1}(N-n)^{1-\lambda_2}} = N^{\lambda_1+\lambda_2-1} \sum_{n=1}^{N-1} \frac{\frac{1}{N}}{\left(\frac{n}{N}\right)^{1-\lambda_1}\left(1-\frac{n}{N}\right)^{1-\lambda_2}}.$$

For $n/N \leq x \leq (n+1)/N$ let $x = n/N + \theta/N$ $(0 \leq \theta \leq 1)$. Then we have

$$\frac{1}{\left(\frac{n}{N}\right)^{1-\lambda_1}\left(1-\frac{n}{N}\right)^{1-\lambda_2}} - \frac{1}{x^{1-\lambda_1}(1-x)^{1-\lambda_2}}$$

$$= \frac{1}{\left(\frac{n}{N}\right)^{1-\lambda_1}\left(1-\frac{n}{N}\right)^{1-\lambda_2}}\left(1-\left(1+\frac{\theta}{n}\right)^{\lambda_1-1}\left(1-\frac{\theta}{N-n}\right)^{\lambda_2-1}\right)$$

$$= \frac{1}{\left(\frac{n}{N}\right)^{1-\lambda_1}\left(1-\frac{n}{N}\right)^{1-\lambda_2}}\left(O\left(\frac{1}{n}\right)+O\left(\frac{1}{N-n}\right)\right).$$

Hence

$$\sum_{n=1}^{N-1} \frac{1}{n^{1-\lambda_1}(N-n)^{1-\lambda_2}} = N^{\lambda_1+\lambda_2-1}\left(\int_0^1 x^{\lambda_1-1}(1-x)^{\lambda_2-1}\,dx\right.$$

$$\left.+\,O\left(\sum_{n=1}^{N-1} \frac{\frac{1}{nN}}{\left(\frac{n}{N}\right)^{1-\lambda_1}\left(1-\frac{n}{N}\right)^{1-\lambda_2}} + \sum_{n=1}^{N-1} \frac{\frac{1}{(N-n)N}}{\left(\frac{n}{N}\right)^{1-\lambda_1}\left(1-\frac{n}{N}\right)^{1-\lambda_2}}\right)\right)$$

$$= N^{\lambda_1+\lambda_2-1}\frac{\Gamma(\lambda_1)\,\Gamma(\lambda_2)}{\Gamma(\lambda_1+\lambda_2)} + O\left(\sum_{n=1}^{N-1}\frac{1}{n^{2-\lambda_1}(N-n)^{1-\lambda_2}}\right.$$

$$\left.+\sum_{n=1}^{N-1}\frac{1}{n^{1-\lambda_1}(N-n)^{2-\lambda_2}}\right).$$

Since

$$\sum_{n=1}^{N-1}\frac{1}{n^{2-\lambda_1}(N-n)^{1-\lambda_2}} = \sum_{n\leq\frac{1}{2}N}\frac{1}{n^{2-\lambda_1}(N-n)^{1-\lambda_2}} + \sum_{N>n>\frac{1}{2}N}\frac{1}{n^{2-\lambda_1}(N-n)^{1-\lambda_2}}$$

$$\ll N^{\lambda_2-1}\sum_{n\leq\frac{1}{2}N}\frac{1}{n^{2-\lambda_1}} + N^{\lambda_1-2}\sum_{N>n>\frac{1}{2}N}\frac{1}{(N-n)^{1-\lambda_2}}$$

$$\ll N^{\lambda_2-1}$$

and

$$\sum_{n=1}^{N-1} \frac{1}{n^{1-\lambda_1}(N-n)^{2-\lambda_2}} \ll N^{\lambda_1+\lambda_2-1-\min(1,\lambda_2)} \begin{cases} 1 & \text{if } \lambda_2 \neq 1, \\ \log N & \text{if } \lambda_2 = 1, \end{cases}$$

we obtain the lemma.

Lemma 7.18.

$$\sum_{\substack{n_1+\cdots+n_s=N \\ n_\nu>0}} \frac{1}{n_1^{1-a}\cdots n_s^{1-a}} = \frac{\Gamma^s(a)}{\Gamma(sa)} N^{sa-1}(1+O(N^{-a})).$$

Proof. By Lemma 7.17 we know that the lemma is true for $s = 2$. Now suppose that the lemma is true for $s - 1$. Then by Lemma 7.17 we know that

$$\sum_{\substack{n_1+\cdots+n_s=N \\ n_\nu>0}} \frac{1}{n_1^{1-a}\cdots n_s^{1-a}} = \sum_{n_1=1}^{N-s+1} \frac{1}{n_1^{1-a}} \sum_{n_2+\cdots+n_s=N-n_1} \frac{1}{n_2^{1-a}\cdots n_s^{1-a}}$$

$$= \sum_{n_1} \frac{1}{n_1^{1-a}} \frac{\Gamma^{s-1}(a)}{\Gamma((s-1)a)} (N-n_1)^{(s-1)a-1} + O\left(\sum_{n_1} \frac{1}{n_1^{1-a}(N-n)^{1-(s-2)a}}\right)$$

$$= \frac{\Gamma^s(a)}{\Gamma(sa)} N^{sa-1}(1+O(N^{-a})).$$

Lemma 7.19.

$$\sum_{\substack{n_1+\cdots+n_s=N \\ n_\nu>1}} \frac{1}{n_1^{1-a}\log\frac{n_1}{A}\cdots n_s^{1-a}\log\frac{n_s}{A}} = \frac{\Gamma^s(a)}{\Gamma(sa)} \frac{N^{sa-1}}{\log^s N}\left(1+O\left(\frac{\log L}{L}\right)\right).$$

Proof. Let

$$\Psi_0(N) = \sum_{\substack{n_1+\cdots+n_s=N \\ n_\nu>1}} \frac{1}{n_1^{1-a}\cdots n_s^{1-a}},$$

$$\Psi_\mu(N) = \sum_{\substack{n_1+\cdots+n_s=N \\ n_\nu>1}} \frac{1}{n_1^{1-a}\log\frac{n_1}{A}\cdots n_\mu^{1-a}\log\frac{n_\mu}{A}\cdot n_{\mu+1}^{1-a}\cdots n_s^{1-a}}, \quad 0<\mu\leqslant s.$$

Then

$$\Psi_\mu(N) = \frac{1}{L}\Psi_{\mu-1}(N) + O\left(\frac{\Psi_\mu(N)\log L}{L}\right) + O\left(\frac{N^{sa-1}}{L^{s+1}}\right). \tag{1}$$

The proof of this equality is as follows: split the sum into two parts:

$$\Psi_\mu(N) = \sum_{n_\mu\leqslant NL^{-\delta}} + \sum_{n_\mu>NL^{-\delta}} = S_1 + S_2.$$

Then

$$S_1 \ll \sum_{\substack{n_1+\cdots+n_s=N \\ n_\mu \leqslant NL^{-\delta}}} \frac{1}{n_1^{1-a}\cdots n_s^{1-a}}$$

$$\ll \sum_{n_\mu \leqslant NL^{-\delta}} \frac{1}{n_\mu^{1-a}} \sum_{n_1+\cdots+n_{\mu-1}+n_{\mu+1}+\cdots+n_s=N-n_\mu} \frac{1}{n_1^{1-a}\cdots n_{\mu-1}^{1-a}\, n_{\mu+1}^{1-a}\cdots n_s^{1-a}}$$

$$\ll \sum_{n_\mu \leqslant NL^{-\delta}} \frac{1}{n_\mu^{1-a}} (N-n_\mu)^{(s-1)a-1}$$

$$\ll N^{(s-1)a-1}(NL^{-\delta})^a = N^{sa-1}L^{-\delta a} \ll N^{sa-1}L^{-s-1}.$$

Here $\delta = k(s+1)$. Further,

$$S_2 = \frac{1}{\log N} \sum_{\substack{n_1+\cdots+n_s=N \\ n_\mu > NL^{-\delta}}} \frac{1}{n_1^{1-a}\log\frac{n_1}{A}\cdots n_{\mu-1}^{1-a}\log\frac{n_{\mu-1}}{A}\cdot n_\mu^{1-a}\cdots n_s^{1-a}}$$

$$+ \sum \frac{1}{n_1^{1-a}\log\frac{n_1}{A}\cdots n_\mu^{1-a}\cdots n_s^{1-a}} \left(\frac{1}{\log\frac{n_\mu}{A}} - \frac{1}{\log N}\right)$$

$$= \frac{1}{\log N}\Psi_{\mu-1}(N) + O\left(\frac{N^{sa-1}}{L^{s+1}}\right) + O\left(\frac{\log L}{L}\Psi_\mu(N)\right).$$

This completes the proof of (1).

By (1) we know that

$$\Psi_\mu(N) = \frac{1}{\log N}\Psi_{\mu-1}(N) + O\left(\frac{\Psi_{\mu-1}(N)\log L}{L^2}\right) + O\left(\frac{N^{sa-1}}{L^{s+1}}\right),$$

and, repeating this process, we deduce that

$$\Psi_s(N) = \frac{1}{\log^s N}\Psi_0(N) + O\left(\frac{\Psi_0(N)\log L}{L^{s+1}}\right) + O\left(\frac{N^{sa-1}}{L^{s+1}}\right)$$

$$= \frac{1}{\log^s N}\Psi_0(N) + O\left(\frac{N^{sa-1}}{L^{s+1}}\log L\right).$$

By Lemma 7.18 we obtain the lemma.

By Theorem 11′ and Lemma 7.19 we obtain the theorem presented at the beginning of this chapter (Theorem 11).

CHAPTER VIII

SINGULAR SERIES

§1. FORMULATION OF THEOREM 12

Let us now study the properties of the singular series when $f(x) = x^k$.

Let $p^\theta \| k$,

$$\gamma = \begin{cases} \theta + 2 & \text{if } p = 2, 2 | k, \\ \theta + 1 & \text{otherwise,} \end{cases}$$

and

$$K = \prod_{(p-1)|k} p^\gamma .$$

Theorem 12. *Suppose that* $s \geq 3k + 1$, *and for all* p *satisfying* $(p - 1)|k$ *we have* $s \equiv N \pmod{p^\gamma}$. *Further, take* $f(x) = x^k$. *Then* $\mathfrak{S}(N) \geq A > 0$, *where* A *is independent of* N.

§2. LEMMAS PERTAINING TO TRIGONOMETRIC SUMS

Lemma 8.1. *If* $(q_1, q_2) = 1$, *then*

$$W_{h, q_1 q_2} = W_{h q_1^{k-1}, q_2} W_{h q_2^{k-1}, q_1}$$

and

$$B_s(N, q_1 q_2) = B_s(N, q_1) B_s(N, q_2) .$$

Proof. Letting $l = l_1 q_2 + l_2 q_1$, then

$$W_{h, q_1 q_2} = \sum_{\substack{l_1=1 \\ (l_1, q_1)=1}}^{q_1} \sum_{\substack{l_2=1 \\ (l_2, q_2)=1}}^{q_2} e_{q_1 q_2}(h q_2^k l_1^k + h q_1^k l_2^k) = W_{h q_1^{k-1}, q_2} W_{h q_2^{k-1}, q_1} .$$

Further, if we let $h = h_1 q_2 + h_2 q_1$, then

$$B_s(N, q_1 q_2) = \sum_{\substack{h_1=1\\(h_1,q_1)=1}}^{q_1} \sum_{\substack{h_2=1\\(h_2,q_2)=1}}^{q_2} \left(\frac{W_{h_2 q_1^k, q_2}}{\varphi(q_2)}\right)^s \left(\frac{W_{h_1 q_2^k, q_1}}{\varphi(q_1)}\right)^s e_{q_1}(-h_1 N)\, e_{q_2}(-h_2 N)$$

$$= \sum_{\substack{h_1=1\\(h_1,q_1)=1}}^{q_1} \sum_{\substack{h_2=1\\(h_2,q_2)=1}}^{q_2} \left(\frac{W_{h_2, q_2}}{\varphi(q_2)}\right)^s \left(\frac{W_{h_1, q_1}}{\varphi(q_1)}\right)^s e_{q_1}(-h_1 N)\, e_{q_2}(-h_2 N)$$

$$= B_s(N, q_1)\, B_s(N, q_2).$$

Lemma 8.2. *Let*

$$\mu \geqslant \begin{cases} 1 & \text{if } p > 2, \\ 2 & \text{if } p = 2. \end{cases}$$

If

$$x \equiv y + z p^{\mu} \pmod{p^{\mu+1}},$$

then

$$x^p \equiv y^p + y^{p-1} z p^{\mu+1} \pmod{p^{\mu+2}}.$$

Proof. Write

$$x = y + z p^{\mu} + m p^{\mu+1}.$$

Since $3\mu \geq \mu + 2$, we know that

$$x^p \equiv (y + z p^{\mu})^p \equiv y^p + y^{p-1} z p^{\mu+1} + \frac{1}{2}(p-1) p y^{p-2} z^2 p^{2\mu} \pmod{p^{\mu+2}}.$$

If $p > 2$, we have

$$\frac{1}{2}(p-1) p y^{p-2} z^2 p^{2\mu} \equiv 0 \pmod{p^{\mu+2}}.$$

Since $\mu \geq 2$, $2\mu \geq \mu + 2$, it follows for $p = 2$ that

$$\frac{1}{2} p (p-1) y^{p-2} z^2 p^{2\mu} \equiv 0 \pmod{p^{\mu+2}}.$$

From these two congruences we obtain the lemma.

Lemma 8.3. *If* $t > \gamma$ *and* $p \nmid h$, *then*

$$W_{h, p^t} = 0.$$

Proof. Let $l = l_1 + l_2 p^{t-\theta-1}$. Then by repeated application of Lemma 8.2, we obtain

$$l^{p^\theta} \equiv l_1^{p^\theta} + l_1^{p^\theta - 1} l_2 p^{t-1} \pmod{p^t}.$$

Therefore

$$l^k \equiv l_1^k + k\, l_1^{k-1}\, l_2\, p^{t-\theta-1} \qquad (\mathrm{mod}\; p^t).$$

Hence we deduce that

$$W_{h,\,p^t} = \sum_{\substack{l_1=1\\(l_1,\,p)=1}}^{p^{t-\theta-1}} \sum_{l_2=1}^{p^{\theta+1}} e_{p^t}\left(h\,(l_1^k + p^{t-\theta-1}\, k l_1^{k-1}\, l_2)\right) = 0$$

(since $p \nmid l_1 k p^{-\theta}$).

Lemma 8.4. *The congruence*

$$x^k \equiv a\;(\mathrm{mod}\; p), \qquad p \nmid a,$$

is either insolvable or has $(k, p-1)$ *solutions. When* x *runs through* $1, 2, \cdots$ $\cdots, p-1\;(\mathrm{mod}\,p)$, x^k *runs through* $(p-1)/(k, p-1)$ *mutually incongruent numbers* $\mathrm{mod}\; p$.

Proof. The congruence $x^k \equiv 1\;(\mathrm{mod}\,p)$ has $(p-1, k)$ solutions, as follows from the fact that $x^{p-1} \equiv 1\;(\mathrm{mod}\,p)$. Let

$$a_1, \cdots, a_{(k,\,p-1)}$$

denote these solutions. If $x_1^k \equiv a\;(\mathrm{mod}\,p)$, then

$$x_1 a_1, \cdots, x_1 a_{(k,\,p-1)}$$

are all the solutions and the only solutions of $x^k \equiv a\;(\mathrm{mod}\,p)$. Therefore the congruence

$$x^k \equiv a\;(\mathrm{mod}\; p), \qquad p \nmid a,$$

may be insolvable or may have $(k, p-1)$ solutions. Hence we obtain the lemma.

Lemma 8.5. *If* $(h, q) = 1$, *then*

$$|W_{h,\,q}| \leqslant c_1(k, \varepsilon)\, q^{1/2+\varepsilon}.$$

Proof. 1) Suppose that q is mutually prime to p. Then by Lemma 8.4 we know that

$$\frac{1}{p} \sum_{h=1}^{p} \left| \sum_{x=1}^{p} e_p(h x^k) \right|^2 = \sum \sum_{x^k \equiv y^k \;(\mathrm{mod}\; p)} 1 = (k, p-1)(p-1) + 1.$$

Consider the sum

$$\sum_{x=1}^{p} e_p(h x^k) = \sum_{x=1}^{p} e_p(h(\lambda x)^k) = \sum_{x=1}^{p} e_p(h \lambda^k x^k), \qquad \lambda = 1, \cdots, p-1.$$

Since λ^k runs through $(p-1)/(k, p-1)$ mutually incongruent integers mod p, it follows that

$$\frac{p-1}{(k, p-1)} \left| \sum_{x=1}^{p} e_p(h x^k) \right|^2 \leqslant \sum_{h=1}^{p} \left| \sum_{x=1}^{p} e_p(h x^k) \right|^2$$
$$\leqslant \Big((k, p-1)(p-1) + 1 \Big) p.$$

Hence

$$\left| \sum_{x=1}^{p} e_p(h x^k) \right| \leqslant \sqrt{\frac{k^2 p^2}{p-1}} \leqslant 2k\sqrt{p},$$

and thus

$$|W_{h,p}| \leqslant 3k\sqrt{p}.$$

2) If $p|k$, it is easily seen from Lemma 8.3 that

$$W_{h,p^t} = O(1).$$

Moreover, by Lemma 8.3, we see that when $p \nmid k$ and $t > \gamma = \theta + 1 = 1$ we also have

$$W_{h,p^t} = O(1).$$

By 1) we know that for all p we always have

$$|W_{h,p}| \leqslant 3k\sqrt{p},$$

and accordingly when $p \geq (3k)^{1/\epsilon}$

$$|W_{h,t}| \leqslant p^{\frac{1}{2}+\epsilon}.$$

Let $q = p_t^{l_1} \cdots p_t^{l_t}$, $p_1 < p_2 < \cdots < p_t$. Then by Lemma 8.1 we know that

$$|W_{h,q}| = \prod_{p_i \leqslant k^{1/\epsilon}} |W_{h_i, p_i^{l_i}}| \prod_{p_i > k^{1/\epsilon}} |W_{h_i, p_i^{l_i}}| = O(q^{\frac{1}{2}+\epsilon}).$$

§3. LEMMAS PERTAINING TO CONGRUENCES

Lemma 8.6. *$M_s(p^t, N)$ denote the number of solutions of the congruence*

$$x_1^k + \cdots + x_s^k \equiv N \pmod{p^t}, \quad p \nmid x_1 \cdots x_s, \quad 0 < x_\nu < p^t$$

Then

$$\varphi(p^t)^{-s}\, p^t M_s(p^t, N) = 1 + \sum_{d=1}^{t} B_s(N, p^d).$$

Proof. We have

$$M_s(p^t, N) = p^{-t} \sum_{\substack{l_1=1 \\ p\nmid l_1}}^{p^t} \cdots \sum_{\substack{l_s=1 \\ p\nmid l_s}}^{p^t} \sum_{h=1}^{p^t} e_{p^t}(h(l_1^k + \cdots + l_s^k - N))$$

$$= p^{-t} \sum_{h=1}^{p^t} W^s{}_{h,\,p^t}\, e_{p^t}(-hN) = p^{-t} \varphi^s(p^t)\,(1 + \sum_{d=1}^{t} B_s(N, p^d)).$$

Lemma 8.7 (Cauchy). *Assume that* $x_1, x_2, \cdots, x_m$ *and* $y_1, y_2, \cdots, y_n$ *belong respectively to* m *and to* n *distinct residue classes* $(\bmod\, p^l)$, *and that* $y_i - y_j \not\equiv 0 \pmod p$ *for* $i \neq j$; *then the number of distinct residue classes* $(\bmod\, p^l)$ *represented by* $x_u + y_v$ $(1 \le u \le m,\ 1 \le v \le n)$ *is*

$$\geqslant \min(m + n - 1, p^l).$$

Proof. When $n = 1$, the lemma is obviously true. Let us now assume that $n \ge 2$, and we may suppose that y_1 satisfies $y_i \not\equiv y_1 \pmod p$ $(i \neq 1)$. Let $z_1, \cdots$ $\cdots, z_t$ represent all the distinct residue classes $(\bmod\, p^l)$ of the form $x_u + y_v$. If $t = p^l$, the lemma is established, and therefore we can assume that $t < p^l$. Let X, Y and Z represent the sets $x_1, x_2, \cdots, x_m$; $y_1, y_2, \cdots, y_n$ and $z_1, z_2, \cdots, z_t$, respectively.

Since $p \nmid y_n - y_1$, it follows that when λ runs through $\lambda = 0, 1, \cdots, p^l - 1$, the quantity $x_1 + y_1 + \lambda(y_n - y_1)$ runs through a complete set of residue classes modulo p^l, and therefore the numbers expressed by it definitely do not belong to Z. Let λ_0 be the least λ $(0 \le \lambda \le p^l - 1)$ such that $x_1 + y_1 + \lambda(y_n - y_1)$ does not belong to Z. It is easily seen that $\lambda_0 \ge 2$. Letting

$$\delta = x_1 + y_1 + \lambda_0(y_n - y_1) + y_1$$

we obviously have

$$\delta - y_1 \notin Z, \qquad \delta - y_n \in Z.$$

Let us now rearrange $y_1, \cdots, y_n$ so that

$$\begin{cases} \delta - y_s \notin Z & (1 \leqslant s \leqslant r), \\ \delta - y_{s'} \in Z & (r < s' \leqslant n), \end{cases}$$

Obviously $r \leq n - 1$. Further, let Z' denote the set formed by $x_u + y_s$ $(1 \leq u \leq m,\ 1 \leq s \leq r)$. Then Z' is a subset of Z.

We shall prove

$$\delta - y_{s'} \notin Z',$$

in fact, if $\delta - y_{s'} \in Z'$, then from $\delta - y_{s'} = x_u + y_s$ we deduce that

$$\delta - y_s = x_u + y_{s'} \in Z,$$

which contradicts $\delta - y_s \notin Z$, and therefore $\delta - y_{s'} \notin Z$. Let t' be the number of distinct residue classes $(\bmod\, p^l)$ represented by Z'. Then we have

$$t' \leqslant t - (n - r).$$

Thus, assuming by induction that

$$t' \geqslant m + r - 1$$

we obtain the lemma.

Lemma 8.8. *In the case of* $s \geq 3k$ *and* $(p - 1) \nmid k$, *we have*

$$M_s(p^\gamma, N) > 0.$$

To be more specific, if $k \neq p^\theta(p - 1)/2$, *then for* $s \geq 2k$ *the above conclusion is still valid. In the case of* $k = p^\theta(p - 1)/2$, *if we establish only one of*

$$N \equiv \pm s, \pm (s - 2), \pm (s - 4), \cdots, \qquad (\bmod\, p^\gamma),$$

then $M_s(p^\gamma, N) > 0$.

Proof. It is obvious that $p > 2$.

1) $p \nmid k$, so that $\gamma = 1$. From $(p - 1) \nmid k$ and Lemma 8.4 we know that x^k runs through

$$d = \frac{p-1}{(k, p-1)} > 1$$

distinct residue classes mod p. By Lemma 8.7, $x_1^k + \cdots + x_s^k$ $(p \nmid x_1 \cdots x_s)$ runs through

$$\min(d + (d - 1)(s - 1), p)$$

distinct residue classes mod p. But

$$s \geqslant 2k \geqslant \frac{p-1}{\frac{1}{2}d} \geqslant \frac{p-1}{d-1}$$

and hence

$$\min(d + (d - 1)(s - 1), p) = p.$$

2) Suppose that $k = p^\theta k_0$, $p \nmid k_0$. Since

$$x^{p^\theta k_0} \equiv x^{k_0} \pmod p \quad \text{and} \quad (p-1) \nmid k_0,$$

x^k runs through at least $(p-1)/(p-1, k_0)$ (> 1) distinct residue classes mod p. Therefore

$$x_1^k + \cdots + x_s^k, \qquad p \nmid x_1 \cdots x_s,$$

runs through

$$\min\left(\frac{p-1}{(p-1, k_0)} + \left(\frac{p-1}{(p-1, k_0)} - 1\right)(s-1), p^\gamma\right)$$

distinct residue classes mod p^γ.

When $k_0 \nmid (p-1)$, it is easily proved, since $(p-1) \nmid k_0$, that

$$\frac{k_0(p-1)}{(k_0, p-1)} \geqslant k_0 + (p-1),$$

and therefore

$$\frac{2k_0(p-1)}{(k_0, p-1)} \geqslant 2k_0 + p.$$

Furthermore, when $p - 1 = mk_0$ with $m > 2$, it is still not difficult to prove the above inequality. Hence, when $k \neq p^\theta(p-1)/2$ with $s \geq 2k$, we deduce that

$$s - 1 \geqslant 2p^\theta k_0 - 1 \geqslant \frac{p^\gamma}{\dfrac{p-1}{(p-1, k_0)} - 1} - 1.$$

Hence $x_1^k + \cdots + x_s^k$ $(p \nmid x_1 \cdots x_s)$ runs through p^γ distinct residue classes.

Further, if $k = p^\theta(p-1)/2 = \phi(p^\gamma)/2$, then $x^k \equiv \pm 1 \pmod{p^\gamma}$, and therefore, provided $N \equiv \pm s, \pm(s-2), \pm(s-4), \cdots, \pm(s - 2[s/2]) \pmod{p^\gamma}$, we have $M_s(p^\gamma, N) > 0$. But if $s \geq 3k$, it is not difficult to prove, since $s \geq p^\gamma$, that $\pm s, \pm(s-2), \pm(s-4), \cdots, \pm(s-2[s/2])$ runs through all the residue classes mod p^γ. Hence we have the proof of the lemma.

Lemma 8.9. *If* $s \equiv N \pmod{p^\gamma}$, *then*

$$M_s(p^\gamma, N) > 0.$$

The proof of this lemma is obvious.

§4. POSITIVENESS OF THE SINGULAR SERIES

Lemma 8.10. *When* $s > 4$, *the singular series* $\mathfrak{S}(N)$ *is absolutely convergent. When* $k = 1$, *this result can be improved to* $s > 2$.

Proof. We have, by Lemma 8.5,

$$|\mathfrak{S}(N)| \leqslant \sum_{q=1}^{\infty} |B_s(N, q)| \ll \sum_{q=1}^{\infty} q^{1-\frac{1}{2}s+\varepsilon}.$$

If $k = 1$, then $W_{k,q} = \mu(q)$ (the Möbius function). But $|\mu(q)| \leq 1$, and therefore

$$|\mathfrak{S}(N)| \leqslant \sum_{q=1}^{\infty} |B_s(N, q)| \ll \sum_{q=1}^{\infty} q^{1-s+\varepsilon}.$$

Lemma 8.11. *When* $s > 4$,

$$\mathfrak{S}(N) = \prod_p \chi_p(N),$$

where

$$\chi_p(N) = 1 + \sum_{t=1}^{\gamma} B_s(N, p^t).$$

When $k = 1$, *this result can be improved to* $s > 2$.

Proof. We can deduce the lemma directly from Lemmas 8.1, 8.3 and 8.10.

Lemma 8.12. *There exists a constant* A *such that when* $s \geq 3k$

$$\mathfrak{S}(N) \geqslant A > 0.$$

To be more specific, if $k \neq p^{\theta}(p-1)/2$, *the above conclusion is still true when* $s \geq 2k$. *If* $k = p^{\theta}(p-1)/2$ *with*

$$N \equiv \pm s, \pm (s-2), \pm (s-4), \cdots, \pm \left(s - 2\left[\frac{1}{2}s\right]\right) \pmod{p^{\gamma}}$$

the above result is still valid for any s.

Proof. We know, by Lemmas 8.6, 8.8 and 8.9, that for all p

$$\chi_p(N) > 0.$$

Further

$$|B_s(N, p)| \leqslant p\left(\frac{3k\sqrt{p}}{p-1}\right)^s \leqslant (6k)^s p^{-\frac{1}{2}s+1}.$$

Therefore, when $p > (6k)^{4s}$,

$$\chi_p > 1 - p^{-s/2+1+1/4}.$$

Further, when $s > 4$,

$$\mathfrak{S}(N) \geqslant \prod_{p \leqslant (6k)^{4s}} \chi_p \prod_{p > (6k)^{4s}} (1 - p^{-5/4}) \geqslant A > 0.$$

The same method applies for the cases $k = 1$ and $s > 2$.

Obviously, we can deduce Theorem 12 from Lemma 8.12.

§5. COROLLARIES OF THEOREMS 11 AND 12

It is easy to obtain the following theorem: *Suppose that* $s \geq s_0$, *with*

$$s_0 \geqslant \begin{cases} 2^k + 1 & \textit{if } 1 \leqslant k \leqslant 10, \\ 2k^2(2\log k + \log\log k + 2.5) & \textit{if } k > 10. \end{cases}$$

Every sufficiently large integer $N \equiv s \pmod{K}$ *can be expressed as the sum of* s *kth powers of primes.*

To be more specific, we introduce several immediate corollaries:

Corollary 1. *Every sufficiently large odd integer is the sum of three primes.*

Corollary 2. *Every sufficiently large integer* $\equiv 5 \pmod{24}$ *can be expressed as the sum of five squares of primes.*

Corollary 3. *Every sufficiently large odd integer can be expressed as the sum of nine cubes of primes.*

Corollary 4. *Every sufficiently large integer* $\equiv 17 \pmod{240}$ *can be expressed as the sum of* 17 *fourth powers of primes.*

To conclude this chapter, we introduce the following definition. Let $H(k)$ denote the least integer s such that every sufficiently large integer $\equiv s \pmod{K}$ can be expressed as the sum of s kth powers of primes. The results of this chapter can be summed up by the following formula:

$$H(k) \leqslant \begin{cases} 2^k + 1 & \text{if } 1 \leqslant k \leqslant 10, \\ 2k^2(2\log k + \log\log k + 2.5) & \text{if } k > 10. \end{cases}$$

CHAPTER IX

A FURTHER STUDY OF THE WARING-GOLDBACH PROBLEM

§1. INTRODUCTION

The object of this chapter is to obtain a result better than that of §5 of Chapter VIII. Let us now first introduce the concept of exponential density.

Definition. Let $\mathfrak{U}$ be a set of distinct natural numbers. Use u to denote the elements in $\mathfrak{U}$, and let

$$U(X) = \sum_{u \leqslant X} 1$$

denote the number of the elements in $\mathfrak{U}$ not greater than X. If ν is the greatest real number such that for any $\epsilon > 0$

$$U(X) \gg X^{\nu-\varepsilon},$$

then ν is called the exponential density of the set $\mathfrak{U}$.

In the discussion developed in this chapter we always assume that $k \geq 4$. Furthermore, let $a = 1/k$,

$$b = \begin{cases} 2k^2\,(2\log k + \log\log k + 3) & \text{if } k > 12, \\ 2^{k-1} & \text{if } k \leqslant 12, \end{cases}$$

and

$$m = \left[\frac{\log\frac{1}{2}\,b + \log(1-2a)}{-\log(1-a)}\right].$$

The principal theorem in the chapter is:

Theorem 13. *Let N be a sufficiently large (i.e., $\geq c(k)$) integer, let $\mathfrak{U}$ be a set of natural numbers whose exponential density is not smaller than ν, and let*

$$\delta = k - 1 + \max_{1 \leqslant r \leqslant k-2} \min\left(2^{1-r}, \frac{r + 1 - \nu(k-1)}{2^r - 1 + \nu}\right).$$

If

$$1 + \nu\delta > k\left(1 - \frac{2}{b}\right),$$

and if the number of distinct solutions of

$$u + u' \equiv N - 2k - 3 \pmod{K}, \quad u, u' \in \mathfrak{U}, \quad u, u' \leqslant X$$

is always $\gg U^2(X)$, *then*

i) *for* $k \neq p^\theta(p-1)/2$ $(p \neq 2)$ *it is possible to express* N *in the form*

$$p_1^k + p_2^k + \cdots + p_{2k+3}^k + u + u', \qquad u, u' \in \mathfrak{U}; \tag{1}$$

ii) *for* $k = p^\theta(p-1)/2$ $(p \neq 2)$, *and for any* l *such that the exponential density of the set* $\mathfrak{U}_l$ *formed by the elements in* $\mathfrak{U}$ *satisfying*

$$u \equiv l \pmod{p}$$

is not smaller than ν, *it is possible to express* N *in the form* (1).

Lemma 9.1. *The number of sets of integral solutions of the equation*

$$x_0^k + \cdots + x_{m-1}^k + x_m^k + x_m'^k = y_0^k + \cdots + y_{m-1}^k + y_m^k + y_m'^k \tag{2}$$

in the interval

$$2^{-i} P^{(1-a)^i} \leqslant x_i, y_i \leqslant 2^{1-i} P^{(1-a)^i} \qquad (0 \leqslant i \leqslant m) \tag{3}$$

is

$$O\left(P^{k-(k-2)(1-a)^m} L^{c_3}\right).$$

Proof. From (2) and (3) we obtain: when P is sufficiently large, $x_i = y_i$ $(i = 0, \cdots, m-1)$. In fact, assuming that μ is the first index such that $x_\mu \neq y_\mu$, then

$$\left| x_\mu^k - y_\mu^k \right| = k \left| \int_{y_\mu}^{x_\mu} t^{k-1}\, dt \right| \geqslant k\left(2^{-\mu} P^{(1-a)^\mu}\right)^{k-1}.$$

The right member of this inequality, when P is sufficiently large, is greater than

$$y_{\mu+1}^k + \cdots + y_m^k + y_m'^k,$$

and therefore (2) becomes an impossibility. This proves that $x_i = y_i$ $(i = 0, \cdots, m-1)$. Further, by Theorem 4 the number of solutions of the equation

$$x_m^k + x_m'^k = y_m^k + y_m'^k$$

is $O(P^{2(1-a)^m} L^{C_3})$. The lemma is proved.

Lemma 9.2. *Let $q \geq 1$, let $l_0, \cdots, l_{m+1}$ be a set of integers, and let $(l_i, q) = 1$. Let $\mathfrak{U}$ denote the set of distinct integers of the form*

$$u = p_0^k + \cdots + p_{m+1}^k, \qquad p_i \equiv l_i \pmod q, \tag{4}$$

where p_i $(0 \leq i \leq m+1)$ runs through the primes in the arithmetic progression $qx + l_i$. Then the exponential density of $\mathfrak{U}$ is

$$\geqslant 1 - (1-2a)(1-a)^m.$$

Proof. Let $P = [(X/(m+2))^a/2]$. It is easily seen that $P^k \ll X \ll P^k$. The numbers in $\mathfrak{U}$ not greater than X obviously include u satisfying

$$2^{-i} P^{(1-a)^i} \leqslant p_i \leqslant 2^{1-i} P^{(1-a)^i} \qquad (0 \leqslant i \leqslant m), \tag{5}$$
$$2^{-m} P^{(1-a)^m} \leqslant p_{m+1} \leqslant 2^{1-m} P^{(1-a)^m}.$$

Let $r(u)$ denote the number of distinct sets of prime solutions of equation (4) in interval (5). Then by Cauchy's inequality we obtain

$$\Big(\sum_u r(u)\Big)^2 \leqslant U(X) \sum_u r^2(u).$$

By Lemma 9.1, it is easily seen that

$$\sum_u r^2(u) \ll P^{k-(k-2)(1-a)^m+\varepsilon};$$

moreover, by Lemma 7.14 we know that

$$\sum_u r(u) \gg P^{k-(k-2)(1-a)^m-\varepsilon};$$

therefore we obtain

$$U(X) \gg P^{k-(k-2)(1-a)^m-\varepsilon} \gg X^{1-(1-2a)(1-a)^m-\varepsilon},$$

which is the lemma in question.

In Theorem 13, take $\mathfrak{U}$ to be the set of distinct integers in the form

$$u = p_0^k + \cdots + p_{m+1}^k$$

and take $\nu = 1 - (1-2a)(1-a)^m$. Since $\delta > k - 1$, we can easily show that $1 + \nu\delta > k(1 - 2/b)$. Further, when $k = p^\theta(p-1)/2$ $(p > 2)$, we must have $k \geq 9$, from which it readily follows that $m + 2 \geq 3k$, and therefore, by Lemma 8.8, the congruence

$$l_0^k + \cdots + l_{m+1}^k \equiv l \pmod{p^\gamma}, \quad p \nmid l_0 \cdots l_{m+1},$$

is solvable, and consequently, by Lemma 9.2, we know that the exponential density of $\mathfrak{U}_l$ also is $\geq \nu$. Hence we obtain:

Theorem 14. *Let* $s_0 = s_0(k) = 2k + 2m + 7$ *and* $s \geq s_0$. *Then all sufficiently large integers* N *congruent to* $s \pmod K$ *are the sum of* s k*th powers of primes. In other words,*

$$H(k) \leqslant 2k + 2m + 7.$$

When k is sufficiently large,

$$m \sim 2k \log k$$

and

$$s_0 \sim 4k \log k.$$

This result, when $k \geq 5$, is better than that in §5 of the preceding chapter.

§2. DAVENPORT'S LEMMA

Lemma 9.3 (Davenport).[1] *Let* $\mathfrak{U}$ *denote a set of distinct natural numbers. Let* $f(x)$ *denote an integral-valued polynomial of the* k*th degree, let* δ *be a real number satisfying* $k - 1 < \delta \leq k$, *and let* P *be a positive integer. Then the number of distinct solutions of the equation*

$$f(x_1) + u_1 = f(x_2) + u_2, \quad P \leqslant x_1, x_2 \leqslant 2P, \quad u_1, u_2 \leqslant P^\delta \tag{1}$$

is

$$\ll P^{1+\varepsilon} U(P^\delta) \left(1 + P^{\delta-k+1-2^{1-r}} + P^{(1-2^{-r})(\delta-k+1)-(r+1)2^{-r}} (U(P^\delta))^{2^{-r}}\right),$$

where r *satisfies* $1 \leq r \leq k - 2$, *and the constants involved in the sign* $\ll$ *depend only on* k *and* ϵ.

Proof. We will use the notation

$$t_1 \Delta f(x) = f(x + t_1) - f(x)$$

and

$$t_1 \cdots t_r \Delta^r f(x) = t_r \Delta (t_1 \cdots t_{r-1} \Delta^{r-1} f(x)).$$

1) Let N_r $(r \geq 1)$ denote the number of solutions of

$$t_1 \cdots t_r \Delta^r f(x) + u_1 = u,$$

$$P \leqslant x \leqslant 2P, \quad u_1, u \leqslant P^\delta, \quad t_1 \cdots t_r \ll P^{\delta-k+r}, \quad t_i > 0. \tag{2}$$

For fixed $t_1, \cdots, t_r$ and u, let $r(u, t)$ denote the number of solutions of (2). We

---

1) The author is indebted to Dr. Rao for valuable suggestions concerning this lemma.

shall prove that

$$N_r \ll U(P^\delta)\, P^{\delta-k+r} + (U(P^\delta)\, P^{\delta-k+r} N_{r+1})^{\frac{1}{2}}. \tag{3}$$

By Cauchy's inequality, we know that

$$N_r = \sum_t \sum_u r(u, t) \leqslant \Big(\sum_t \sum_u 1\Big)^{\frac{1}{2}} \Big(\sum_t \sum_u r^2(u, t)\Big)^{\frac{1}{2}}$$
$$\ll \Big(P^{\delta-k+r}\, U(P^\delta) \sum_t \sum_u r^2(u, t)\Big)^{\frac{1}{2}},$$

where $\Sigma_t \Sigma_u r^2(u, t)$ is the number of solutions of

$$t_1 \cdots t_r\, \Delta^r f(x_1) + u_1 = t_1 \cdots t_r\, \Delta^r f(x_2) + u_2, \tag{4}$$

and both sides of this equality belong to $\mathfrak{U}$. The number of distinct $t_1 \cdots t_r \Delta^r f(x_2) + u_2$ in $\mathfrak{U}$ is obviously N_r. Therefore, when $x_1 = x_2$, the number of solutions of (4) is N_r. Let us now assume that $x_1 > x_2$, and let $x_1 = x + t_{r+1}$ and $x_2 = x$; then we obtain

$$t_1 \cdots t_{r+1}\, \Delta^{r+1} f(x) + u_1 = u_2. \tag{5}$$

Since

$$\Delta^{r+1} f(x) \gg x^{k-r-1} \gg P^{k-r-1},$$

we know that

$$t_1 \cdots t_{r+1} \ll P^{\delta-k+r+1}.$$

Therefore the number of solutions of (4) satisfying $x_1 > x_2$ is $\ll N_{r+1}$. Hence we obtain

$$N_r \ll \{P^{\delta-k+r}\, U(P^\delta)\, (N_r + N_{r+1})\}^{\frac{1}{2}},$$

i.e.,

$$N_r \ll P^{\delta-k+r}\, U(P^\delta) + (P^{\delta-k+r}\, U(P^\delta)\, N_{r+1})^{\frac{1}{2}}.$$

2) When $1 \le r \le k-2$,

$$N_1 \ll U(P^\delta)\, P^{\delta-k+2-2^{1-r}} + (U(P^\delta))^{1-2^{-r}}\, P^{(\delta-k+1)(1-2^{-r})+1-(r+1)2^{-r}}\, N_{r+1}^{2^{-r}}. \tag{6}$$

When $r = 1$, we obtain (6) from (3). Let us now assume that (6) is true for $r-1$. By (3), we obtain

$$N_1 \ll U(P^\delta)\, P^{\delta-k+2-2^{2-r}} + (U(P^\delta))^{1-2^{1-r}}\, P^{(\delta-k+1)(1-2^{1-r})+1-r2^{1-r}}\, N_r^{2^{1-r}} \ll$$

$$\ll U(P^\delta)\, P^{\delta-k+2-2^{2-r}} + (U(P^\delta))^{1-2^{1-r}}\, P^{(\delta-k+1)(1-2^{1-r})+1-r2^{1-r}}$$
$$\times\, \left(U(P^\delta)\, P^{\delta-k+r} + (P^{\delta-k+r}\, U(P^\delta)\, N_{r+1})^{\frac{1}{2}}\right)^{2^{1-r}}$$
$$\ll U(P^\delta)\, P^{\delta-k+2-2^{1-r}} + (U(P^\delta))^{1-2^{-r}}\, P^{(\delta-k+1)(1-2^{-r})+1-(r+1)2^{-r}}\, N_{r+1}^{2^{-r}}.$$

3) Let N denote the number of solutions of (1). We shall prove

$$N \ll PU(P^\delta) + N_1.$$

If $x_1 = x_2$, the number of solutions of (1) is $\ll PU(P^\delta)$. If $x_1 \neq x_2$, the number of solutions of (1) is $\ll N_1$.

By (6) and the obvious inequality

$$N_{r+1} \ll \sum_{u_1}\sum_{u_2} d^r(u_2 - u_1) \ll (U(P^\delta))^2 P^\varepsilon$$

we obtain the lemma.

§3. PROOF OF THEOREM 13

Let $\mathfrak{U}$ be a set of distinct natural numbers with exponential density $\geq \nu$. Further, let

$$\delta = k - 1 + \max_{1\leqslant r\leqslant k-2} \min\left(2^{1-r}, \frac{r+1-\nu(k-1)}{2^r-1+\nu}\right).$$

Obviously, when $\nu > 1/k$ we have $\delta < k$.

Let

$$Q(\alpha) = \sum_{u\leqslant P^\delta}{}' e^{2\pi i u\alpha},$$

$$T(\alpha) = \sum_{P\leqslant n\leqslant 2P} e^{2\pi i n^k\alpha},$$

$$\mathfrak{T}(\alpha) = \sum_{P<p\leqslant 2P} e^{2\pi i p^k\alpha},$$

$$\mathfrak{T}^*(\alpha, h, q) = \frac{W_{h,q}}{\varphi(q)} \sum_{P^k<n\leqslant(2P)^k} \frac{e(n\beta)}{n^{1-a}\log n}.$$

Taking $f(x) = x^k$ in Lemma 9.3, we accordingly obtain

$$\int_0^1 |T(\alpha)\, Q(\alpha)|^2\, d\alpha \ll P^{1+\varepsilon}\, Q(0). \qquad (1)$$

Lemma 9.4.

$$\int_0^1 |T^{k+1}(\alpha)\, Q(\alpha)|^2\, d\alpha \ll P^{k+2} Q^2(0).$$

Proof. Dissect $-1/\tau \le \alpha \le 1 - 1/\tau$ as in §3 of Chapter VII.

1) When α falls in E, we know by Lemma 3.6 and Theorem 9 that

$$T(\alpha) \ll P^{1-\frac{1}{b}+\varepsilon},$$

therefore by (1) we obtain

$$\int_E |T^{k+1}(\alpha)\, Q(\alpha)|^2\, d\alpha \ll P^{2k\left(1-\frac{1}{b}\right)+\varepsilon} \int_0^1 |T(\alpha)\, Q(\alpha)|^2\, d\alpha$$

$$\ll P^{2k\left(1-\frac{1}{b}\right)+\varepsilon} P^{1+\varepsilon} Q(0) \ll P^{k+2} Q^2(0).$$

(Here we have assumed that $1 + \nu\delta > k(1 - 2/b)$.)

2) By Lemma 7.12 we have

$$\sum_{\mathfrak{M}} \int_{\mathfrak{M}} |T^{k+1}(\alpha)\, Q(\alpha)|^2\, d\alpha \ll Q^2(0) \sum_{\mathfrak{M}} \int_{\mathfrak{M}} |T^{k+1}(\alpha)|^2\, d\alpha$$

$$\ll P^{k+2} Q^2(0).$$

Hence the lemma is proved.

Lemma 9.5.

$$\int_0^1 \mathfrak{T}^{2k+3}(\alpha)\, Q^2(\alpha)\, e(-N\alpha)\, d\alpha$$

$$= \Psi(N) \sum_{u \le P^\delta} \sum_{u' \le P^\delta} \mathfrak{S}(N - u - u') + O(Q^2(0) P^{k+3} L^{-\eta}).$$

Here η is a constant greater than $2k + 4$ and $\mathfrak{S}(N)$ is the singular series when $s = 2k + 3$; while

$$\Psi(N) = \sum_{\substack{n_1+\cdots+n_{2k+3}=N \\ P^k \le n_i \le (2P)^k}} \frac{1}{\prod_{i=1}^{2k+3} n_i^{1-a} \log n_i}.$$

Proof. Dissect $-1/\tau \le \alpha \le 1 - 1/\tau$ as in §7 of Chapter VII, but let σ be so chosen that σ_0 in Theorem 10 is greater than η.

1) By Theorem 10, we obtain

$$\int_E |\mathfrak{T}^{2k+3}(\alpha)\, Q^2(\alpha)|\, d\alpha \ll \max_{\alpha \in E} |\mathfrak{T}(\alpha)| \int_0^1 |T^{k+1}(\alpha)\, Q(\alpha)|^2\, d\alpha$$

$$\ll Q^2(0) P^{k+3} L^{-\eta}.$$

2) When $\alpha \in \mathfrak{M}(h, q)$,

$$\left|Q(\alpha) - Q\left(\frac{h}{q}\right)\right| \ll \sum_{u \leqslant P^\delta} \left| e\left(u\left(\frac{h}{q} + \beta\right)\right) - e\left(u \frac{h}{q}\right)\right|$$

$$\ll \sum_{u \leqslant P^\delta} |\beta|\, u \ll Q(0)\, P^\delta (qNL^{-\sigma})^{-1} \ll P^{\delta-k+\varepsilon}\, Q(0)$$

and we at once obtain

$$\left|Q^2(\alpha) - Q^2\left(\frac{h}{q}\right)\right| \ll P^{\delta-k+\varepsilon}\, Q^2(0).$$

Therefore by Lemma 7.16 we know that

$$\sum_{\mathfrak{M}} \int_{\mathfrak{M}} |\mathfrak{T}^{2k+3}(\alpha)| \left|Q^2(\alpha) - Q^2\left(\frac{h}{q}\right)\right| d\alpha$$

$$\ll P^{\delta-k+\varepsilon} Q^2(0) \sum_{q \leqslant L^\sigma} q \cdot q^{-(2+3a)+\varepsilon} \left(\int_0^{P^{-k}} P^{2k+3}\, d\beta + \int_{P^{-k}} \beta^{-2-3a}\, d\beta\right)$$

$$\ll Q^2(0)\, P^{\delta+3+\varepsilon} \ll Q^2(0)\, P^{k+3} L^{-\eta}.$$

3) By 3) in the proof of Theorem 11$'$ we know that

$$\sum_{\mathfrak{M}} Q^2\left(\frac{h}{q}\right) \int_{\mathfrak{M}} (\mathfrak{T}^{2k+3}(\alpha) - \mathfrak{T}^{*2k+3}(\alpha, h, q))\, e(-\alpha N)\, d\alpha$$

$$\ll Q^2(0) \sum_{q \leqslant L^\sigma} q \cdot q^{-(2+2a)+\varepsilon} P^{k+3} e^{-c\sqrt{L}}$$

$$\ll Q^2(0)\, P^{k+3} L^{-\eta}.$$

4) By 4) in the proof of Theorem 11$'$ we know that

$$\sum_{\mathfrak{M}} Q^2\left(\frac{h}{q}\right)\left(\int_{-\frac{1}{2}}^{\frac{1}{2}} - \int_{\mathfrak{M}}\right) \mathfrak{T}^{*2k+3}(\alpha, h, q)\, e(-N\alpha)\, d\beta$$

$$\ll Q^2(0) \sum_{q \leqslant L^\sigma} q \cdot q^{-(2+3a)+\varepsilon} \int_{q^{-1}N^{-1}L^\sigma} \beta^{-(2+3a)}\, d\beta \ll Q^2(0)\, P^{k+3} L^{-\eta}.$$

(We have used $3a\sigma > \sigma_0 > \eta$ here.)

5) Since

$$\int_{-\frac{1}{2}}^{\frac{1}{2}} \mathfrak{T}^{*2k+3}(\alpha, h, q)\, e(-N\beta)\, d\beta = \left(\frac{W_{h,q}}{\varphi(q)}\right)^{2k+3} \Psi(N),$$

we have, by Lemma 7.19,

$$\Psi(N)\Big(\sum_{u\leqslant P^\delta}\sum_{u'\leqslant P^\delta}\mathfrak{S}(N-u-u')-\sum_{\mathfrak{M}}Q^2\Big(\frac{h}{q}\Big)e\Big(-N\frac{h}{q}\Big)\Big(\frac{W_{h,q}}{\varphi(q)}\Big)^{2k+3}\Big)$$
$$\ll Q^2(0)P^{k+3}L^{-\eta}.$$

The lemma follows at once.

By Lemma 7.19 it is easily seen that

$$P^{k+3}L^{-2k-3}\ll\Psi(N)\ll P^{k+3}L^{-2k-3}.$$

Hence, by Lemmas 9.5 and 8.12, we have the proof of Theorem 13.

§4. APPENDIX

Let $f(x)$ be an integral-valued polynomial of the kth degree with positive leading coefficient.

Lemma 9.6. *Let $\mathfrak{U}$ denote a set whose exponential density is $\geq \nu$, and let $\mathfrak{B}$ denote a set of distinct integers of the form*

$$v=f(p)+u.$$

Then the exponential density of $\mathfrak{B}$ is not less than $a(1+\delta\nu)$. For the definition of δ, see Theorem 13.

Proof. Let x_0 be the greatest positive root of the equation $X=f(x)$, and let $P=[x_0/4]$. Obviously we have $P^k\ll X\ll P^k$.

When X is sufficiently large, the numbers in $\mathfrak{B}$ not greater than X obviously include

$$f(p)+u,\qquad P\leqslant p\leqslant 2P,\qquad u\leqslant P^\delta.$$

Let $r(v)$ denote the number of solutions of the equation

$$v=f(p)+u,\qquad P\leqslant x\leqslant 2P,\qquad u\leqslant P^\delta.$$

Then by Cauchy's inequality we obtain

$$\Big(\sum_v r(v)\Big)^2\leqslant\Big(\sum_v 1\Big)\Big(\sum_v r^2(v)\Big).$$

Since $\sum_v r^2(v)$ is not greater than the number of solutions of

$$f(x_1)+u_1=f(x_2)+u_2,\quad P\leqslant x_1,x_2\leqslant 2P,\quad u_1,u_2\leqslant P^\delta,$$

therefore by Lemma 9.3 we obtain

$$\sum_v r^2(v) \ll P^{1+\varepsilon} U(P^\delta).$$

Further, since

$$\sum_v r(v) \gg P^{1-\varepsilon} U(P^\delta), \quad \text{and} \quad U(P^\delta) \gg P^{\nu\delta-\varepsilon},$$

we obtain

$$V(X) \gg \sum_v 1 \gg P^{1+\nu\delta-\varepsilon} \gg X^{a(1+\nu\delta)-\varepsilon},$$

from which the lemma follows.

Lemma 9.7. *Let $f(x)$ denote an integral-valued polynomial of the 4th degree with positive leading coefficient and let $\mathfrak{B}_4$ denote a set of distinct integers of the form*

$$v = f(p_1) + f(p_2) + f(p_3) + f(p_4).$$

Then the exponential density of $\mathfrak{B}_4$ is $\geq 331/412$.

Proof. 1) Let $\mathfrak{U}$ be a set of distinct integers of the form

$$u = f(p_1) + f(p_2).$$

The numbers in $\mathfrak{U}$ not greater than X obviously include

$$u = f(p_1) + f(p_2), \qquad P \leqslant p_1, p_2 \leqslant 2P.$$

Here $P = [x_0/4]$, where x_0 is the greatest positive root of $X = f(x)$. Further, let $r(u)$ denote the number of solutions of the above form. Then since

$$\sum_u r(u) \gg P^{2-\varepsilon} \gg X^{\frac{1}{2}-\varepsilon},$$

we obtain from Theorem 4

$$\sum_u r^2(u) \leqslant \int_0^1 \left| \sum_{x=1}^{2P} e(\alpha f(x)) \right|^4 d\alpha \ll P^{2+\varepsilon} \ll X^{\frac{1}{2}+\varepsilon},$$

and Cauchy's formula

$$\left(\sum_u r(u)\right)^2 \leqslant \left(\sum_u 1\right)\left(\sum_u r^2(u)\right).$$

Hence we obtain

$$U(X) \gg \sum_u 1 \gg X^{\frac{1}{2}-\varepsilon}.$$

2) Taking $\nu = 1/2$, $r = 2$, $\delta = 24/7$ in Lemma 9.6, the exponential density of a set of distinct integers of the form

$$f(p_1) + f(p_2) + f(p_3)$$

is

$$\geqslant \frac{1}{4}\left(1 + \frac{1}{2} \cdot \frac{24}{7}\right) = \frac{19}{28}.$$

Further, using Lemma 9.6 but taking $\nu = 19/28$, $r = 2$, $\delta = 336/103$, we conclude that the exponential density of $\mathfrak{B}_4$ is

$$\geqslant \frac{1}{4}\left(1 + \frac{19}{28} \cdot \frac{336}{103}\right) = \frac{331}{412}.$$

For the sake of clarity, we indicate the proof in the table below: The n in the table is the number of distinct $f(x)$, and ν_n denotes the exponential density of the set of distinct integers in the form

$$f(p_1) + f(p_2) + \cdots + f(p_n).$$

n	r	δ	$\nu_n \geqslant$
2	—	—	$\frac{1}{2}$
3	2	$\frac{24}{7}$	$\frac{19}{28}$
4	2	$\frac{336}{103}$	$\frac{331}{412}$

Lemma 9.8. *Let $f(x)$ denote an integral-valued polynomial of the 5th degree, and let $\mathfrak{B}_7$ denote the set of distinct integers in the form*

$$f(p_1) + f(p_2) + \cdots + f(p_7).$$

Then the exponential density of $\mathfrak{B}_7$ is

$$\geqslant \frac{1}{5} \cdot \frac{127{;}6889}{29{,}1873}.$$

The proof of this lemma is indicated by the following table:

n	r	δ	$v_n \geqslant$
2	—	—	$\frac{2}{5}$
3	2	$5\cdot\frac{15}{17}$	$\frac{1}{5}\cdot\frac{47}{17}$
7	3	—	$\frac{1}{5}\cdot\frac{127{,}6889}{29{,}1873}$

Explanation: $\nu_4, \cdots, \nu_7$ are obtained by repeated application of the formula

$$v_{n+1} \geqslant \frac{1}{5}\left(1+\frac{32v_n}{7+v_n}\right) \qquad (n \geqslant 3),$$

starting with $\nu_3 \geq (1/5)\cdot(47/17)$. In calculating, it is more convenient to apply the formula

$$\frac{5v_{n+1}+7}{1-v_{n+1}} \geqslant \frac{10}{7}\,\frac{5v_n+7}{1-v_n} \qquad (n \geqslant 3).$$

Lemma 9.9. *Let $f(x)$ be an integral-valued polynomial of the 6th degree, and let $\mathfrak{B}_{12}$ denote the set of distinct integers of the form*

$$f(p_1)+f(p_2)+\cdots+f(p_{12}).$$

Then the exponential density of $\mathfrak{B}_{12}$ is ≥ 0.934.

This lemma is indicated by the following table:

n	r	δ	$v_n \geqslant$
2	—	—	$\frac{1}{3}$
3	2	$6\cdot\frac{9}{10}$	$\frac{1}{6}\cdot\frac{14}{5}$
4	3	$6\cdot\frac{195}{224}$	$\frac{1}{6}\cdot\frac{55}{16}$
5	3	$6\cdot\frac{624}{727}$	$\frac{1}{6}\cdot\frac{2872}{727}$
12	4	—	0.934

Explanation: The numerical value 0.934 is obtained by repeated application of the formula

$$\nu_{n+1} \geqslant \frac{1}{6}\left(1+\frac{80\nu_n}{15+\nu_n}\right) \quad \left(\text{i.e. } \frac{2\nu_{n+1}+5}{1-\nu_{n+1}} \geqslant \frac{32}{25}\,\frac{2\nu_n+5}{1-\nu_n}\right) \quad (n \geqslant 5),$$

starting with $\nu_5 \geq (1/6)\cdot(2872/727)$.

Lemma 9.10. *Let $f(x)$ represent an integral-valued polynomial of the 7th degree, and let $\mathfrak{B}_{18}$ denote the set of distinct integers of the form*

$$f(p_1)+f(p_2)+\cdots+f(p_{18}).$$

Then the exponential density of $\mathfrak{B}_{18}$ is ≥ 0.9601.

This lemma is indicated by the following table:

n	r'	δ	$\nu_n \geqslant$
2	—	—	$\frac{2}{7}$
3	2	$7\cdot\frac{21}{23}$	$\frac{1}{7}\cdot\frac{65}{23}$
4	3	$7\cdot\frac{529}{596}$	$\frac{1}{7}\cdot\frac{2091}{596}$
5	3	$7\cdot\frac{2,7416}{3,1295}$	$\frac{1}{7}\cdot\frac{12,7481}{3,1295}$
6	4	$7\cdot\frac{297,3025}{341,3456}$	$\frac{1}{7}\cdot\frac{1552,4151}{341,3456}$
7	4	$7\cdot\frac{3,2427,8320}{3,7393,7031}$	$\frac{1}{7}\cdot\frac{18,4873,1376}{3,7393,7031}$
18	5	—	0.9601

Explanation: The numerical value 0.9601 is obtained by repeated application of the formula

$$\nu_{n+1} \geqslant \frac{1}{7}\left(1+\frac{192\nu_n}{31+\nu_n}\right) \quad \left(\text{i.e. } \frac{31+7\nu_{n+1}}{1-\nu_{n+1}} \geqslant \frac{112}{93}\,\frac{31+7\nu_n}{1-\nu_n}\right) \quad (n \geqslant 7),$$

starting with $\nu_7 \geq (1/7)\cdot(18,4873,1376/3,7393,7031)$.

Lemma 9.11. *Let $f(x)$ represent an integral-valued polynomial of the 8th degree, and let $\mathfrak{B}_{28}$ denote the set of distinct integers of the form*

$$f(p_1) + f(p_2) + \cdots + f(p_{28}).$$

Then the exponential density of $\mathfrak{B}_{28}$ is ≥ 0.9838.

This lemma is indicated by the following table:

n	r	δ	$v_n \geqslant$
2	—	—	$\frac{1}{4}$
3	2	$8\cdot\frac{12}{13}$	$\frac{1}{8}\cdot\frac{37}{13}$
4	3	$8\cdot\frac{689}{765}$	$\frac{1}{8}\cdot\frac{2726}{765}$
5	4	$8\cdot\frac{4,2075}{4,7263}$	$\frac{1}{8}\cdot\frac{19,7193}{4,7263}$
6	4	$8\cdot\frac{519,8930}{586,8753}$	$\frac{1}{8}\cdot\frac{2755,9983}{586,8753}$
7	5	$8\cdot\frac{13,0873,1919}{14,8301,0727}$	$\frac{1}{8}\cdot\frac{76,2888,6936}{14,8301,0727}$
8	5	$8\cdot\frac{3307,1139,2121}{3754,1554,7232}$	$\frac{1}{8}\cdot\frac{2595,8216,6745}{469,2694,3404}$
9	5	$8\cdot\frac{10,4647,0837,9092}{11,8974,6413,0937}$	$\frac{1}{8}\cdot\frac{69,7842,8731,5072}{11,8974,6413,0937}$
28	6	—	0.9838

Explanation: The numerical value 0.9838 is obtained by repeated application of the formula

$$v_{n+1} \geqslant \frac{1}{8}\left(1 + \frac{448v_n}{63+v_n}\right) \quad \left(\text{i.e. } \frac{8v_{n+1}+63}{1-v_{n+1}} \geqslant \frac{512}{441}\,\frac{8v_n+63}{1-v_n}\right) \quad (n \geqslant 9),$$

starting with $\nu_9 \geq (1/8)\cdot(69,7842,8731,5072/11,8974,6413,0937)$.

The use of these lemmas can improve the upper limit of $H(k)$ when k is comparatively small, such as, $H(4) \leq 15$, $H(5) \leq 25$ and so forth. However, we should bear in mind that the degree of $T(\alpha)$ in Lemma 9.4 cannot again be taken as $2(k+1)$. For the sake of achieving the above aim, we have yet to revise and improve our method in an adequate way.

CHAPTER X

INDETERMINATE EQUATIONS IN PRIME UNKNOWNS [1)]

§1. INTRODUCTION

In this chapter and the next we shall discuss the indeterminate equations

$$p_1^k + \cdots + p_s^k = N_k,$$

$$\cdots\cdots\cdots\cdots\cdots\cdots$$

$$p_1 + \cdots + p_s = N_1,$$

in which the unknowns $p_1, \cdots, p_s$ are primes. In the present chapter an asymptotic formula for the number of solutions of these equations will be given, with the assumption that $s \geq s_0$, the numerical values of s_0 being given in the following table:

k	2	3	4	5	6	7	8	9	10	≥ 11
s_0	7	19	49	113	243	417	675	1083	1773	$2k^2(3\log k + \log\log k + 4) - 21$

In order to eliminate unnecessary and complicated operations we shall assume in our proof that $k \geq 3$. For the case $k = 2$ the reader can readily make the necessary changes.

§2. LEMMAS NECESSARY FOR THE PROOF OF THEOREM 16

Lemma 10.1. [2)] *Let* $\gamma_k, \cdots, \gamma_1$ *denote* k *real numbers, and let*

1) In regard to the problems mentioned in Chapters X and XI, see also the paper by K. K. Mardžanišvili, *On a problem of the additive theory of numbers*, Izv. Akad. Nauk SSSR Ser. Mat. 4 (1940), 193–214.

2) I. M. Vinogradov, Mat. Sb. 3 (1938), 435–471; for the proof given above see Hua Lo-keng, *A study of the number of solutions of problems on idempotent sums*, Acta Math. Sinica 2 (1952).

$$I=\int_0^1 e(\gamma_k x^k+\cdots+\gamma_1 x)\,dx\,.$$

Then

$$I\ll Z\,,\qquad Z=(\max(1,|\gamma_1|,\cdots,|\gamma_k|))^{-\alpha}\,.$$

Proof. Obviously $|I|\le 1$. Therefore we can assume that $|\gamma_h|\ge 1$, $(1\le h\le k)$. We have

$$I^k=\int_0^1\cdots\int_0^1 e(\psi)\,dx_1\cdots dx_k\,,$$

where

$$\psi=(x_1^k+\cdots+x_k^k)\gamma_k+\cdots+(x_1+\cdots+x_k)\gamma_1\,.$$

Obviously we have

$$I^k=k!\int\cdots\int_{0\le x_1\le x_2\le\cdots\le x_k\le 1} e(\psi)\,dx_1\cdots dx_k\,.$$

Let us now discuss the transformation

$$\left.\begin{array}{l}(x_1^k+\cdots+x_k^k)|\gamma_k|=y_k\\ \cdots\cdots\cdots\cdots\cdots\cdots\cdots\cdots\\ (x_1+\cdots+x_k)|\gamma_1|=y_1\end{array}\right\}.$$

Let $\mathfrak{N}$ represent the domain determined by $y_1,\cdots,y_k$ when $x_1,\cdots,x_k$ belong to the domain $0\le x_1\le x_2\le\cdots\le x_k\le 1$. The functional determinant of the transformation

$$\frac{\partial(x_1,\cdots,x_k)}{\partial(y_1,\cdots,y_k)}=g(y_1,\cdots,y_k)$$

is always positive. Using Lemma 7.5, we obtain

$$\begin{aligned}|k!^{-1}I^k|&=\left|\int\underset{\mathfrak{N}}{\cdots}\int e(\pm y_k\pm\cdots\pm y_1)\,g(y_1,\cdots,y_k)\,dy_1\cdots dy_k\right|\\
&\le\int\cdots\int dy_1\cdots dy_{h-1}\,dy_{h+1}\cdots dy_k\left|\int e(\pm y_h)\,g(y_1,\cdots,y_k)\,dy_h\right|\\
&\ll\max_{0\le\xi\le 1}\int\cdots\int dy_1\cdots dy_{h-1}\,dy_{h+1}\cdots dy_k\max_{v}\int_{v\le y_h\le v+\xi} g(y_1,\cdots,y_k)\,dy_h\\
&\ll\max_{\substack{0\le\xi\le 1\\ v}}\underset{v\le y_h\le v+\xi}{\int_0^1\cdots\int_0^1} dx_1\cdots dx_k\,.\end{aligned}\tag{1}$$

We now have

$$\underset{v\leqslant y_h\leqslant v+\xi}{\int_0^1\cdots\int_0^1} dx_1\cdots dx_k \leqslant \underset{v\leqslant y_h\leqslant v+\xi}{\int\cdots\int} dx_1\cdots dx_k \leqslant \underset{v\leqslant y_h\leqslant v+1}{\int\cdots\int} dx_1\cdots dx_k$$

$$= V(v+1)-V(v), \tag{2}$$

where $V(v)$ is the volume of the domain defined by

$$y_h = |\gamma_h|(x_1^h+\cdots+x_k^h)\leqslant v, \quad x_\nu \geqslant 0.$$

Since

$$V(v)=\eta\left(\frac{v}{|\gamma_h|}\right)^{k/h}$$

(where η is a constant depending only on h and k) it follows that

$$\begin{aligned} V(v+1)-V(v) &\ll \left(\frac{v+1}{|\gamma_h|}\right)^{k/h} - \left(\frac{v}{|\gamma_h|}\right)^{k/h} \\ &\ll |\gamma_h|^{-k/h}\int_v^{v+1} t^{k/h-1}\,dt \\ &\ll |\gamma_h|^{-k/h}(v+1)^{k/h-1} \\ &\ll |\gamma_h|^{-k/h}(|\gamma_h|\,k+1)^{k/h-1} \end{aligned} \tag{3}$$

(where we have used $v\leq k|\gamma_h|$). Summing up (1), (2) and (3), we have

$$\begin{aligned} I^k &\ll |\gamma_h|^{-k/h}(|\gamma_h|\,k+1)^{k/h-1} \\ &\ll |\gamma_h|^{-k/h-1+k/h} = |\gamma_h|^{-1}. \end{aligned}$$

This proves the lemma.

Lemma 10.2. *As in the hypothesis of Lemma* 10.1, *let* $\delta_\nu = \max(1, |\gamma_\nu|)$. *Then*

$$I \ll \prod_{\nu=1}^{k}\delta_\nu^{-a^2}.$$

Further, when $0<\delta\leq 1$,

$$\int_0^\delta e(\gamma_k x^k+\cdots+\gamma_1 x)\,dx \ll \prod_{\nu=1}^{k}\delta_\nu^{-a^2}.$$

Also, when $g>k^2$,

$$\int_{-\infty}^{\infty}\cdots\int_{-\infty}^{\infty}|I|^g\,d\gamma_k\cdots d\gamma_1$$

is convergent.

Proof. Since

$$\prod_{\nu=1}^{k} \delta_\nu = \prod_{\nu=1}^{k} \max(1, |\gamma_\nu|) \leqslant \max(1, |\gamma_1|, \cdots, |\gamma_k|)^k,$$

we at once obtain the first inequality by Lemma 10.1.

Further,

$$\begin{aligned}\int_0^\delta e(\gamma_k x^k + \cdots + \gamma_1 x)\, dx &= \delta \int_0^1 e(\gamma_k \delta^k y^k + \cdots + \gamma_1 \delta y)\, dy \\ &\ll \delta \left(\prod_{\nu=1}^{k} \max(1, \delta^\nu |\gamma_\nu|) \right)^{-a^2} \\ &\ll \delta \left(\prod_{\nu=1}^{k} \max(\delta^\nu, \delta^\nu |\gamma_\nu|) \right)^{-a^2} \\ &\ll \delta^{\frac{1}{2}-\frac{1}{2}a} \left(\prod_{\nu=1}^{k} \delta_\nu \right)^{-a^2} \ll \left(\prod_{\nu=1}^{k} \delta_\nu \right)^{-a^2}.\end{aligned}$$

This proves the second inequality.

Also, the integral

$$\int_{-\infty}^{\infty} \cdots \int_{-\infty}^{\infty} |I|^g\, d\gamma_k \cdots d\gamma_1 \ll \prod_{\nu=1}^{k} \int_{-\infty}^{\infty} \delta_\nu^{-a^2 g}\, d\gamma_\nu$$

is obviously convergent when $g > k^2$.

Lemma 10.3. *If $q_1, \cdots, q_k$ are positive integers, $H = q_1 \cdots q_k$, the least common multiple of $q_1, \cdots, q_k$ is denoted by Q, and*

$$B\left(\frac{h_k}{q_k}, \cdots, \frac{h_1}{q_1}\right) = \frac{1}{H} \sum_{y=1}^{H} e\left(\frac{h_k}{q_k} y^k + \cdots + \frac{h_1}{q_1} y\right), \ (h_\nu, q_\nu) = 1,$$

then

$$B\left(\frac{h_k}{q_k}, \cdots, \frac{h_1}{q_1}\right) \ll Q^{-a+\varepsilon},$$

and the series

$$\sum_{q_1=1}^{\infty} \cdots \sum_{q_k=1}^{\infty} \sum_{\substack{h_1=1 \\ (h_1, q_1)=1}}^{q_1} \cdots \sum_{\substack{h_k=1 \\ (h_k, q_k)=1}}^{q_k} \left| B\left(\frac{h_k}{q_k}, \cdots, \frac{h_1}{q_1}\right) \right|^g$$

is convergent when $g > k(k+1)$.

Proof. Let us first prove that

$$\left(\frac{h_k}{q_k}Q, \cdots, \frac{h_1}{q_1}Q, Q\right) = 1.$$

Assume the contrary; then there must be a prime p such that

$$p \,\Big|\, \left(\frac{h_k}{q_k}Q, \cdots, \frac{h_1}{q_1}Q, Q\right).$$

Suppose Q is divisible by p^b but not by p^{b+1}. Then according to the definition of Q there exists a q, say q_l, that is divisible by p^b but not by p^{b+1}; i.e., $(h_l/q_l)Q$ is not a multiple of p. But this contradicts the above hypothesis.

We know by Theorem 1 that

$$B\left(\frac{h_k}{q_k}, \cdots, \frac{h_1}{q_1}\right) = \frac{1}{Q}\sum_{x=1}^{Q} e(g(x)/Q) \ll Q^{-a+\varepsilon},$$

where

$$g(x) = Q\frac{h_k}{q_k}x^k + \cdots + Q\frac{h_1}{q_1}x.$$

Hence we deduce that the infinite series of the lemma is

$$\ll \sum_{q_1=1}^{\infty} \cdots \sum_{q_k=1}^{\infty} \sum_{h_1=1}^{q_1} \cdots \sum_{h_k=1}^{q_k} Q^{-ag+\varepsilon} \leqslant \sum_{q_1=1}^{\infty} \cdots \sum_{q_k=1}^{\infty} q_1 \cdots q_k Q^{-ag+\varepsilon}.$$

Let us discuss for a fixed Q the sum

$$\sigma(Q) = \sum \cdots \sum q_1 \cdots q_k,$$

which runs through all sets of integers $q_1, \cdots, q_k$ having Q as their least common multiple. We know by Lemma 2.1 that

$$\sigma(Q) \leqslant \left(\sum_{q|Q} q\right)^k \ll Q^k(d(Q))^k \ll Q^{k+\varepsilon}.$$

Therefore such a series is

$$\ll \sum_{Q=1}^{\infty} Q^{k-ag+\varepsilon}.$$

Obviously this series is convergent when $k - ag < -1$; i.e., the original series is convergent when $g > k(k+1)$.

Remark. The domain of convergence in Lemmas 10.2 and 10.3 can still be improved. See the article by Hua Lo-keng, Acta Math. Sinica 2.

Lemma 10.4. *Let*

$$f(x) = \frac{h_k}{q_k} x^k + \cdots + \frac{h_1}{q_1} x, \quad (h_\nu, q_\nu) = 1, \quad q_\nu \geqslant 1.$$

Further, let Q_1 *be the least common multiple of* $q_k, \cdots, q_2$, *so that* Q *is the least common multiple of* Q_1 *and* q_1. *If* $Q_1 < Q$, *then*

$$\sum_{x=1}^{P} e(f(x)) \ll Q.$$

Proof. This lemma is obviously true when $Q \geq P$. Suppose $Q < P$. Let $x = Q_1 y + z$, where

$$1 \leqslant z \leqslant Q_1, \quad 0 \leqslant y \leqslant (P-z)/Q_1.$$

Since Q_1 is not divisible by q_1, it follows that

$$\left| \sum_{x=1}^{P} e(f(x)) \right| = \left| \sum_{z=1}^{Q_1} e(f(z)) \sum_{y=0}^{(P-z)/Q_1} e^{2\pi i h_1 Q_1 y/q_1} \right|$$

$$\leqslant Q_1 \max_z \left| \sum_y e^{2\pi i h_1 Q_1 y/q_1} \right|$$

$$\leqslant \frac{Q_1}{\{h_1 Q_1/q_1\}} \leqslant \frac{Q_1 q_1}{(Q_1, q_1)} = Q.$$

(Here we have made use of Lemma 1.8.)

Lemma 10.5. *Let* σ *be a positive number smaller than* $a/4$, *and*

$$f(x) = \alpha_k x^k + \cdots + \alpha_1 x.$$

Further, let

$$\alpha_\nu = \frac{h_\nu}{q_\nu} + \frac{\theta_\nu}{q_\nu \tau_\nu}, \quad |\theta_\nu| \leqslant 1, \quad (h_\nu, q_\nu) = 1,$$

where

$$\tau_1 = P^{\frac{1}{2}}, \quad \tau_\nu = P^{\nu - \frac{1}{2}a + \sigma}, \quad 2 \leqslant \nu \leqslant k.$$

Suppose that

$$P^{\frac{1}{2} - \frac{1}{2}a + \sigma} < q_1 \leqslant \tau_1, \quad q_\nu \leqslant P^{\frac{1}{2}a - 2\sigma}, \quad 2 \leqslant \nu \leqslant k.$$

Then

$$\sum_{x=1}^{P} e(f(x)) \ll P^{1-\sigma}.$$

Proof. Let

$$S_n = \sum_{x \leqslant n} e\left(\frac{h_k}{q_k} x^k + \cdots + \frac{h_1}{q_1} x\right).$$

Since $Q_1 \leq q_2 \cdots q_k < P^{(k-1)(\frac{1}{2}a-2\sigma)} = P^{\frac{1}{2}-\frac{1}{2}a-2\sigma(k-1)} < P^{\frac{1}{2}-\frac{1}{2}a+\sigma} < q_1$, we know by Lemma 10.4 that

$$\begin{aligned} S_n &\ll Q \leqslant q_1 \cdots q_k \\ &\leqslant P^{\frac{1}{2}} \cdot P^{(\frac{1}{2}a-2\sigma)(k-1)} \ll P^{1-\frac{1}{2}a-2\sigma(k-1)}. \end{aligned}$$

Similarly, if we let $\theta_\nu / q_\nu \tau_\nu = \beta_\nu$, $(1 \leq \nu \leq k)$, then

$$\begin{aligned} \sum_{x=1}^{P} e(f(x)) &= \sum_{n=1}^{P} (S_n - S_{n-1})\, e(\beta_k n^k + \cdots + \beta_1 n) \\ &= \sum_{n=1}^{P} S_n (e(\beta_k n^k + \cdots + \beta_1 n) - e(\beta_k (n+1)^k + \cdots + \beta_1 (n+1))) \\ &\qquad + S_P\, e(\beta_k (P+1)^k + \cdots + \beta_1 (P+1)). \end{aligned}$$

Since

$$\begin{aligned} &| e(\beta_k (n+1)^k + \cdots + \beta_1 (n+1)) - e(\beta_k n^k + \cdots + \beta_1 n) | \\ &\ll | \beta_k | P^{k-1} + | \beta_{k-1} | P^{k-2} + \cdots + | \beta_1 | \\ &\ll \frac{P^{k-1}}{\tau_k} + \frac{P^{k-2}}{\tau_{k-1}} + \cdots + \frac{P}{\tau_2} + \frac{1}{q_1 \tau_1} \\ &\ll P^{-1+\frac{1}{2}a-\sigma} + P^{-\frac{1}{2}-\frac{1}{2}+\frac{1}{2}a-\sigma} \ll P^{-1+\frac{1}{2}a-\sigma}, \end{aligned}$$

it follows that

$$\begin{aligned} \sum_{x=1}^{P} e(f(x)) &\ll \sum P^{1-\frac{1}{2}a-2\sigma(k-1)} P^{-1+\frac{1}{2}a-\sigma} \\ &\ll P^{1-\sigma(2k-1)} \ll P^{1-\sigma}. \end{aligned}$$

§3. RESULTS RELATED TO TARRY'S PROBLEM

Theorem 15. *Let*

$$S(\alpha_k, \cdots, \alpha_1) = \sum_{x \leqslant P} e(\alpha_k x^k + \cdots + \alpha_1 x).$$

Let t_0 denote a positive integer dependent on k according to the following table:

k	2	3	4	5	6	7	8	9	10	≥ 11
t_0	3	8	23	55	120	207	336	540	885	$[k^2(3 \log k + \log\log k + 4)] - 11$

Then when $t > t_0$ *we have the following results:*

$$T(P) = \int_0^1 \cdots \int_0^1 |S(\alpha_k, \cdots, \alpha_1)|^{2t} d\alpha_k \cdots d\alpha_1$$
$$= c_1 c_2 P^{2t-\frac{1}{2}k(k+1)} + O(P^{2t-\frac{1}{2}k(k+1)-c(k)}),$$

where

$$c_1 = \int_{-\infty}^{\infty} \cdots \int_{-\infty}^{\infty} \left| \int_0^1 e(\beta_k x^k + \cdots + \beta_1 x)\, dx \right|^{2t} d\beta_k \cdots d\beta_1$$

and

$$c_2 = \sum_{q_1=1}^{\infty} \cdots \sum_{q_k=1}^{\infty} \sum_{\substack{h_1=1\\(h_1,q_1)=1}}^{q_1} \cdots \sum_{\substack{h_k=1\\(h_k,q_k)=1}}^{q_k} \left| B\left(\frac{h_k}{q_k}, \cdots, \frac{h_1}{q_1}\right)\right|^{2t},$$

with

$$B\left(\frac{h_k}{q_k}, \cdots, \frac{h_1}{q_1}\right) = \frac{1}{q_1 \cdots q_k} \sum_{x=1}^{q_1 \cdots q_k} e\left(\frac{h_k}{q_k} x^k + \cdots + \frac{h_1}{q_1} x\right).$$

Proof. 1) Because of the periodicity of $S(\alpha_k, \cdots, \alpha_1)$, we have

$$T(P) = \int_{-\frac{1}{\tau_1}}^{1-\frac{1}{\tau_1}} d\alpha_1 \cdots \int_{-\frac{1}{\tau_k}}^{1-\frac{1}{\tau_k}} |S(\alpha_k, \cdots, \alpha_1)|^{2t} d\alpha_k.$$

Let us now take

$$\tau_1 = P^{\frac{1}{2}}, \quad \tau_\nu = P^{\nu - \frac{1}{2}a + \sigma}, \quad 2 \leqslant \nu \leqslant k,$$

with $\sigma = a^3$.

We know by Lemma 7.1 that for each point $(\alpha_k, \cdots, \alpha_1)$ in k-dimensional space there exists a rational point $(h_k/q_k, \cdots, h_1/q_1)$ such that

$$\alpha_\nu = \frac{h_\nu}{q_\nu} + \beta_\nu, \quad (h_\nu, q_\nu) = 1, \quad |\beta_\nu| \leqslant \frac{1}{q_\nu \tau_\nu}, \quad 0 < q_\nu \leqslant \tau_\nu.$$

We now consider all rational points satisfying the condition

$$1 \leqslant q_\nu \leqslant P^{\frac{1}{2}a - 2\sigma} \quad (2 \leqslant \nu \leqslant k), \quad 1 \leqslant q_1 \leqslant P^{\frac{1}{2} - \frac{1}{2}a + \sigma}.$$

To correspond with such a point $(h_k/q_k, \cdots, h_1/q_1)$, we form an interval in the k-dimensional space by taking all $(\alpha_k, \cdots, \alpha_1)$ that satisfy

$$|\beta_\nu| \leqslant \frac{1}{q_\nu \tau_\nu}, \quad 1 \leqslant \nu \leqslant k,$$

and denote it by $\mathfrak{M}(h_k/q_k, \cdots, h_1/q_1)$.

It is easily proved that no two $\mathfrak{M}$ have a common point. For let us suppose that there exists a point which is common to

$$\mathfrak{M}\left(\frac{h_k}{q_k}, \cdots, \frac{h_1}{q_1}\right) \quad \text{and} \quad \mathfrak{M}\left(\frac{h_k'}{q_k'}, \cdots, \frac{h_1'}{q_1'}\right).$$

Because the intervals are not identical with each other, there must be a ν such that $h_\nu/q_\nu \neq h'_\nu/q'_\nu$, and

$$\frac{1}{q_\nu q_\nu'} \leqslant \frac{|h_\nu q_\nu' - h_\nu' q_\nu|}{q_\nu q_\nu'} = \left| \frac{h_\nu}{q_\nu} - \frac{h_\nu'}{q_\nu'} \right| \leqslant \frac{1}{q_\nu \tau_\nu} + \frac{1}{q_\nu' \tau_\nu}$$

$$\leqslant \frac{2}{\tau_\nu} \max\left(\frac{1}{q_\nu}, \frac{1}{q_\nu'}\right);$$

i.e.,

$$\tau_\nu \leqslant 2 \max(q_\nu, q_\nu') \leqslant \begin{cases} 2P^{\frac{1}{2}a - 2\sigma} & \text{if } \nu > 1, \\ 2P^{\frac{1}{2} - \frac{1}{2}a + \sigma} & \text{if } \nu = 1. \end{cases}$$

But this is impossible.

Let E denote the part of

$$-\frac{1}{\tau_\nu} \leqslant \alpha_\nu \leqslant 1 - \frac{1}{\tau_\nu}, \quad 1 \leqslant \nu \leqslant k,$$

that remains after taking away all $\mathfrak{M}$. Letting

$$T_{(1)} = \int \cdots \int_E | S(\alpha_k, \cdots, \alpha_1) |^{2t} \, d\alpha_1 \cdots d\alpha_k,$$

and

$$T_{(2)} = \sum_{\mathfrak{M}} K\left(\frac{h_k}{q_k}, \cdots, \frac{h_1}{q_1}\right),$$

$$K\left(\frac{h_k}{q_k}, \cdots, \frac{h_1}{q_1}\right) = \int \cdots \int_{\mathfrak{M}} | S |^{2t} \, d\alpha_1 \cdots d\alpha_k,$$

then

$$T(P) = T_{(1)} + T_{(2)}. \tag{1}$$

2) Let $H = q_1 \cdots q_k$ and

$$x = H\xi + \eta, \quad \eta = 1, \cdots, H, \quad -\eta/H < \xi \leqslant (P - \eta)/H.$$

Then over $\mathfrak{M}(h_1/q_1, \cdots, h_k/q_k)$,

$$S(\alpha_k, \cdots, \alpha_1) = \sum_\eta W_\eta \, e\left(\frac{h_k}{q_k}\eta^k + \cdots + \frac{h_1}{q_1}\eta\right),$$

where

$$W_\eta = \sum_{-\frac{\eta}{H} < \xi \leqslant \frac{P-\eta}{H}} e(\beta_k(H\xi + \eta)^k + \cdots + \beta_1(H\xi + \eta)).$$

Let

$$\varphi(\xi) = \beta_k(H\xi + \eta)^k + \cdots + \beta_1(H\xi + \eta).$$

Then when P is sufficiently large,

$$|\varphi'(\xi)| \leqslant \frac{kHP^{k-1}}{q_k \tau_k} + \cdots + \frac{H}{q_1 \tau_1}$$

$$\ll \sum_{\nu=2}^{k} P^{(\frac{1}{2}a-2\sigma)(k-2)} P^{\frac{1}{2}-\frac{1}{2}a+\sigma} \frac{P^{\nu-1}}{P^{\nu-\frac{1}{2}a+\sigma}} + P^{(\frac{1}{2}a-2\sigma)(k-1)} \frac{1}{P^{\frac{1}{2}}}$$

$$\ll P^{-a-2\sigma(k-2)} + P^{-\frac{1}{2}a-2\sigma(k-1)} = o(1);$$

i.e., when P is sufficiently large $|\phi'(\xi)| \leq 1/2$. Therefore we know by 2) of Lemma 7.5 that

$$W_\eta = \int_{-\eta/H}^{(P-\eta)/H} e(\varphi(z))\, dz + O(1).$$

Letting $x = P^{-1}(zH + \eta)$, and $\gamma_\nu = \beta_\nu P^\nu$ $(1 \leq \nu \leq k)$, we obtain

$$W_\eta = \frac{P}{H} R + O(1),$$

where

$$R = \int_0^1 e(\gamma_k x^k + \cdots + \gamma_1 x)\, dx.$$

Hence

$$S = B\left(\frac{h_k}{q_k}, \cdots, \frac{h_1}{q_1}\right) P R + O(H). \tag{2}$$

3) Since

$$Q \geqslant \max(q_1, \cdots, q_k) \geqslant (q_1 \cdots q_k)^a = H^a,$$

we know by Lemmas 10.1 and 10.3 that

$$B\left(\frac{h_k}{q_k}, \cdots, \frac{h_1}{q_1}\right) PR \ll PQ^{-a+\varepsilon} Z \ll PH^{-a^2+\varepsilon} Z. \tag{3}$$

Further, with α in $\mathfrak{M}$,

$$\begin{aligned} H = q_1 \cdots q_k &\leqslant P^{\frac{1}{2} - \frac{1}{2}a + \sigma + (k-1)(\frac{1}{2}a - 2\sigma)} \\ &\leqslant P^{1-a-(2k-3)\sigma} \leqslant P^{1-a} \end{aligned}$$

and

$$\begin{aligned} Z &= \min(1, |\gamma_1|^{-a}, \cdots, |\gamma_k|^{-a}) \\ &= \min(1, (P|\beta_1|)^{-a}, \cdots, (P^k|\beta_k|)^{-a}) \\ &\geqslant \min(1, (P/\tau_1)^{-a}, \cdots, (P^k/\tau_k)^{-a}) \\ &\geqslant \min(1, P^{-\frac{1}{2}a}) = P^{-\frac{1}{2}a}. \end{aligned}$$

Therefore

$$\begin{aligned} H &= H^{-a^2+\varepsilon} \cdot H^{1+a^2-\varepsilon} \\ &\leqslant H^{-a^2+\varepsilon} P^{(1+a^2-\varepsilon)(1-a)} \\ &\leqslant H^{-a^2+\varepsilon} P \cdot P^{-\frac{1}{2}a} \ll P H^{-a^2+\varepsilon} Z. \end{aligned} \tag{4}$$

We know by (2), (3) and (4) that over $\mathfrak{M}$

$$S \ll P H^{-a^2+\varepsilon} Z. \tag{5}$$

4) By (2), (3) and (5), and the simple inequality

$$||\xi|^{2t} - |\eta|^{2t}| \leqslant 2t|\xi - \eta|(|\xi|^{2t-1} + |\eta|^{2t+1}),$$

we know that

$$|S|^{2t} - \left|B\left(\frac{h_k}{q_k}, \cdots, \frac{h_1}{q_1}\right)\right|^{2t} P^{2t}|R|^{2t} \ll H(PH^{-a^2+\varepsilon} Z)^{2t-1}.$$

Integrating over $\mathfrak{M}(h_k/q_k, \cdots, h_1/q_1)$, we obtain

$$K\left(\frac{h_k}{q_k}, \cdots, \frac{h_1}{q_1}\right) = \left|B\left(\frac{h_k}{q_k}, \cdots, \frac{h_1}{q_1}\right)\right|^{2t} P^{2t} \int_{-q_k^{-1}\tau_k^{-1}}^{q_k^{-1}\tau_k^{-1}} \cdots \int_{-q_1^{-1}\tau_1^{-1}}^{q_1^{-1}\tau_1^{-1}} |R|^{2t} d\beta_1 \cdots d\beta_k$$

$$+ O\left(HP^{2t-1} \cdot H^{-(2t-1)a^2+\varepsilon} \int_{-\infty}^{\infty} \cdots \int_{-\infty}^{\infty} Z^{2t-1} d\beta_1 \cdots d\beta_k\right).$$

By Lemma 10.2, we know (since $2t - 1 > k^2$) that

$$\begin{aligned} \int_{-\infty}^{\infty} \cdots \int_{-\infty}^{\infty} Z^{2t-1} d\beta_k \cdots d\beta_1 &\leqslant P^{-\frac{1}{2}k(k+1)} \int_{-\infty}^{\infty} \cdots \int_{-\infty}^{\infty} Z^{2t-1} d\gamma_k \cdots d\gamma_1 \\ &\ll P^{-\frac{1}{2}k(k+1)}. \end{aligned}$$

Hence we deduce

$$K\left(\frac{h_k}{q_k}, \ldots, \frac{h_1}{q_1}\right)$$

$$= \left| B\left(\frac{h_k}{q_k}, \ldots, \frac{h_1}{q_1}\right)\right|^{2t} P^{2t} \int_{-q_k^{-1}\tau_k^{-1}}^{q_k^{-1}\tau_k^{-1}} \cdots \int_{-q_1^{-1}\tau_1^{-1}}^{q_1^{-1}\tau_1^{-1}} |R|^{2t} d\beta_1 \cdots d\beta_k$$

$$+ O(P^{2t-\frac{1}{2}k(k+1)-1} H^{1-a^2(2t-1)+\varepsilon})$$

$$= \left| B\left(\frac{h_k}{q_k}, \ldots, \frac{h_1}{q_1}\right)\right|^{2t} P^{2t-\frac{k}{2}(k+1)} \int_{-q_k^{-1}\tau_k^{-1}P^k}^{q_k^{-1}\tau_k^{-1}P^k} \cdots \int_{-q_1^{-1}\tau_1^{-1}P}^{q_1^{-1}\tau_1^{-1}P} |R|^{2t} d\gamma_1 \cdots d\gamma_k$$

$$+ O(P^{2t-\frac{1}{2}k(k+1)-1} H^{1-a^2(2t-1)+\varepsilon}). \tag{6}$$

5) It is easily seen that

$$\left| \int_{-q_k^{-1}\tau_k^{-1}P^k}^{q_k^{-1}\tau_k^{-1}P^k} \cdots \int_{-q_1^{-1}\tau_1^{-1}P}^{q_1^{-1}\tau_1^{-1}P} |R|^{2t} d\gamma_1 \cdots d\gamma_k - \int_{-\infty}^{\infty} \cdots \int_{-\infty}^{\infty} |R|^{2t} d\gamma_1 \cdots d\gamma_k \right|$$

$$\ll \max_j M_j \int_{-\infty}^{\infty} \cdots \int_{-\infty}^{\infty} |R|^{2t-1} d\gamma_1 \cdots d\gamma_k,$$

where M_j is the maximum of $|R|$ when $|\gamma_j| > q_j^{-1}\tau_j^{-1}P^j$. Since

$$\frac{P^j}{\tau_j q_j} \geqslant \frac{P^j}{P^{\frac{1}{2}a-2\sigma} P^{j-\frac{1}{2}a+\sigma}} = P^\sigma \quad \text{for } 2 \leqslant j \leqslant k,$$

and

$$\frac{P}{\tau_1 q_1} \geqslant \frac{P}{P^{\frac{1}{2}-\frac{1}{2}a+\sigma} P^{\frac{1}{2}}} = P^{\frac{1}{2}a-\sigma} \geqslant P^\sigma,$$

it follows by Lemma 10.2 that

$$M_j \ll \max_{|\gamma_j| \geqslant P^\sigma} \delta_j^{-a^2} \ll P^{-a^2\sigma},$$

and we accordingly have

$$\int_{-q_k^{-1}\tau_k^{-1}P^k}^{q_k^{-1}\tau_k^{-1}P^k} \cdots \int_{-q_1^{-1}\tau_1^{-1}P}^{q_1^{-1}\tau_1^{-1}P} |R|^{2t} d\gamma_1 \cdots d\gamma_k = c_1 + O(P^{-a^2\sigma}). \tag{7}$$

Combining (6) and (7), we know that

$$K\left(\frac{h_k}{q_k}, \ldots, \frac{h_1}{q_1}\right) = c_1 \left| B\left(\frac{h_k}{q_k}, \ldots, \frac{h_1}{q_1}\right)\right|^{2t} P^{2t-\frac{1}{2}k(k+1)}$$

$$+ O(P^{2t-\frac{1}{2}k(k+1)-1} H^{1-a^2(2t-1)+\varepsilon})$$

$$+ O(P^{2t-\frac{1}{2}k(k+1)-a^2\sigma} H^{-2ta^2+\varepsilon}). \tag{8}$$

Let

$$A = \sum_{q_k \leqslant P^{\frac{1}{2}a-2\sigma}} \cdots \sum_{q_2 \leqslant P^{\frac{1}{2}a-2\sigma}} \sum_{q_1 \leqslant P^{\frac{1}{2}-\frac{1}{2}a+\sigma}} \sum_{\substack{h_1=1 \\ (h_1, q_1)=1}}^{q_1} \cdots \sum_{\substack{h_k=1 \\ (h_k, q_k)=1}}^{q_k} \left| B\left(\frac{h_k}{q_k}, \ldots, \frac{h_1}{q_1}\right)\right|^{2t}.$$

We know by (8) that

$$T_{(2)} = c_1 A P^{2t-\frac{1}{2}k(k+1)} + O\big(P^{2t-\frac{1}{2}k(k+1)-1} \sum H^{1-a^2(2t-1)+\varepsilon}\big)$$
$$+ O\big(P^{2t-\frac{1}{2}k(k+1)-a^2\sigma} \sum H^{-2ta^2+\varepsilon}\big).$$

Because of the convergence of

$$\sum_q \sum_h H^{-2ta^2+\varepsilon} \leqslant \sum_{q_1, \ldots, q_k} H^{1-2ta^2+\varepsilon} \leqslant \Big(\sum_{q=1}^{\infty} q^{1-2ta^2+\varepsilon}\Big)^k$$

when $t > k^2$ and the convergence of

$$\sum_q \sum_h H^{1-a^2(2t-1)+\varepsilon} \leqslant \Big(\sum_q q^{2-a^2(2t-1)+\varepsilon}\Big)^k$$

when $2t < 3k^2 + 1$, we know that

$$T_{(2)} = c_1 A P^{2t-\frac{1}{2}k(k+1)} + O\big(P^{2t-\frac{1}{2}k(k+1)-c_4}\big). \tag{9}$$

Suppose that $t > k^2$ and $2t > 3k^2 + 1$ are established only when $k \geq 4$ and $k \geq 5$, respectively. Then for $k = 3, 4$ we use the following supplementary argument to obtain (9).

When $k = 3$,

$$\sum_q \sum_h H^{-2ta^2+\varepsilon} \leqslant \sum_{q_1 \leqslant P^{\frac{1}{2}-\frac{1}{6}+\sigma}} \sum_{q_2 \leqslant P^{\frac{1}{6}-2\sigma}} \sum_{q_3 \leqslant P^{\frac{1}{6}-2\sigma}} (q_1 q_2 q_3)^{1-\frac{18}{9}+\varepsilon}$$
$$\ll P^{(\frac{1}{3}+\sigma+\frac{1}{6}-2\sigma+\frac{1}{6}-2\sigma)\varepsilon};$$

$$\sum_q \sum_h H^{1-a^2(2t-1)+\varepsilon}$$
$$\leqslant \sum_{q_1 \leqslant P^{\frac{1}{2}-\frac{1}{6}+\sigma}} \sum_{q_2 \leqslant P^{\frac{1}{6}-2\sigma}} \sum_{q_3 \leqslant P^{\frac{1}{6}-2\sigma}} (q_1 q_2 q_3)^{2-(18-1)/9+\varepsilon}$$
$$\ll P^{(\frac{1}{3}+\sigma+\frac{1}{6}-2\sigma+\frac{1}{6}-2\sigma)10/9+\varepsilon} \ll P^{\frac{20}{27}+\varepsilon};$$

and when $k = 4$,

$$\sum_{q_1 < P^{\frac12-\frac18+\sigma}} q_1^{2-(48-1)/16+\epsilon}\Big(\sum_{q \leqslant P^{\frac18-2\sigma}} q^{2-(48-1)/16+\epsilon}\Big)^3$$

$$\ll P^{\frac{1}{16}\left(\frac{25}{64}+\frac{18}{64}\right)+\epsilon} \ll P^{\frac{3}{64}+\epsilon}.$$

6) We now find the absolute value of the difference between c_2 and A. Since the least common multiple Q of $q_1, \cdots, q_k$ is $> \max(q_1, \cdots, q_k)$, therefore

$$|c_2 - A| \leqslant F \sum_{q_1=1}^{\infty} \cdots \sum_{q_k=1}^{\infty} \sum_{h_1} \cdots \sum_{h_k} \left| B\left(\frac{h_k}{q_k}, \cdots, \frac{h_1}{q_1}\right)\right|^{2t-1},$$

where

$$F = \max_{Q \geqslant P^{\frac12-\frac12 a+\sigma}} \left| B\left(\frac{h_k}{q_k}, \cdots, \frac{h_1}{q_1}\right)\right|.$$

We know by Lemma 10.3 that

$$F \ll Q^{-a+\epsilon} \ll P^{-a(\frac12-\frac12 a+\sigma)+\epsilon}$$

and by the same lemma that $\Sigma_q \Sigma_h |B|^{2t-1}$ is convergent (because $2t > k(k+1)+1$). Therefore

$$c_2 = A + O(P^{-c_5}).$$

Combining this with (9), we see that

$$T_{(2)} = c_1 c_2 P^{2t-\frac12 k(k+1)} + O(P^{2t-\frac12 k(k+1)-c_6}). \tag{10}$$

7) Let us now discuss $T_{(1)}$. If $(\alpha_k, \cdots, \alpha_1)$ belongs to E, it must satisfy one of the following k conditions:

$$P^{\frac12 a-2\sigma} < q_\nu \leqslant P^{\nu-\frac12 a+\sigma}, \quad 2 \leqslant \nu \leqslant k,$$
$$P^{\frac12-\frac12\sigma+\sigma} < q_1 \leqslant P^{\frac12}.$$

If one of the first inequalities is established, there is a ν such that $P^{\frac12 a-2\sigma} < q_\nu \le P^{\nu-\frac12 a+\sigma}$. Then we know by Theorem 9 and Lemma 5.12 that when $k > 11$,

$$S(\alpha_k, \cdots, \alpha_1) \ll P^{1-\lambda}, \quad \lambda = \frac{1}{50k^3 \log k}. \tag{11}$$

We also know by Theorem 9 and Lemma 5.11 that this formula holds when $k \le 11$.

If it does not satisfy the first inequality, then the condition in question must satisfy the hypothesis of Lemma 10.5, and we have

$$S \ll P^{1-\sigma} \ll P^{1-\lambda}, \quad \lambda = \frac{1}{50k^3 \log k}.$$

In other words, (11) always holds over E.

8) We shall now prove

$$T_{(1)} \ll P^{2t-\frac{1}{2}k(k+1)-c_7}. \tag{12}$$

8.1) If $k < 11$, then by Theorem 7 and the inequality (11),

$$T_{(1)} \ll P^{2(1-\lambda)} \int_0^1 \cdots \int_0^1 |S|^{2t-2} \, d\alpha_1 \cdots d\alpha_k$$
$$\ll P^{2t-\frac{1}{2}k(k+1)-c_7}.$$

8.2) Now suppose that $k \geq 11$, and take $t = t_1 + k^2$ according to Theorem 5. Then

$$T_{(1)} \ll P^{2k^2(1-\lambda)} \int_0^1 \cdots \int_0^1 |S|^{2t_1} \, d\alpha_1 \cdots d\alpha_k$$
$$\ll P^{2k^2(1-\lambda)+2t_1-\frac{1}{2}k(k+1)+\frac{1}{2}k(k+1)(1-a)^l+\varepsilon}$$
$$\ll P^{2t-\frac{1}{2}k(k+1)-c_5},$$

where

$$c_5 = \frac{1}{25\, k \log k} - \frac{1}{2} k(k+1)(1-a)^l - \varepsilon.$$

Take

$$l = \left[\frac{\log (13k^2(k+1) \log k)}{-\log (1-a)}\right] + 1.$$

This insures $c_5 > 0$. Also, when $k \geq 11$,

$$l < \frac{3 \log k + \log \log k + \log (1+a) + \log 13}{-\log (1-a)} + 1$$
$$< k(3 \log k + \log \log k + \log (1+a) + \log 13)\left(1 - \frac{1}{3} a\right) + 1.$$

Therefore

$$t = t_1 + k^2 \leqslant lk + \frac{1}{4}(k^2 + k + 2) + k^2$$
$$\leqslant k^2(3 \log k + \log \log k + \log (1+a) + \log 13)\left(1 - \frac{1}{3} a\right)$$
$$+ \frac{5}{4}(k^2 + k) + \frac{1}{2} <$$

$$< k^2\left(3\log k + \log\log k + \log\frac{12}{11} + \log 13 + \frac{5}{4}\right)$$
$$- k\left(\log k - \frac{5}{4} - \frac{1}{2}a\right)$$
$$< k^2(3\log k + \log\log k + 4) - 11.$$

By (1), (10) and (12), Theorem 15 is proved.

Remarks. We have not presented the part of Theorem 15 with $k = 2$ since it is not difficult for the reader to supplement the proof for himself. Furthermore, with $k = 2$, it is possible to find the two constants c_1 and c_2.

§4. FORMULATION OF THEOREM 16

Theorem 16. *Let k denote an integer which is ≥ 2. Let s be an integer which is $\geq s_0$, where s_0 is defined according to the following table:*

k	2	3	4	5	6	7	8	9	10	≥ 11
s_0	7	19	49	113	243	417	675	1083	1773	$2k^2(3\log k + \log\log k + 4) - 21$

Let $I(N_k, \cdots, N_1)$ denote the number of sets of prime solutions $p_1, \cdots, p_s$ of the equations

$$\left.\begin{aligned} p_1 + p_2 + \cdots + p_s &= N_1, \\ p_1^2 + p_2^2 + \cdots + p_s^2 &= N_2, \\ &\cdots\cdots\cdots\cdots \\ p_1^k + p_2^k + \cdots + p_s^k &= N_k. \end{aligned}\right\} \qquad (1)$$

Let $N_k^a = P$. Then the number of sets of solutions of (1) can be expressed as

$$I(N_k, \cdots, N_1) = \frac{b_1 P^{s-\frac{1}{2}k(k+1)}\mathfrak{S}(N_k, \cdots, N_1)}{L^s} + O\left(\frac{P^{s-\frac{1}{2}k(k+1)}}{L^{s+1}}\log L\right),$$

where

$$b_1 = \int_{-\infty}^{\infty}\cdots\int_{-\infty}^{\infty}\left(\int_0^1 e(\gamma_k x^k + \cdots + \gamma_1 x)\,dx\right)^s e\left(-\frac{N_k}{P^k}\gamma_k - \cdots - \frac{N_1}{P}\gamma_1\right)d\gamma_k\cdots d\gamma_1,$$

$$\mathfrak{S}(N_k, \cdots, N_1) = \sum_{q_1, \cdots, q_k = 1}^{\infty} A(q_k, \cdots, q_1),$$

$$A(q_k, \cdots, q_1) = \sum_{h_1, \cdots, h_k}' T^s e\left(-\frac{h_k}{q_k} N_k - \cdots - \frac{h_1}{q_1} N_1\right),$$

where $h_1, \cdots, h_k$ *run separately through a partitioned set of residues* mod $q_1, \cdots$ $\cdots$, mod q_k, *and*

$$T = \frac{1}{\varphi(Q)} \sum_x' e\left(\frac{h_k}{q_k} x^k + \cdots + \frac{h_1}{q_1} x\right),$$

where Q *is the least common multiple of* $q_1, \cdots, q_k$, *with* x *running through a partitioned set of residues* mod Q.

§5. PROOF OF THE THEOREM

1) Let

$$S(\alpha_k, \cdots, \alpha_1) = \sum_{p \leqslant P} e(f(p)), \quad f(x) = \alpha_k x^k + \cdots + \alpha_1 x.$$

Then

$$I(N_k, \cdots, N_1) = \int_0^1 d\alpha_1 \cdots \int_0^1 S^s(\alpha_k, \cdots, \alpha_1)\, e(-N_k \alpha_k - \cdots - N_1 \alpha_1)\, d\alpha_k$$

$$= \int_{-\tau_1^{-1}}^{1-\tau_1^{-1}} d\alpha_1 \cdots \int_{-\tau_k^{-1}}^{1-\tau_k^{-1}} S^s(\alpha_k, \cdots, \alpha_1)\, e(-N_k \alpha_k - \cdots - N_1 \alpha_1)\, d\alpha_k,$$

where $\tau_\nu = P^\nu L^{-\sigma_\nu}$ and

$$\sigma_\nu \geqslant 2^{6k+1}(\sigma_k + \cdots + \sigma_{\nu+1} + s_1 + 1), \quad \sigma_k > 2k^2,$$

with s_1 an arbitrary positive integer.

For an arbitrary α_ν in $(-\tau_\nu^{-1}, 1 - \tau_\nu^{-1})$ we have two integers h_ν and q_ν such that

$$\alpha_\nu - \frac{h_\nu}{q_\nu} = \beta_\nu, \quad |\beta_\nu| \leqslant \frac{1}{q_\nu \tau_\nu}, \quad (h_\nu, q_\nu) = 1, \quad 0 < q_\nu \leqslant \tau_\nu.$$

Hence all the points $(\alpha_k, \cdots, \alpha_1)$ must fall within a domain like

$$\left|\alpha_\nu - \frac{h_\nu}{q_\nu}\right| \leqslant \frac{1}{q_\nu \tau_\nu}, \quad 1 \leqslant \nu \leqslant k.$$

We divide all domains of this type into the following categories:

1°. For those q_k satisfying $L^{\sigma k} \le q_k \le \tau_k$, we use $\mathfrak{m}_k$ to denote their mean.

2°. For those q_k satisfying $0 < q_k < L^{\sigma k}$, and q_{k-1} satisfying $L^{\sigma k-1} \le q_{k-1} \le \tau_{k-1}$, we use $\mathfrak{m}_{k-1}$ to denote their mean.

....

ν°. In the case of $0 < q_k < L^{\sigma k}, \cdots, 0 < q_{k-\nu+2} < L^{\sigma k-\nu+2}$, with the restriction $L^{\sigma k-\nu+1} \le q_{k-\nu+1} \le \tau_{k-\nu+1}$, we use $\mathfrak{m}_{k-\nu+1}$ to denote their mean.

....

k°. In the case of $0 < q_k < L^{\sigma k}, \cdots, 0 < q_2 < L^{\sigma 2}$ with the restriction $L^{\sigma 1} < q_1 \le \tau_1$, we use $\mathfrak{m}_1$ to denote their mean.

$(k+1)$°. We use $\mathfrak{M} = \mathfrak{M}(h_k/q_k, \cdots, h_1/q_1)$ to denote the domain which satisfies $0 < q_\nu < L^{\sigma\nu}$, $1 \le \nu \le k$.

It is easily proved that when P is sufficiently large there are no two $\mathfrak{M}$ that have a common point. Using $\mathfrak{N}$ to denote the set of all points outside of $\mathfrak{M}$, we have

$$I(N_k, \cdots, N_1) = \left(\sum_{\mathfrak{M}} \int_{\mathfrak{M}} + \int_{\mathfrak{N}}\right) S^s\, e(-\alpha_k N_k - \cdots - \alpha_1 N_1)\, d\alpha_k \cdots d\alpha_1 .$$

2) **Lemma 10.6.** *Let*

$$S^*(\beta_k, \cdots, \beta_1) = \int_2^P \frac{e(\Psi(x))}{\log x}\, dx, \quad \Psi(x) = \beta_k x^k + \cdots + \beta_1 x .$$

Then over $\mathfrak{M}(h_k/q_k, \cdots, h_1/q_1)$

$$S(\alpha_k, \cdots, \alpha_1) = T\left(\frac{h_k}{q_k}, \cdots, \frac{h_1}{q_1}\right) \frac{1}{\varphi(Q)}\, S^*(\beta_k, \cdots, \beta_1) + O(P\, e^{-c_1\sqrt{L}}),$$

where

$$T\left(\frac{h_k}{q_k}, \cdots, \frac{h_1}{q_1}\right) = \sum_{\substack{x=1 \\ (x, Q)=1}}^{Q} e\left(\frac{h_k}{q_k} x^k + \cdots + \frac{h_1}{q_1} x\right),$$

with Q *being the least common multiple of* $q_k, \cdots, q_1$.

Proof. Obviously we have $Q < L^{\sigma 1 + \cdots + \sigma k}$. Let

$$S_m = \sum_{2 \le p \le m} e\left(\frac{h_k}{q_k} p^k + \cdots + \frac{h_1}{q_1} p\right), \quad S_1 = 0 .$$

Then by Lemma 7.14

$$S_m = \sum_{\substack{x=1\\(x,Q)=1}}^{Q} e\left(\frac{h_k}{q_k}x^k + \cdots + \frac{h_1}{q_1}x\right) \sum_{\substack{p\leqslant m\\ p\equiv x(Q)}} 1 + O(Q^\varepsilon)$$

$$= T\left(\frac{h_k}{q_k}, \cdots, \frac{h_1}{q_1}\right)\frac{\operatorname{li} m}{\varphi(Q)} + O(Pe^{-c_2\sqrt{L}}).$$

We have

$$S(\alpha_k, \cdots, \alpha_1) = \sum_{2\leqslant m\leqslant P} (S_m - S_{m-1})\, e(\Psi(m))$$

$$= \sum_{2\leqslant m\leqslant P} S_m(e(\Psi(m)) - e(\Psi(m+1))) + S_P\, e(\Psi(P+1))$$

$$= \frac{T\left(\frac{h_k}{q_k}, \cdots, \frac{h_1}{q_1}\right)}{\varphi(Q)}\left(\sum_{2\leqslant m\leqslant P} \operatorname{li} m(e(\Psi(m)) - e(\Psi(m+1)))\right.$$

$$\left. + \operatorname{li} P\, e(\Psi(P+1))\right) + O(P\, e^{-c_3\sqrt{L}}),$$

since

$$P\, e^{-c_2\sqrt{L}} \left(\sum_{2\leqslant m\leqslant P} |\, e(\Psi(m)) - e(\Psi(m+1))\,| + 1\right)$$

$$\ll P\, e^{-c_2\sqrt{L}}\, L^{\sigma_1+\sigma_2+\cdots+\sigma_k} \ll P\, e^{-c_4\sqrt{L}}.$$

Further,

$$\sum_{2\leqslant m\leqslant P} \operatorname{li} m(e(\Psi(m)) - e(\Psi(m+1))) + \operatorname{li} P\, e(\Psi(P+1))$$

$$= \sum_{3\leqslant m\leqslant P} e(\Psi(m)) \int_{m-1}^{m} \frac{dx}{\log x}$$

$$= \sum_{3\leqslant m\leqslant P} \int_{m-1}^{m} \frac{e(\Psi(x))}{\log x}\, dx + O(L^{\sigma_1+\cdots+\sigma_k})$$

$$= S^*(\beta_k, \cdots, \beta_1) + O(L^{\sigma_1+\cdots+\sigma_k}),$$

from which the lemma follows.

Lemma 10.7. *Let $\gamma_k, \cdots, \gamma_1$ denote real numbers, and $\Phi(y) = \gamma_k y^k + \cdots$ $\cdots + \gamma_1 y$. Further, let $W = \prod_{\nu=1}^{k} \delta_\nu^{-a^2}$, $\delta_\nu = \max(1, |\gamma_\nu|)$. Then*

$$\int_{2/P}^{1} \frac{e(\Phi(y))}{\log yP}\, dy = \frac{1}{L}\int_0^1 e(\Phi(y))\, dy + O\left(\frac{\log L}{L^2} W\right),$$

and hence (Lemma 10.2)

$$\int_{2/P}^{1} \frac{e(\Phi(y))}{\log yP}\, dy \ll \frac{W}{L}.$$

Proof. By the second mean-value theorem and Lemma 10.2, we obtain

$$\begin{aligned}\frac{1}{L}\int_0^1 e(\Phi(y))\, dy - \int_{2/P}^{1} \frac{e(\Phi(y))}{\log yP}\, dy &= \frac{1}{L}\int_0^{L^{-8}} e(\Phi(y))\, dy \\ &\quad - \int_{2/P}^{L^{-8}} \frac{e(\Phi(y))}{\log y + L}\, dy + \frac{1}{L}\int_{L^{-8}}^{1} \frac{\log y}{\log y + L}\, e(\Phi(y))\, dy \\ &\ll L^{-8}\prod_{\nu=1}^{k} \max(1, L^{-8\nu}\,|\,\gamma_\nu\,|)^{-\epsilon^2} + \frac{\log L}{L^2} W \\ &\ll L^{-4(1-\epsilon)} W + \frac{\log L}{L^2} W \\ &\ll WL^{-2}\log L.\end{aligned}$$

3) **Lemma 10.8.** *Over* $\mathfrak{N}$,

$$S(\alpha_k, \cdots \alpha_1) \ll PL^{-s_1}.$$

Proof. Suppose that α is in $\mathfrak{m}_n$. Let

$$S_0 = S\left(\frac{h_k}{q_k}, \cdots, \frac{h_n}{q_n}, \alpha_{n-1}, \cdots, \alpha_1\right).$$

Let Q_n denote the least common multiple of $q_k, \cdots, q_{n+1}$. Then $Q_n \ll L^{\sigma_k + \cdots + \sigma_{n+1}}$. By Theorem 10, we have

$$\begin{aligned}|\,S_0\,| &\leqslant \sum_{t=1}^{Q_n} \left|\sum_{\substack{p \leqslant P \\ p \equiv t \pmod{Q_n}}} e\left(\frac{h_n}{q_n} p^n + \cdots + \alpha_1 p\right)\right| \\ &\ll PL^{-s_1 - \sigma_k - \cdots - \sigma_{n+1}}\end{aligned}$$

(since $\sigma_n \geq 2^{6k+1}(\sigma_h + \cdots + \sigma_{n+1} + s_1 + 1)$).

Letting

$$S(m) = \sum_{2 \leqslant p \leqslant m} e\left(\frac{h_k}{q_k} p^k + \cdots + \frac{h_n}{q_n} p^n + \alpha_{n-1} p^{n-1} + \cdots + \alpha_1 p\right),$$

we obtain

$$S(\alpha_k, \cdots, \alpha_1) = \sum_{2 \leqslant m \leqslant P} (S(m) - S(m-1))\, e(\Psi_1(m))$$
$$= \sum_{2 \leqslant m \leqslant P} S(m)\,(e(\Psi_1(m)) - e(\Psi_1(m+1))) + S(P)\, e(\Psi_1(P+1)),$$

where

$$\Psi_1(x) = \beta_k x^k + \cdots + \beta_n x^n.$$

Therefore we obtain

$$S(\alpha_k, \cdots, \alpha_1) \ll P L^{-s_1-\sigma_k-\cdots-\sigma_{n+1}} \sum_{2 \leqslant m \leqslant P} (P^{-1}(L^{\sigma_k} + \cdots + L^{\sigma_{n+1}}) + P^{-1})$$
$$+ P L^{-s_1-\sigma_k-\cdots-\sigma_{n+1}} \ll P L^{-s_1}.$$

4) When $k \geq 3$, we obtain, by Theorem 15 and Lemma 10.8,

$$\int \cdots \int_{\mathfrak{N}} |S(\alpha_k, \cdots, \alpha_1)|^s \, d\alpha_k \cdots d\alpha_1 \ll (P L^{-s_1})^{s-s_0+1} \int \cdots \int_{\mathfrak{N}} |S(\alpha_k, \cdots, \alpha_1)|^{s_0-1} \, d\alpha_k \cdots d\alpha_1$$
$$\ll P^{s-\frac{1}{2}k(k+1)} L^{-s_1}.$$

When $k = 2$, we obtain, by Theorem 7 (theorem B_2'),

$$\iint_{\mathfrak{N}} | S(\alpha_2, \alpha_1) |^7 \, d\alpha_2 \, d\alpha_1 \ll P L^{-s_1} \int_0^1 \int_0^1 | S(\alpha_2, \alpha_1) |^6 \, d\alpha_2 \, d\alpha_1$$
$$\ll P^{s-\frac{1}{2}k(k+1)} L^{-s_1+3}.$$

5) **Lemma 10.9.** *In the case* $g \geq k^2 + 1$,

$$\int_{-\infty}^{\infty} \cdots \int_{-\infty}^{\infty} | S^*(\beta_k, \cdots, \beta_1) |^g \, d\beta_k \cdots d\beta_1 \ll P^{g-\frac{1}{2}k(k+1)} L^{-g}.$$

Proof. The integral in the left member is

$$\int_{-\infty}^{\infty} \cdots \int_{-\infty}^{\infty} \left| \int_2^P \frac{e(\beta_k x^k + \cdots + \beta_1 x)}{\log x} \, dx \right|^g d\beta_k \cdots d\beta_1.$$

If we set $x = Py$ and $\beta_\nu = \gamma_\nu P^{-\nu}$, this integral is equal to

$$P^{g-\frac{1}{2}k(k+1)} \int_{-\infty}^{\infty} \cdots \int_{-\infty}^{\infty} \left| \int_{2/P}^1 \frac{e(\gamma_k y^k + \cdots + \gamma_1 y)}{\log yP} \, dy \right|^g d\gamma_k \cdots d\gamma_1$$
$$\ll P^{g-\frac{1}{2}k(k+1)} L^{-g} \int_{-\infty}^{\infty} \cdots \int_{-\infty}^{\infty} W^g \, d\gamma_k \cdots d\gamma_1.$$

Here we have made use of Lemma 10.7. By Lemma 10.2, we obtain the lemma in question.

Lemma 10.10. *When* $s > k(k+1)$, $\mathfrak{S}(N_k, \cdots, N_1)$ *is absolutely convergent.*

The proof of this lemma is similar to that of Lemma 10.3, but Corollary 1.3 of Chapter I is used instead of Theorem 1.

6) We need the simple inequality

$$|\xi^s - \eta^s| \leqslant s|\xi - \eta|(|\xi|^{s-1} + |\eta|^{s-1}).$$

By Lemma 10.6, we obtain

$$\begin{aligned}
&\sum_{\mathfrak{M}} \int \cdots \int_{\mathfrak{M}} S^s(\alpha_k, \cdots, \alpha_1)\, e(-N_k\alpha_k - \cdots - N_1\alpha_1)\, d\alpha_k \cdots d\alpha_1 \\
&- \sum_{\mathfrak{M}} \left(\frac{T\left(\frac{h_k}{q_k}, \cdots, \frac{h_1}{q_1}\right)}{\varphi(Q)}\right)^s e\left(-\frac{N_k h_k}{q_k} - \cdots - \frac{N_1 h_1}{q_1}\right) \\
&\times \int \cdots \int_{\mathfrak{M}} S^{*s}(\beta_k, \cdots, \beta_1)\, e(-N_k\beta_k - \cdots - N_1\beta_1)\, d\beta_k \cdots d\beta_1 \\
&\ll P e^{-c_1\sqrt{L}} \left(\int_0^1 \cdots \int_0^1 |S(\alpha_k, \cdots, \alpha_1)|^{s-1} d\alpha_k \cdots d\alpha_1\right. \\
&\left. + \sum_q \sum_h Q^{-(s-1)a+\varepsilon} \int_{-\infty}^{\infty} \cdots \int_{-\infty}^{\infty} |S^*(\beta_k, \cdots, \beta_1)|^{s-1} d\beta_k \cdots d\beta_1\right) \\
&\ll P^{s-\frac{1}{2}k(k+1)} e^{-c_1\sqrt{L}}.
\end{aligned}$$

In the process of obtaining this formula, we have relied on the following facts: by Theorem 15 we have

$$\int_0^1 \cdots \int_0^1 |S(\alpha_k, \cdots, \alpha_1)|^{s-1} d\alpha_k \cdots d\alpha_1 \ll P^{s-1-\frac{1}{2}k(k+1)}.$$

(Some changes should be made when $k = 2$, but they are not difficult.) Further, by Lemma 10.9,

$$\int_{-\infty}^{\infty} \cdots \int_{-\infty}^{\infty} |S^*|^{s-1} d\beta_k \cdots d\beta_1 \ll P^{s-1-\frac{1}{2}k(k+1)}$$

and

$$\sum_q \sum_h Q^{-(s-1)a+\varepsilon} \leqslant \sum_q (q_1 \cdots q_k)^{1-(s-1)a^2+\varepsilon} = O(L^{c_5})$$

(since the least common multiple of $q_1, \cdots, q_k$ is $\geq (q_1 \cdots q_k)^a$).

7) We have

$$\left(\sum_{\mathfrak{M}} - \sum_{q_k \leq L^{\frac{1}{2}\sigma_k}} \cdots \sum_{q_1 \leq L^{\frac{1}{2}\sigma_1}} \sum_{h_1}{}' \cdots \sum_{h_k}{}'\right)\left(\frac{T\left(\frac{h_k}{q_k}, \ldots, \frac{h_1}{q_1}\right)}{\varphi(Q)}\right)^s e\left(-\frac{N_k h_k}{q_k} - \cdots - \frac{N_1 h_1}{q_1}\right)$$

$$\times \int \underset{\mathfrak{M}}{\cdots} \int S^{*s} e(-N_k \beta_k - \cdots - N_1 \beta_1)\, d\beta_k \cdots d\beta_1$$

$$\ll M \sum_{q_k=1}^{\infty} \cdots \sum_{q_1=1}^{\infty} \sum_{h_1}{}' \cdots \sum_{h_k}{}' \left| \frac{T\left(\frac{h_k}{q_k}, \ldots, \frac{h_1}{q_1}\right)}{\varphi(Q)} \right|^{s-1} \int_{-\infty}^{\infty} \cdots \int_{-\infty}^{\infty} |S^*|^s\, d\beta_k \cdots d\beta_1, \quad (1)$$

where

$$M = \max_{\nu} \max_{q_\nu \geq L^{\frac{1}{2}\sigma_\nu}} \left| \frac{T\left(\frac{h_k}{q_k}, \ldots, \frac{h_1}{q_1}\right)}{\varphi(Q)} \right|.$$

By Corollary 1.3 of Chapter I, it is easily seen that

$$M \ll \max_{\nu} \max_{q_\nu \geq L^{\frac{1}{2}\sigma_\nu}} Q^{-a+\varepsilon} \ll \max_{\nu} \max_{q_\nu \geq L^{\frac{1}{2}\sigma_\nu}} q_\nu^{-a+\varepsilon}$$

$$\ll L^{-\frac{1}{2}a\sigma_k+\varepsilon} \ll L^{-1}$$

and by Lemma 10.10 that the series in (1) is convergent; also, by Lemma 10.9, the integral part of (1) is $\ll P^{s-\frac{1}{2}k(k+1)} L^{-s}$. Hence we know that the right member of (1) is $\ll P^{s-\frac{1}{2}k(k+1)} L^{-s-1}$.

8) When $q_\nu \leq L^{\frac{1}{2}\sigma_\nu}$, $1 \leq \nu \leq k$, we have

$$\left(\int_{-\infty}^{\infty} \cdots \int_{-\infty}^{\infty} - \int \underset{\mathfrak{M}}{\cdots} \int\right) |S^*|^s\, d\beta_1 \cdots d\beta_k$$

$$\ll M \int_{-\infty}^{\infty} \cdots \int_{-\infty}^{\infty} |S^*|^{s-1}\, d\beta_1 \cdots d\beta_k, \quad (2)$$

where

$$M = \max_{\nu} \max_{|\beta_\nu| > q_\nu^{-1} P^{-\nu} L^{-\sigma_\nu}} |S^*|.$$

By Lemma 10.7 and

$$|\gamma_\nu| = P^\nu |\beta_\nu| > q_\nu^{-1} L^{\sigma_\nu} \geq L^{\frac{1}{2}\sigma_\nu},$$

we know that

$$M \ll \frac{P}{L} \max_{\nu} \max_{|\gamma_\nu| > L^{\frac{1}{2}\sigma_\nu}} \min(1, |\gamma_\nu|^{-a^2}) \ll \frac{P}{L} L^{-\frac{1}{2}a^2\sigma_k} \ll P L^{-2}.$$

Further, by Lemma 10.9, the right member of (2) is $\ll P^{s-\frac{1}{2}k(k+1)}L^{-s-1}$. Combining (1) with (2), we obtain

$$\sum_{\mathfrak{M}} \left(\frac{T\left(\frac{h_k}{q_k}, \cdots, \frac{h_1}{q_1}\right)}{\varphi(Q)} \right)^s e\left(-\frac{h_k}{q_k} N_k - \cdots - \frac{h_1}{q_1} N_1\right) \int \cdots_{\mathfrak{M}} \int S^{*s}(\beta_k, \cdots, \beta_1)$$

$$\times e(-N_k \beta_k - \cdots - N_1 \beta_1)\, d\beta_k \cdots d\beta_1$$

$$= \sum_{q_k \leq L^{\frac{1}{2}\sigma_k}} \cdots \sum_{q_1 \leq L^{\frac{1}{2}\sigma_1}} \sum_{h_k}{}' \cdots \sum_{h_1}{}' \left(\frac{T\left(\frac{h_k}{q_k}, \cdots, \frac{h_1}{q_1}\right)}{\varphi(Q)} \right)^s e\left(-\frac{h_k}{q_k} N_k - \cdots - \frac{h_1}{q_1} N_1\right)$$

$$\times \int_{-\infty}^{\infty} \cdots \int_{-\infty}^{\infty} S^{*s}(\beta_k, \cdots, \beta_1)\, e(-\beta_k N_k - \cdots - \beta_1 N_1)\, d\beta_k \cdots d\beta_1$$

$$+ O(P^{s-\frac{1}{2}k(k+1)} L^{-s-1}). \tag{3}$$

9) When $k \geq 3$, we have

$$\mathfrak{S}(N_k, \cdots, N_1) - \sum_{q_k \leq L^{\frac{1}{2}\sigma_k}} \cdots \sum_{q_1 \leq L^{\frac{1}{2}\sigma_1}} \sum_{h_k}{}' \cdots \sum_{h_1}{}' \left(\frac{T\left(\frac{h_k}{q_k}, \cdots, \frac{h_1}{q_1}\right)}{\varphi(Q)} \right)^s$$

$$\times e\left(-\frac{h_k}{q_k} N_k - \cdots - \frac{h_1}{q_1} N_1\right)$$

$$\ll M \sum_{q_k=1}^{\infty} \cdots \sum_{q_1=1}^{\infty} \sum_{h_1}{}' \cdots \sum_{h_k}{}' \left| \frac{1}{\varphi(Q)} T\left(\frac{h_k}{q_k}, \cdots, \frac{h_1}{q_1}\right) \right|^{s-1}, \tag{4}$$

where

$$M = \max_{\nu} \max_{q_\nu \geq L^{\frac{1}{2}\sigma_\nu}} \left| \frac{1}{\varphi(Q)} T\left(\frac{h_k}{q_k}, \cdots, \frac{h_1}{q_1}\right) \right|.$$

By $M \ll L^{-\frac{1}{2}a\sigma_k + \epsilon} \ll L^{-1}$ and Lemma 10.10, the right member of (4) is $\ll L^{-1}$. (Some changes must be made when $k = 2$.)

Hence we obtain

$$\sum_{\mathfrak{M}} \left(\frac{T\left(\frac{h_k}{q_k}, \cdots, \frac{h_1}{q_1}\right)}{\varphi(Q)} \right)^s e\left(-\frac{h_k N_k}{q_k} - \cdots - \frac{h_1 N_1}{q_1}\right)$$

$$\times \int \underset{\mathfrak{M}}{\cdots} \int S^{*s} e(-N_k \beta_k - \cdots - N_1 \beta_1)\, d\beta_k \cdots d\beta_1$$

$$= \mathfrak{S}(N_k, \cdots, N_1) \int_{-\infty}^{\infty} \cdots \int_{-\infty}^{\infty} S^{*s}(\beta_k, \cdots, \beta_1)\, e(-\beta_k N_k - \cdots - \beta_1 N_1)\, d\beta_k \cdots d\beta_1$$

$$+ O(P^{s-\frac{1}{2}k(k+1)} L^{-s-1}).$$

10) We have

$$\int_{-\infty}^{\infty} \cdots \int_{-\infty}^{\infty} S^{*s}(\beta_k, \cdots, \beta_1)\, e(-N_k \beta_k - \cdots - N_1 \beta_1)\, d\beta_k \cdots d\beta_1$$

$$= P^{s-\frac{1}{2}k(k+1)} \int_{-\infty}^{\infty} \cdots \int_{-\infty}^{\infty} \left(\int_{2/P}^{1} \frac{e(\gamma_k x^k + \cdots + \gamma_1 x)}{\log x P} dx \right)^s e\left(-\frac{N_k}{P^k}\gamma_k - \cdots - \frac{N_1}{P}\gamma_1\right) d\gamma_k \cdots d\gamma_1.$$

By Lemma 10.7,

$$\int_{-\infty}^{\infty} \cdots \int_{-\infty}^{\infty} \left(\int_{2/P}^{1} \frac{e(\gamma_k x^k + \cdots + \gamma_1 x)}{\log x P} dx \right)^s e\left(-\frac{N_k}{P^k}\gamma_k - \cdots - \frac{N_1}{P}\gamma_1\right) d\gamma_k \cdots d\gamma_1$$

$$= \frac{1}{L^s} \int_{-\infty}^{\infty} \cdots \int_{-\infty}^{\infty} \left(\int_0^1 e(\gamma_k x^k + \cdots + \gamma_1 x)\, dx \right)^s e\left(-\frac{N_k}{P^k}\gamma_k - \cdots - \frac{N_1}{P}\gamma_1\right) d\gamma_k \cdots d\gamma_1$$

$$+ O\left(\frac{\log L}{L^{s+1}}\right) \int_{-\infty}^{\infty} \cdots \int_{-\infty}^{\infty} W^s\, d\gamma_k \cdots d\gamma_1 = \frac{b_1}{L^s} + O\left(\frac{\log L}{L^{s+1}}\right).$$

Therefore, we finally obtain

$$\sum_{\mathfrak{M}} \int_{\mathfrak{M}} S^s(\alpha_k, \cdots, \alpha_1)\, e(-\alpha_k N_k - \cdots - \alpha_1 N_1)\, d\alpha_k \cdots d\alpha_1$$

$$= b_1 \mathfrak{S}(N_k, \cdots N_1) \frac{P^{s-\frac{1}{2}k(k+1)}}{L^s} + O\left(\frac{P^{s-\frac{1}{2}k(k+1)}}{L^{s+1}} \log L\right),$$

where

$$b_1 = \int_{-\infty}^{\infty} \cdots \int_{-\infty}^{\infty} \left(\int_0^1 e(\gamma_k x^k + \cdots + \gamma_1 x)\, dx \right)^s e\left(-\frac{N_k}{P^k}\gamma_k - \cdots - \frac{N_1}{P}\gamma_1\right) d\gamma_k \cdots d\gamma_1.$$

Hence we obtain the lemma.

In the case $b_1 \geq b > 0$ and $\mathfrak{S}(N_k, \cdots, N_1) \geq c > 0$ (where b and c are independent of N), we obtain: when N_k is sufficiently large, the indeterminate equation

$$\sum_{\nu=1}^{s} p_\nu^h = N_h, \quad 1 \leqslant h \leqslant k,$$

is solvable in primes $p_1, \cdots, p_s$. The condition guaranteeing $b_1 \geq b > 0$ is called the condition of "positive solvability," while that guaranteeing $c_1 \geq c > 0$ is known as the condition of "congruent solvability."

§6. APPENDIX

It was mentioned in the beginning of this chapter that in order to avoid complications we would dispense with the condition $k = 2$. With slight changes in the above argument, however, it is not difficult to prove the theorem of this chapter when $k = 2$. Moreover, we can also calculate more specifically the integrals subject to the condition of positive solvability and the singular series subject to the condition of congruent solvability. To avoid taking up too much space, we shall omit some of the more detailed calculations.

1) **A study of the condition of positive solvability.**

In calculating, we shall use the following results:

1°. Let $\delta > 0$, $\alpha > 0$. We have the inequality

$$(\delta - x_1 - \cdots - x_n)^2 + \alpha(x_1^2 + \cdots + x_n^2) \geqslant \frac{\alpha}{n+\alpha}\delta^2. \tag{1}$$

The equality sign holds only for $x_1 = \cdots = x_n = \delta/(n+\alpha)$.

2°. Let $a < 0$ and $b > 0$. Further, let $f(x)$ be a continuous function in (a, b). Then

$$\lim_{\omega\to\infty} \int_a^b \frac{\sin 2\pi x\omega}{\pi x} f(x)\, dx = f(0). \tag{2}$$

3°. Let $Q(x_1, \cdots, x_n) = \sum_{i,j=1}^n q_{ij}x_ix_j$ be a positive definite quadratic form with determinant $|Q|$ and let $L(x_1, \cdots, x_n)$ be a homogeneous linear form, with L also denoting the vector of its coefficients. Further, let $A > 0$. Let R denote the interior of the hyperellipsoid

$$A + 2L(x_1, \cdots, x_n) - Q(x_1, \cdots, x_n) > 0.$$

Use $|\Delta|$ to denote the absolute value of the determinant of the square matrix

$$\begin{pmatrix} A & L \\ L' & -Q \end{pmatrix}.$$

Here L' denotes the coefficients of L arranged from top to bottom as a column vector. Then

$$\int\cdots\int_R \frac{dx_1\cdots dx_n}{\sqrt{A+2L(x_1,\cdots,x_n)-Q(x_1,\cdots,x_n)}}=|Q|^{-\frac{1}{2}n}|\Delta|^{\frac{1}{2}(n-1)}\frac{\pi^{\frac{1}{2}(n+1)}}{\Gamma(\frac{1}{2}(n+1))}. \quad (3)$$

4°. Letting Δ_n be the determinant of the quadratic form $(x_1+\cdots+x_n)^2+2x_1^2+\cdots+2x_n^2$, we have $\Delta_n=(n+2)2^{n-1}$. Further, letting U be the determinant of the quadratic form

$$u\,x_0^2+2v\,x_0(x_1+\cdots+x_n)+(x_1+\cdots+x_n)^2+2x_1^2+\cdots+2x_n^2,$$

we have

$$U=2^{n-1}((n+2)(u+v^2)-2(n+1)v^2).$$

Let us now study the definite integral

$$J(\delta)=\int_{-\infty}^{\infty}\int_{-\infty}^{\infty}\left(\int_0^1 e^{2\pi i(\alpha_2x^2+\alpha_1x)}\,dx\right)^s e^{-2\pi i(\alpha_2+\alpha_1\delta)}\,d\alpha_2\,d\alpha_1$$

under the condition of positive solvability. We treat it as the limit of

$$J_\omega(\delta)=\int_{-\omega}^{\omega}\int_{-\omega}^{\omega}\left(\int_0^1 e^{2\pi i(\alpha_2x^2+\alpha_1x)}\,dx\right)^s e^{-2\pi i(\alpha_2+\alpha_1\delta)}\,d\alpha_2\,d\alpha_1.$$

Let

$$X=x_1^2+\cdots+x_s^2-1,\qquad Y=x_1+\cdots+x_s-\delta.$$

Then

$$\begin{aligned}J_\omega(\delta)&=\int_0^1\cdots\int_0^1\frac{\sin 2\pi X\omega}{\pi X}\;\frac{\sin 2\pi Y\omega}{\pi Y}\,dx_1\cdots dx_s\\&=2\int_0^1\cdots\int_0^1\frac{\sin 2\pi X\omega}{\pi X}\;\frac{\sin 2\pi Y\omega}{\pi Y}\,dx_1\cdots dx_s.\\[-4pt]&\qquad{\scriptstyle x_1>x_2}\end{aligned}$$

We now have

$$J_\omega(\delta)=\iint\frac{\sin 2\pi X\omega}{\pi X}\;\frac{\sin 2\pi Y\omega}{\pi Y}\,dX\,dY\int_0^1\cdots\int_0^1\frac{dx_3\cdots dx_s}{x_1-x_2}.$$

By 2° we obtain

$$J(\delta) = \lim_{\omega\to\infty} J_\omega(\delta) = \underset{\substack{x_1^2+\cdots+x_s^2=1 \\ x_1+\cdots+x_s=\delta \\ x_1>x_2}}{\int\cdots\int} \frac{dx_3\cdots dx_s}{x_1-x_2}$$

$$= \underset{\mathfrak{D}}{\int\cdots\int} \frac{dx_3\cdots dx_s}{\sqrt{2(1-x_3^2-\cdots-x_s^2)-(\delta-x_3-\cdots-x_s)^2}} .$$

The domain $\mathfrak{D}$ over which this integral is taken is restricted by the following conditions:

$$2(1-x_3^2-\cdots-x_s^2) \geqslant (\delta-x_3-\cdots-x_s)^2 , \tag{4}$$

$$(\delta-x_3-\cdots-x_s)^2 \geqslant 1-x_3^2-\cdots-x_s^2 , \tag{5}$$

$$x_\nu \geqslant 0 . \tag{6}$$

By 1° we know that $(\delta-x_3-\cdots-x_s)^2 + 2(x_3^2+\cdots+x_s^2) \geq 2\delta^2/s$. But this shows, in the case $s<\delta^2$, that (4) is impossible; i.e., if $s<\delta^2$, then $J(\delta)=0$. Further, by (6), it is seen that $x_3+\cdots+x_s \leq \delta$ within the domain of integration. In the case of $\delta<1$, it follows from

$$1-x_3^2-\cdots-x_s^2 \geqslant 1-(x_3+\cdots+x_s)^2 \geqslant (1-x_3-\cdots-x_s)^2 \geqslant (\delta-x_3-\cdots-x_s)^2$$

that (5) is impossible. Hence if $\delta \leq 1$, then $J(\delta)=0$.

Now suppose $s \geq \delta^2$. Then (4) holds in the interior of the hyperellipsoid $2(1-x_3^2-\cdots-x_s^2)=(\delta-x_3-\cdots-x_s)^2$ and (5) holds in the interior of the hyperellipsoid $1-x_3^2-\cdots-x_s^2=(\delta-x_3-\cdots-x_s)^2$. It is easily seen that there must be points on the first hyperellipsoid outside the second hyperellipsoid, and those on the second hyperellipsoid must be inside the first hyperellipsoid. In other words, the first hyperellipsoid must include the second. The common parts $x_3+\cdots+x_s=\delta$ and $x_3^2+\cdots+x_s^2=1$ of these two hyperellipsoids form a domain of less than $s-2$ dimensions, and therefore, there exists a part, which has a positive n-dimensional volume, satisfying (4), (5) and (6). We accordingly obtain

Lemma 10.11. *Let* $s \geq 3$. *If* $s \geq \delta^2 > 1$, *then* $J(\delta) > 0$.

If we assume further that $\delta^2 > s-1$, then we can still find the function $J(\delta)$. Inequality (5) obviously holds because when $\delta^2 > s-1$ we know by

1° that

$$x_3^2+\cdots+x_s^2+(\delta-x_3-\cdots-x_s)^2\geqslant\frac{1}{s-1}\delta^2>1,$$

which naturally satisfies (5).

Further, the condition (6) also obviously holds: by (4), we know that $x_\nu\le 1$, and in the case of $x_3+\cdots+x_s<0$,

$$(\delta-x_3-\cdots-x_s)^2\geqslant\delta^2>s-1\geqslant 2,$$

which contradicts (4). Therefore, among $x_3,\cdots,x_s$, there is at least one of the terms that is positive. Suppose that there is also one in this set which is negative. We can assume that $x_3\ge 0$, $x_4<0$. Then

$$\begin{aligned}&(\delta-(x_3+x_4)-x_5-\cdots-x_s)^2+2(x_3^2+\cdots+x_s^2)\\&\geqslant(\delta-(x_3+x_4)-x_5-\cdots-x_s)^2+2((x_3+x_4)^2+x_5^2+\cdots+x_s^2)\\&\geqslant\frac{2}{s-1}\delta^2>2\end{aligned}$$

(by 1°). This contradicts (4). Therefore from (4) we can deduce (5) and (6). Hence we obtain

$$J(\delta)=\underset{(\delta-x_3-\cdots-x_s)^2<2(1-x_3^2-\cdots-x_s^2)}{\int\cdots\int}\frac{dx_3\cdots dx_s}{\sqrt{2(1-x_3^2-\cdots-x_s^2)-(\delta-x_3-\cdots-x_s)^2}}.$$

In 3° take $n=s-2$, $A=2-\delta^2$, $L(x_1,\cdots,x_n)=\delta(x_3+\cdots+x_s)$ and $Q(x_3,\cdots,x_s)=(x_3+\cdots+x_s)^2+2(x_3^2+\cdots+x_s^2)$. Then by 4° we know that

$$|Q|=s\cdot 2^{s-3},\quad |\Delta|=2^{s-2}(s-\delta^2).$$

Hence by 3° we obtain

Lemma 10.12. *If* $s\ge 3$ *and* $s\ge\delta^2>s-1$, *then*

$$J(\delta)=s^{1-\frac{1}{2}s}(s-\delta^2)^{\frac{1}{2}(s-3)}\frac{\pi^{\frac{1}{2}(s-1)}}{\Gamma(\frac{1}{2}(s-1))}.$$

2) A study of the condition of congruent solvability.

It is less simple to calculate $\mathfrak{S}(N_2,N_1)$. Here we give only a general explanation of the process for calculating it and describe the important conclusions as follows:

We rewrite

$$T\left(\frac{u}{p^l}, \frac{v}{p^l}\right) = T(u, v, p^l) . \quad (u, v) = 1 .$$

We use

$$S(u, p^l) = \sum_{x=1}^{p^l} e_{p^l}(u x^2)$$

to denote the usual Gaussian sum. For the numerical values of this sum we obviously have the following results:

1°.

$$S(u, p^l) = \left(\frac{u}{p}\right)^l S(1, p^l) \qquad \text{if } p > 2, \tag{7}$$

$$S(u, 2^l) = (-1)^{\frac{1}{8}(u^2-1)l} i^{-\frac{1}{4}(u-1)^2} S(1, 2^l), \tag{8}$$

$$S(1, p^l) = i^{\frac{1}{4}(p^l-1)^2} p^{\frac{1}{2}l} \qquad \text{if } p > 2, \tag{9}$$

$$S(1, 2^l) = \begin{cases} 0 & \text{if } l = 1, \\ (1+i)\, 2^{\frac{1}{2}l} & \text{if } l > 1. \end{cases} \tag{10}$$

2°. We introduce the integer γ defined by

$$p^\gamma \| (2u, v) .$$

Hence we have the following lemma.

Lemma 10.13. *Suppose $l > 2\gamma + 1$. If the congruence*

$$2ux + v \equiv 0 \pmod{p^{\gamma+1}}, \quad p \nmid x \tag{11}$$

is not solvable, then

$$T(u, v, p^l) = 0 . \tag{12}$$

If otherwise, let x_0 be a solution of

$$2ux + v \equiv 0 \pmod{p^{l+\gamma}}. \tag{13}$$

Then

$$T(u, v, p^l) = e_{p^l}(-u x_0^2)\, S(u, p^l) = e_{p^l}(-v^2/(4u))\, S(u, p^l), \tag{14}$$

where $v^2/4u$ and ux_0^2 are a pair of integers taken modulo p^l.

Proof. Let $x = y + p^{l-\gamma-1}z$. Then

$$T(u, v, p^l) = \sum_{y, p^{l-\gamma-1}}^{*} e_{p^l}(uy^2 + vy) \sum_{z, p^{\gamma+1}} e_{p^l}((2uy + v)\, p^{l-\gamma-1} z)$$

$$= p^{\gamma+1} \sum_{\substack{y, p^{l-\gamma-1} \\ 2uy+v\equiv 0 \pmod{p^{\gamma+1}}}} e_{p^l}(uy^2 + vy),$$

where Σ_{y, p^l} denotes a sum with y running through a set of residues $\bmod p^l$, and Σ^*_{y, p^l} denotes a sum with y running through a reduced set of residues $\bmod p^l$.

Obviously, when (11) is insolvable, these sums are equal to zero. Otherwise, let x_0 be a solution satisfying (13). Then all the solutions of (11) can be expressed in the form

$$x = x_0 + py, \qquad 1 \leqslant y \leqslant p^{l-1}.$$

Substituting this into the original sum, we accordingly obtain

$$T(u, v, p^l) = \sum_{y, p^{l-1}} e_{p^l}(u(x_0 + py)^2 + v(x_0 + py))$$

$$= e_{p^l}(ux_0^2 + vx_0) \sum_{y, p^{l-1}} e_{p^{l-2}}(uy^2)$$

$$= e_{p^l}\left(-\frac{v^2}{4u}\right) p\, S(u, p^{l-2})$$

$$= e_{p^l}\left(-\frac{v^2}{4u}\right) S(u, p^l).$$

3°. If $l \leq 2\gamma + 1$, then $T(u, v, p^l)$ is completely determined; in particular, if $p > 2$, then $\gamma = 0$, and we have

$$T(u, v, p) = \sum_{x, p} e(ux^2 + vx) - 1$$

$$= \begin{cases} e_p\left(-\dfrac{v^2}{4u}\right) S(u, p) - 1 & \text{if } p \nmid u, \\ -1 & \text{if } p \mid u. \end{cases} \tag{15}$$

If $p = 2$, then $l \leq 3$, and we can directly find

$$\left.\begin{aligned} T(u, v, 2) &= (-1)^{u+v}, \\ T(u, v, 4) &= i^{u+v}(1 + (-1)^v), \\ T(u, v, 8) &= \left(\frac{1+i}{\sqrt{2}}\right)^{u+v} (1 + i^v)(1 + (-1)^v). \end{aligned}\right\} \tag{16}$$

At this point we already have ample means of finding the numerical values of $T(u, v, p^l)$.

4°. Let

$$A(p^l) = \sum_{\substack{u=1 \\ p \nmid (u,v)}}^{p^l} \sum_{v=1}^{p^l} \left(\frac{T(u, v, p^l)}{\varphi(p^l)} \right) e_{p^l}(-N_2 u - N_1 v).$$

After considerable calculation we obtain the following two lemmas.

Lemma 10.14. *Suppose $l > 1$. If p^l is sufficiently large, then*

$$A(p^l) = 0.$$

In proving this lemma we use $sN_2 - N_1^2 \neq 0$, which is guaranteed by the condition of positive solvability $N_1^2 < sN_2$.

Lemma 10.15.

$$A(p) \ll p^{1-\frac{1}{2}s}.$$

Let

$$\partial_p = \sum_{l=0}^{\infty} A(p^l).$$

By Lemma 10.14 we know that the series ∂_p is finite. Also, when p is sufficiently large,

$$\partial_p = 1 + A(p).$$

Further, by Lemma 10.15, we know that for $s \geq 5$ the infinite product

$$\prod_p \partial_p$$

is absolutely convergent. Hence we have the following lemma.

Lemma 10.16. *If $s \geq 5$, then the product*

$$\mathfrak{S}(N_2, N_1) = \prod_p \partial_p$$

is absolutely convergent.

5°. With a more detailed calculation we can show the following results.

If $s \geq 5$ and $p \geq 5$, then $\partial_p > 0$. Further, if $2|(s - N_1)$ and $8|(s - N_2)$, then $\partial_2 > 0$, and if $3|(s - N_2)$, then $\partial_3 > 0$. To sum up, we can prove the following lemma.

Lemma 10.17. *Let* $s \geq 5$. *In the case of* $2|(s-N_1)$ *and* $24|(s-N_2)$,

$$\mathfrak{S}(N_2, N_1) > 0 .$$

Combining the results in this section with Theorem 17, we arrive at the following more lucid and precise conclusion.

Let $N_1(t)$ *and* $N_2(t)$ *be two sets of positive integers with* t *approaching infinity. Suppose that*

$$1 < \overline{\lim_{t\to\infty}} \frac{N_1^2(t)}{N_2(t)} < 7 .$$

Suppose further that $N_1(t)$ *are odd numbers, and* $N_2(t) \equiv 7 \pmod{24}$. *Then when* t *is sufficiently large there exist seven primes* $p_1, \cdots, p_7$ *such that*

$$p^2 + \cdots + p_7^2 = N_2 ,$$

$$p_1 + \cdots + p_7 = N_1 .$$

CHAPTER XI

A FURTHER STUDY OF THE PROBLEM OF THE PRECEDING CHAPTER

§1. INTRODUCTION

In this chapter we clarify the meaning of the condition of "positive solvability" and of "congruent solvability" and give a condition to insure positive solvability and congruent solvability. Under this condition when $s > 2k^2(3 \log k + \log \log k + 4)$ and N is sufficiently large, there exist prime solutions to the equations

$$\begin{aligned} p_1^k + \cdots + p_s^k &= N_k, \\ &\cdots\cdots \\ p_1 + \cdots + p_s &= N_1. \end{aligned} \tag{1}$$

Another object of this chapter is to reduce the restriction on s. In other words, we shall reduce the numbers smaller than s to

$$2k^2 + 3 + k \log (50 k^3 \log k) \Big/ \log \frac{1}{1-a} \sim 3k^2 \log k;$$

i.e., when s is greater than the above numbers and the sufficiently large $N_k, \cdots \cdots, N_1$ satisfy the conditions of positive solvability and congruent solvability, there exist solutions to the above equations.

§2. A STUDY OF THE CONDITION OF POSITIVE SOLVABILITY

Let

$$b_1 = \int_{-\infty}^{\infty} \cdots \int_{-\infty}^{\infty} \left(\int_0^1 e(\gamma_k x^k + \cdots + \gamma_1 x)\, dx \right)^s e(-\gamma_k \delta_k - \gamma_{k-1} \delta_{k-1} - \\ - \cdots - \gamma_1 \delta_1)\, d\gamma_k \cdots d\gamma_1 .$$

Let

$$B(\omega_k, \cdots, \omega_1) = \int_{-\omega_k}^{\omega_k} d\gamma_k \cdots$$

$$\cdots \int_{-\omega_1}^{\omega_1} \left(\int_0^1 e(\gamma_k x^k + \cdots + \gamma_1 x)\, dx \right)^s e(-\gamma_k \delta_k - \gamma_{k-1}\delta_{k-1} - \cdots - \gamma_1 \delta_1)\, d\gamma_1 .$$

Then

$$b_1 = \lim_{\omega_k \to \infty} \cdots \lim_{\omega_1 \to \infty} B(\omega_k, \cdots, \omega_1).$$

Interchanging the order of integration, we obtain

$$B(\omega) = B(\omega_k, \cdots, \omega_1) = \int_0^1 \cdots \int_0^1 dx_1 \cdots dx_s$$

$$\times \int_{-\omega_k}^{\omega_k} \cdots \int_{-\omega_1}^{\omega_1} e(\gamma_k (x_1^k + \cdots + x_s^k - \delta_k) + \cdots + \gamma_1 (x_1 + \cdots + x_s - \delta_1))\, d\gamma_k \cdots d\gamma_1$$

$$= \int_0^1 \cdots \int_0^1 \frac{\sin 2\pi \omega_k (x_1^k + \cdots + x_s^k - \delta_k)}{\pi (x_1^k + \cdots + x_s^k - \delta_k)} \cdots \frac{\sin 2\pi \omega_1 (x_1 + \cdots + x_s - \delta_1)}{\pi (x_1 + \cdots + x_s - \delta_1)}\, dx_1 \cdots dx_s .$$

Let

$$\left. \begin{array}{l} X_1 = x_1 + \cdots + x_s - \delta_1 \\ \cdots\cdots\cdots\cdots\cdots\cdots \\ X_k = x_1^k + \cdots + x_s^k - \delta_k \end{array} \right\},$$

so that the functional determinant

$$J = \frac{D(x_1, \cdots, x_k)}{D(X_1, \cdots, X_k)} = \frac{1}{k!} \begin{vmatrix} 1, & \cdots, & 1 \\ x_1, & \cdots, & x_k \\ \cdots & \cdots & \cdots \\ x_1^{k-1}, & \cdots, & x_k^{k-1} \end{vmatrix}^{-1} = \frac{1}{k! \prod_{k \geqslant i > j \geqslant 1} (x_i - x_j)} .$$

We partition the k-dimensional unit cube into several parts D_j in such a way that the sign of J does not vary in each part. Then we obtain

$$B(\omega) = \sum_j \int \cdots \int_{D_j} \frac{\sin 2\pi \omega_1 X_1}{\pi X_1} \cdots \frac{\sin 2\pi \omega_k X_k}{\pi X_k}\, dX_1 \cdots dX_k$$

$$\times \underset{\substack{0 \leqslant x_1 \leqslant 1 \\ \cdots \\ 0 \leqslant x_k \leqslant 1}}{\int_0^1 \cdots \int_0^1} \frac{dx_{k+1} \cdots dx_s}{k! \prod (x_i - x_j)} .$$

By Dirichlet's theorem, we know that if there exist positive solutions for the equations

$$X_\mu = x_1^\mu + \cdots + x_s^\mu - \delta_\mu = 0, \qquad x_\nu \leqslant 1, \quad 1 \leqslant \mu \leqslant k, \tag{2}$$

then

$$\lim_{\omega\to\infty} B(\omega) = \underset{\substack{0\leqslant x_\nu \leqslant 1\\ X_\nu = 0}}{\int_0^1 \cdots \int_0^1} \frac{dx_{k+1}\cdots dx_s}{k!\,|\Pi(x_i - x_j)|} > 0. \tag{3}$$

Therefore, we at once make a change in our procedure by taking up the problem of finding positive solutions for

$$x_1^\mu + \cdots + x_s^\mu = \delta_\mu, \quad 0 \leqslant x_\nu \leqslant 1, \quad 1 \leqslant \mu \leqslant k, \quad 1 \leqslant \nu \leqslant s.$$

Let us here set $\delta_\mu = N_\mu / P^\mu$ and investigate whether there exist positive solutions for

$$Z_1^\mu + \cdots + Z_s^\mu = N_\mu, \qquad 1 \leqslant \mu \leqslant k, \tag{4}$$

This approach is quite reasonable, since an absence of positive solutions would imply an absence of positive integral solutions, not to mention that of prime solutions. We should also note that since $N_k^a = P$, it follows that $\delta_k = 1$, and hence also $x_\nu \leq 1$, so that these inequalities do not need to be included among our hypotheses.

Therefore, the "condition of positive solvability" is one which insures the existence of positive solutions for (4), and is so named for this reason.

Lemma 11.1. *The equations*

$$x_1^h + \cdots + x_k^h = \delta_h, \qquad 1 \leqslant h \leqslant k, \tag{5}$$

have positive solutions $x_i \neq x_j$ $(i \neq j)$ *if and only if the quadratic form*

$$\sum_{i,j=1}^{k} \delta_{i+j-1}\, t_i\, t_j \tag{6}$$

is positive definite, where δ_ν $(\nu > k)$ *is recursively defined by the equation*

$$\begin{vmatrix} \delta_1, & 1, & 0, & \cdots, & 0 \\ \delta_2, & \delta_1, & 2, & \cdots, & 0 \\ \cdots & \cdots & \cdots & \cdots & \cdots \\ \delta_k, & \delta_{k-1}, & \delta_{k-2}, & \cdots, & k \\ \delta_\nu, & \delta_{\nu-1}, & \delta_{\nu-2}, & \cdots, & \delta_{\nu-k} \end{vmatrix} = 0.$$

Proof. 1) Necessity. If (1) is solvable, let

$$R_\nu = t_1 x_\nu + t_2 x_\nu^2 + \cdots + t_k x_\nu^k.$$

Then

$$\sum_{\nu=1}^{k} \frac{1}{x_\nu} R_\nu^2 = \sum_{i,j=1}^{k} \delta_{i+j-1} t_i t_j$$

is obviously a positive definite quadratic form.

2) Sufficiency. The equation (5) is certainly solvable, although this does not settle the question whether the solutions are complex or real. The polynomial of the kth degree with $x_1, \cdots, x_k$ as roots has real coefficients. Therefore, if complex numbers occur among the $x_1, \cdots, x_k$, they must be in pairs of conjugate complex numbers. The $x_1, \cdots, x_k$ are distinct and none of them is zero. For otherwise $R_\nu = 0$ $(1 \le \nu \le k)$ has a nonzero solution $(t_1, \cdots, t_k)$ (by the zero solution we mean the solution $t_1 = 0, \cdots, t_k = 0$). Hence (6) is not a positive definite form. Arrange the roots $x_1, \cdots, x_k$ as

$$\begin{aligned} x_{2m-1} &= y_{2m-1} + i\, y_{2m}, \\ x_{2m} &= y_{2m-1} - i\, y_{2m}, \end{aligned} \qquad y_{2m} \neq 0, \qquad 1 \leqslant m \leqslant g,$$

and

$$x_\nu' = y_\nu, \qquad 2g < \nu \leqslant k,$$

where y is real. Write

$$\begin{aligned} R_{2m-1}/x_{2m-1} &= P_{2m-1} + i\, P_{2m}, \\ R_{2m}\ /x_{2m} &= P_{2m-1} - i\, P_{2m}, \end{aligned} \qquad 1 \leqslant m \leqslant g,$$

where P_ν $(1 \le \nu \le 2g)$ are real linear coefficients of $t_1, \cdots, t_k$. Solve the equations

$$\begin{aligned} P_\nu &= 0, & 3 \leqslant \nu \leqslant 2g, \\ R_\nu &= 0, & 2g < \nu \leqslant k, \end{aligned}$$

and

$$y_1 P_1 = \left(y_2 + \sqrt{y_1^2 + y_2^2}\right) P_2 .$$

These are linear equations, with $k-1$ real coefficients, in the k variables $t_1, \cdots, t_k$. Obviously, there exists a solution $t_1, \cdots, t_k$ different from the zero solution. For this solution

$$\sum_{\nu=1}^{k} \frac{1}{x_\nu} R_\nu^2 = \sum_{\nu=1}^{k} x_\nu \left(\frac{R_\nu}{x_\nu}\right)^2 = x_1 \left(\frac{R_1}{x_1}\right)^2 + x_2 \left(\frac{R_2}{x_2}\right)^2$$

$$= 2 y_1 (P_1^2 - P_2^2) - 4 y_2 P_1 P_2 = 0 .$$

This contradicts the hypothesis that (6) is a positive definite form. Therefore the $x_1, \cdots, x_k$ are all real. From the sum

$$\sum_{\nu=1}^{k} \frac{1}{x_\nu} R_\nu^2$$

we can at once observe that if this sum is positive definite, the x_ν are all positive.

Remark. Because of the continuity, Lemma 11.1 is still true if, on the one hand, the condition $x_i \neq x_j$ is dispensed with, and on the other, the positive definiteness is changed into positive semidefiniteness. We have the following general lemma.

Lemma 11.2. *Let $s \geq k$. The necessary and sufficient condition for the equations*

$$x_1^h + \cdots x_s^h = \delta_h , \qquad 1 \leqslant h \leqslant k ,$$

to have positive real solutions is that there exist $s-k$ positive numbers $\delta_{k+1}, \cdots, \delta_s$ such that

$$\sum_{i,j=1}^{s} \delta_{i+j-1} t_i t_j$$

is a positive semidefinite form, with δ_ν $(\nu > s)$ recursively defined by the following equation:

$$\begin{vmatrix} \delta_1, & 1, & 0, & \cdots, 0 \\ \delta_2, & \delta_1, & 2, & \cdots, 0 \\ \cdots & \cdots & \cdots & \cdots \\ \delta_k, & \delta_{k-1}, & \delta_{k-2}, & \cdots, k \\ \delta_\nu, & \delta_{\nu-1}, & \delta_{\nu-2}, & \cdots, \delta_{\nu-k} \end{vmatrix} = 0 .$$

We shall omit the proof of this lemma, since it is similar to that of Lemma 11.1.

Remark. If we need only real solutions and are not limited to positive solutions, then the positive semidefiniteness of

$$\sum_{i,j=1}^{n} \delta_{i+j-2} t_i t_j , \qquad \delta_0 = s ,$$

guarantees their existence.

Lemma 11.3. *Given* $k-1$ *positive numbers* $\delta_1, \cdots, \delta_{k-1}$ *and* $\delta_k = 1$ *satisfying the conditions of Lemma* 11.2, *let* $N_\nu = [\delta_\nu P^\nu]$. *Then the conditions for positive solutions for the set* $N_1, \cdots, N_k$ *are satisfied.*

The proof of this lemma is obvious. We only need to replace the condition on δ by the condition on N.

§3. SINGULAR SERIES AND THE CONDITION OF CONGRUENT SOLVABILITY

We now use $\Sigma_{x, (q)}$ to denote a sum in which the variable x runs through a complete set of residues $\bmod q$. We further use $\Sigma'_{x, (q)}$ to denote a sum in which the variable x runs through a reduced set of residues $\bmod q$. We have

$$\mathfrak{S} = \mathfrak{S}(N_k, \cdots, N_1) = \sum_{q_1=1}^{\infty} \cdots \sum_{q_k=1}^{\infty} A(q_k, \cdots, q_1) ,$$

$$A(q_k, \cdots, q_1) = \sum_{h_1, (q_1)}' \cdots \sum_{h_k, (q_k)}' T^s e\left(-\frac{h_k}{q_k} N_k - \cdots - \frac{h_1}{q_1} N_1\right),$$

$$T = \frac{1}{\varphi(Q)} T\left(\frac{h_k}{q_k}, \cdots, \frac{h_1}{q_1}\right) = \frac{1}{\varphi(Q)} \sum_{x, (Q)}' e\left(\frac{h_k}{q_k} x^k + \cdots + \frac{h_1}{q_1} x\right),$$

where Q is the least common multiple of $q_1, \cdots, q_k$.

Lemma 11.4. *The* $\mathfrak{S}$ *can also be rewritten as*

$$\mathfrak{S} = \sum_{Q=1}^{\infty} \sum_{\substack{a_k=1 \\ (a_k, \cdots, a_1, Q)=1}}^{Q} \cdots \sum_{a_1=1}^{Q} \left(\frac{1}{\varphi(Q)} \sum_{x, (Q)}{}' e_Q (a_k x^k + \cdots + a_1 x) \right)^s e_Q (-a_k N_k - \cdots - a_1 N_1) .$$

Proof. This lemma is a direct inference from the following fact: by means of the relations

$$h_l Q / q_l = a_l , \qquad l = 1, 2, \cdots, k ,$$

the following two numerical sequences can be put into one-to-one correspondence with each other: (i) the numerical sequence resulting from the original definition of $\mathfrak{S}$,

$$q_l = 1, 2, 3, \cdots, \quad (h_l, q_l) = 1 , \quad 1 \leqslant h_l \leqslant q_l , \quad l = 1, 2, \cdots, k ;$$

and (ii) the numerical sequence in the lemma,

$$Q = 1, 2, 3, \cdots, \quad (a_k, \cdots, a_1, Q) = 1, \quad 1 \leqslant a_l \leqslant Q, \quad l = 1, 2, \cdots, k .$$

We shall not prove this fact, since it is reasonably obvious.

Let $W(m)$ denote the number of solutions of the congruences

$$\left. \begin{array}{l} h_1^k + \cdots + h_s^k \equiv N_k \\ \cdots\cdots\cdots\cdots\cdots\cdots \\ h_1 + \cdots + h_s \equiv N_1 \end{array} \right\} (\mathrm{mod}\ m) , \tag{1}$$

$$1 \leqslant h_\nu \leqslant m , \qquad (h_\nu, m) = 1 , \qquad 1 \leqslant \nu \leqslant s .$$

Obviously we have the following lemma.

Lemma 11.5. *If* $(m_1, m_2) = 1$, *then*

$$W(m_1 m_2) = W(m_1) W(m_2) .$$

Definition.

$$A(Q) = \sum_{\substack{a_k=1 \\ (a_k, \cdots, a_1, Q)=1}}^{Q} \cdots \sum_{a_1=1}^{Q} \left(\frac{1}{\varphi(Q)} T\left(\frac{a_k}{Q}, \cdots, \frac{a_1}{Q}\right) \right)^s e_Q(-a_k N_k - \cdots - a_1 N_1)$$

and

$$\partial_p = \sum_{l=0}^{\infty} A(p^l) , \qquad A(1) = 1 .$$

Lemma 11.6.

$$\sum_{m=0}^{l} A(p^m) = p^{lk} \varphi^{-s}(p^l)\, W(p^l)\,.$$

Proof. Obviously

$$W(p^l) = \frac{1}{p^{lk}} \sum_{h_1=1}^{p^l} \cdots \sum_{h_k=1}^{p^l} \sum_{x_1=1}^{p^l}{}' \cdots \sum_{x_s=1}^{p^l}{}'$$

$$e_{p^l}\Big(h_k (x_1^k + \cdots + x_s^k - N_k) + \cdots + h_1 (x_1 + \cdots + x_s - N_1)\Big)$$

$$= \frac{1}{p^{lk}} \varphi^s(p^l) \sum_{h_1=1}^{p^l} \cdots \sum_{h_k=1}^{p^l} \left(\frac{1}{\varphi(p^l)} T\left(\frac{h_k}{p^l}, \cdots, \frac{h_1}{p^l}\right)\right)^s e_{p^l}(-h_k N_k - \cdots - h_1 N_1)$$

$$= \frac{1}{p^{lk}} \varphi^s(p^l) \Bigg(\sum_{\substack{h_1=1\\ p|h_1}}^{p^l} \cdots \sum_{\substack{h_k=1\\ p\, h_k}}^{p^l} \left(\frac{1}{\varphi(p^l)} T\left(\frac{h_k}{p^l}, \cdots, \frac{h_1}{p^l}\right)\right)^s e_{p^l}(-h_k N_k - \cdots - h_1 N_1)$$

$$+ A(p^l)\Bigg)$$

$$= \frac{1}{p^{lk}} \varphi^s(p^l) \Bigg(\sum_{h_1=1}^{p^{l-1}} \cdots \sum_{h_k=1}^{p^{l-1}} \left(\frac{1}{\varphi(p^{l-1})} T\left(\frac{h_k}{p^{l-1}}, \cdots, \frac{h_1}{p^{l-1}}\right)\right)^s e_{p^{l-1}}(-h_k N_k$$

$$- \cdots - h_1 N_1) + A(p^l)\Bigg).$$

We obtain the lemma by repeated application of this procedure.

Lemma 11.7. *When* $s > k^2$, *the sequence* ∂_p *is convergent. Also, when* $s > k^2 + k$, *we have*

$$|\partial_p - 1| \leqslant 2(2k^3)^s p^{k-as}$$

and

$$\mathfrak{S} = \prod_p \partial_p\,.$$

Proof. We know by the Fundamental Lemma of Chapter 1 that

$$\left|T\left(\frac{h_k}{p^l}, \cdots, \frac{h_1}{p^l}\right)\right| \leqslant k^3 p^{l(1-a)}\,.$$

Hence we know that

$$|A(p^l)| \leqslant (p^{lk} - p^{(l-1)k}) \left(\frac{k^3 p^{l(1-a)}}{p^{l-1}(p-1)}\right)^s < (2k^3)^s p^{l(k-as)}\,.$$

Therefore, when $s > k^2$, the sequence ∂_p is absolutely convergent. Further, when $s > k^2 + k$,

$$|\partial_p - 1| \leqslant (2k^3)^s \sum_{l=1}^{\infty} p^{l(k-as)} \leqslant (2k^3)^s \frac{p^{k-as}}{1-p^{k-as}} \leqslant 2\,(2k^3)^s\, p^{k-as}.$$

The final conclusion follows from the convergence of

$$\sum_p p^{k-as}.$$

Explanatory remark. We know from Lemmas 11.6 and 11.7 that

$$\partial_p = \lim_{l\to\infty} p^{lk}\varphi^{-s}(p^l)\,W(p^l).$$

It is easily seen that if there is an l_0 such that $W(p^{l_0}) = 0$, then obviously $W(p^l)$ is also equal to zero for $l > l_0$. Therefore $\partial_p = 0$ and $\mathfrak{S} = 0$. Consequently, if the congruence (1) is not solvable, then we will have no solution for the problem under discussion. This is a natural phenomenon and is also the reason why the condition of congruent solvability is so named. From Lemma 11.7 we also have the following fact.

Lemma 11.8. *When* $p > (2(2k^3)^s)^{1/as-k}$,

$$\partial_p > 0;$$

i e., congruence (1) *is always solvable when* $m = p^l$.

Let

$$D = \begin{vmatrix} k^{k-1}, \cdots, 2^{k-1}, 1^{k-1} \\ \cdots\cdots\cdots\cdots\cdots\cdots \\ k\ ,\cdots,\ 2,\quad 1 \\ 1\ ,\cdots,\ 1,\quad 1 \end{vmatrix} = (k-1)!\,(k-2)!\cdots 2!\,1!$$

and $p^{\Theta} \| D$. Then $\Theta = 0$ when $p > k$. Let

$$p^{\Theta_\nu} \| \nu, \qquad \nu = p^{\Theta_\nu}\nu_0, \qquad \Theta_0 = \max(\Theta_1, \cdots, \Theta_k).$$

Let $W_1(p^l)$ denote the number of solutions of the congruences

$$\left.\begin{array}{l} y_1^k + \cdots + y_s^k \equiv N_k \\ \cdots\cdots\cdots\cdots\cdots\cdots \\ y_1 + \cdots + y_s \equiv N_1 \end{array}\right\} \pmod{p^l},\quad p\nmid y,$$

where

$$1 \leqslant y_\nu \leqslant p^l, \qquad 1 \leqslant \nu \leqslant k, \qquad 1 \leqslant y_\mu \leqslant p^{l-\Theta-\Theta_0}, \qquad k+1 \leqslant \mu \leqslant s$$

and

$$p^{\Theta} \parallel \begin{vmatrix} y_k^{k-1}, \cdots, y_1^{k-1} \\ \cdots\cdots\cdots\cdots \\ y_k, \cdots, y_1 \\ 1, \cdots, 1 \end{vmatrix}.$$

Lemma 11.9. *The condition for solvability of the congruences*

$$\sum_{\beta=1}^{k} a_{\alpha\beta} x_\beta \equiv b_\alpha \pmod{p^l}, \quad 1 \leqslant \alpha \leqslant k,$$

$$p^\lambda \parallel \begin{vmatrix} a_{11}, \cdots, a_{1k} \\ \cdots\cdots\cdots \\ a_{k1}, \cdots, a_{kk} \end{vmatrix},$$

is

$$p^\lambda \mid \begin{vmatrix} b_1, a_{12}, \cdots, a_{1k} \\ \cdots\cdots\cdots \\ b_k, a_{k2}, \cdots, a_{kk} \end{vmatrix}, \cdots, p^\lambda \mid \begin{vmatrix} a_{11}, \cdots, a_{1,k-1}, b_1 \\ \cdots\cdots\cdots \\ a_{k1}, \cdots, a_{k,k-1}, b_k \end{vmatrix}.$$

Proof. This lemma can be proved by means of the classical method of determinants.

Lemma 11.10. *When* $l \geq 2\Theta + 2\Theta_0 + 1$, *then*

$$W_1(p^{l+1}) \geqslant p^{s-k} W_1(p^l).$$

By repeated application of this inequality, we obtain

$$W_1(p^{l+u}) \geqslant p^{u(s-k)} W_1(p^l).$$

Proof. Suppose that we already have

$$\sum_{\mu=1}^{s} y_\mu^\nu \equiv N_\nu \pmod{p^l}, \tag{2}$$

$$1 \leqslant y_\lambda \leqslant p^l, \quad 1 \leqslant \lambda \leqslant k; \quad 1 \leqslant y_\tau \leqslant p^{l-\Theta-\Theta_0}, \quad k+1 \leqslant \tau \leqslant s.$$

Letting

$$h_\mu = y_\mu + z_\mu p^{l-\Theta_0-\Theta},$$

we have

$$h_\mu^\nu \equiv y_\mu^\nu + \nu y_\mu^{\nu-1} z_\mu p^{l-\Theta_0-\Theta} \pmod{p^{2(l-\Theta_0-\Theta)}},$$

$$\sum_{\mu=1}^{s} h_\mu^\nu \equiv \sum_{\mu=1}^{s} y_\mu^\nu + \nu \sum_{\mu=1}^{s} y_\mu^{\nu-1} z_\mu p^{l-\Theta_0-\Theta} \pmod{p^{l+1}}. \qquad (3)$$

We now discuss the congruence

$$\sum_{\mu=1}^{s} \nu_0 y_\mu^{\nu-1} z_\mu \equiv \frac{N_\nu - \sum_{\mu=1}^{s} y_\mu^\nu}{p^{l-\Theta_0-\Theta+\Theta_\nu}} \pmod{p^{\Theta_0+\Theta+1}}. \qquad (4)$$

If (4) is solvable, then by (3),

$$\sum_{\mu=1}^{s} h_\mu^\nu \equiv N_\nu \pmod{p^{l+1}}. \qquad (5)$$

Since

$$p^\Theta \,\|\, \begin{vmatrix} y_1^{k-1}, \cdots, y_k^{k-1} \\ \cdots\cdots\cdots \\ y_1^0, \cdots, y_k^0 \end{vmatrix}$$

and

$$p^\Theta \,|\, p^{\Theta_0+\Theta-\Theta_\nu} \,|\, \frac{N_\nu - \sum_{\mu=1}^{s} y_\mu^\nu}{p^{l-\Theta_0-\Theta+\Theta_\nu}},$$

congruence (4) is solvable for arbitrary z_τ $(k+1 \le \tau \le s)$. Therefore

$$W_1(p^{l+1}) \geqslant p^{s-k} W_1(p^l).$$

The proof still cannot be considered complete without the following supplement: since $h_\mu \equiv y_\mu \pmod{p^{l-\Theta_0-\Theta}}$, it follows that

$$\begin{vmatrix} y_1^{k-1}, \cdots, y_k^{k-1} \\ \cdots\cdots\cdots \\ y_1^0, \cdots, y_k^0 \end{vmatrix} \equiv \begin{vmatrix} h_1^{k-1}, \cdots, h_k^{k-1} \\ \cdots\cdots\cdots \\ h_1^0, \cdots, h_k^0 \end{vmatrix} \pmod{p^{\Theta+1}},$$

where we used $l > \Theta_0 + 2\Theta$.

Lemma 11.11. *Suppose* $s > k^2 + k$, *and when* $p \le (2(2k^3)^s)^{1/as-k}$,

$$W_1(p^{2\Theta+2\Theta_0}) > 0,$$

Then $\mathfrak{S}(N_k, \cdots, N_1)$ *is greater than a constant independent of* N.

Proof. We know by hypothesis and by Lemma 11.10 that when $p \le (2(2k^3)^s)^{1/as-k}$,

$$\begin{aligned}
\partial_p &= \lim_{l\to\infty} p^{lk}\varphi^{-s}(p^l)\, W(p^l) \\
&\geqslant \lim_{l\to\infty} p^{lk}\varphi^{-s}(p^l)\, W_1(p^l) \\
&\geqslant \lim_{l\to\infty} p^{lk}\varphi^{-s}(p^l)\, p^{(s-k)(l-2\theta-2\theta_0)}\, W_1(p^{2\theta+2\theta_0}) \\
&\geqslant \lim_{l\to\infty} \frac{p^{-l(s-k)}}{(1-1/p)^s}\, p^{(s-k)(l-2\theta-2\theta_0)} \\
&= p^{-(s-k)(2\theta-2\theta_0)}\left(1-\frac{1}{p}\right)^{-s} \geqslant c_1,
\end{aligned}$$

where c_1 (and hereafter c_2 and c_3) is independent of N, and is > 0.

Letting $s = k^2 + k + \delta$, we have

$$\partial_p > 1 - 2\,(2k^3)^s\, p^{-1-\delta a}.$$

Obviously $\partial_p \ge c_2$ when p satisfies $(2(2k^3)^s)^{1/as-k} < p \le (2(2k^3)^s)^{2k/\delta}$

Further, for $p > (2(2k^3)^s)^{2k/\delta}$ we have

$$\partial_p > 1 - p^{-1-\frac{1}{2}\delta a}.$$

Therefore

$$\prod_{p>(2(2k^3)^s)^{2k/\delta}} \partial_p \geqslant c_3.$$

Summing up, we see that

$$\mathfrak{S}(N_k, \cdots, N_1) \geqslant (c_1c_2)\,(2(2k^3)^s)^{2k/\delta}\, c_3.$$

This proves the lemma.

Let us now discuss the condition leading to

$$W_1(p^{2\theta+2\theta_0}) \geqslant 1.$$

Lemma 11.12. *If* $p > k$ *and* $s > (k+1)p$, *then* $W_1(p) \ge 1$.

Proof. The system of congruences

$$x_1(k+1)^\nu + x_2 k^\nu + x_3(k-1)^\nu + \cdots + x_{k+1} 1^\nu \equiv N_\nu \pmod p,\ 1 \leqslant \nu \leqslant k,$$
$$x_1 + x_2 + x_3 + \cdots + x_{k+1} \equiv s \pmod p$$

is always solvable in $0 < x_\nu \le p$. Therefore we can take x_{k+1} such that

$$x_1 + \cdots + x_{k+1} = s.$$

Hence we obtain the lemma.

Lemma 11.13. *The system of congruences*

$$x_1^\nu + \cdots + x_s^\nu \equiv N_\nu \pmod p, \quad p \nmid x, \quad 1 \leqslant \nu \leqslant k,$$

is solvable when $s > 2k$ *and* $p > k^{k(s-k)/(s-2k)}$.

Proof. The number M of sets of solutions of this congruence is obviously equal to

$$\frac{1}{p^k} \sum_{a_1=1}^{p} \cdots \sum_{a_k=1}^{p} \left(\sum_{x=1}^{p-1} e_p(a_k x^k + \cdots + a_1 x) \right)^s e_p(-(a_k N_k + \cdots + a_1 N_1)).$$

Therefore

$$|M - p^{s-k}| \leqslant \frac{1}{p^k} \sum_{a_1=1}^{p} \cdots \sum_{a_k=1}^{p}{}^{*} \left| \sum_{x=1}^{p-1} e_p(a_k x^k + \cdots + a_1 x) \right|^s,$$

where the asterisk means that p cannot simultaneously divide all a. We have, by formulas (2) and (3) of §3 of Chapter I,

$$\begin{aligned} |M - p^{s-k}| &\leqslant \frac{1}{p^k} (k p^{1-a})^{s-2k} \sum_{a_1=1}^{p} \cdots \sum_{a_k=1}^{p} \left| \sum_{x=1}^{p-1} e_p(a_k x^k + \cdots + a_1 x) \right|^{2k} \\ &\leqslant \frac{1}{p^k} (k p^{1-a})^{s-2k} k!\, p^{2k} \\ &\leqslant k^{s-k} p^{s-k-a(s-2k)} \\ &< p^{s-k}, \end{aligned}$$

where we have used the condition $p > k^{k(s-k)/(s-2k)}$. Hence we obtain

$$M \geqslant p^{s-1} - (p^{s-1} - 1) = 1,$$

which is the lemma.

Lemma 11.14. *If* $s > 3k$ *and* $p > k^{k(s-k)/(s-2k)}$, *then*

$$W_1(p) \geqslant 1.$$

Proof. By Lemma 11.13, the congruences

$$x_1^\nu + \cdots + x_t^\nu \equiv N_\nu - 1^\nu - 2^\nu - \cdots - k^\nu \pmod p \quad p \nmid x, \quad 1 \leqslant \nu \leqslant k,$$

are always solvable when $t > 2k$ and $p > k^{k(s-k)/(s-2k)}$. Hence we obtain the lemma.

Remark. The discussion in this section is to be regarded as preliminary; further developments are entirely possible.

§4. SOME LEMMAS

Lemma 11.15. *Let*

$$(2v-1)Q \leqslant x_v \leqslant 2vQ, \qquad 1 \leqslant v \leqslant k.$$

Then the number of sets of integers $x_1, \cdots, x_k$ *for which*

$$x_1^h + \cdots + x_k^h, \qquad 1 \leqslant h \leqslant k,$$

falls within an interval of length $\ll Q^{h-1}$ $(1 \leq h \leq k)$ *is* $\ll 1$.

The proof of this lemma is essentially the same as that of Lemma 4.1.

Lemma 11.16. *Let* R_k *denote the number of sets of integral solutions of the equations*

$$\sum_{j=1}^{n} \sum_{i=1}^{k} x_{ij}^h = \sum_{j=1}^{n} \sum_{i=1}^{h} x_{ij}'^h, \qquad 1 \leqslant h \leqslant k, \tag{1}$$

$$(2i-1)\,P^{(1-a)^{j-1}} \leqslant x_{ij}, x_{ij}' \leqslant 2i\,P^{(1-a)^{j-1}}. \tag{2}$$

Then

$$R_k \leqslant P^{(2k^2-\frac{1}{2}k(k+1))\,(1-(1-a)^n)}.$$

Proof. It is easily seen from (1) and (2) that

$$\sum_{i=1}^{k} x_{i1}^h - \sum_{i=1}^{k} x_{i1}'^h \ll P^{h(1-a)}, \qquad 1 \leqslant h \leqslant k.$$

For fixed x_{i1}' $(i = 1, \cdots, k)$, each of the sums

$$\sum_{i=1}^{k} x_{i1}^k, \ \sum_{i=1}^{k} x_{i1}^{k-1}, \cdots, \sum_{i=1}^{k} x_{i1}$$

falls respectively within an interval of length

$$O(P^{k(1-a)}),\ O(P^{(k-1)\,(1-a)}), \cdots, O(P^{(1-a)}). \tag{3}$$

Divide up the set of intervals (3) into

$$O\left(\frac{P^{k(1-a)}}{P^{k-1}}\ \frac{P^{(k-1)\,(1-a)}}{P^{k-2}} \cdots \frac{P^{2(1-a)}}{P}\ \frac{P^{1-a}}{1}\right) = O(P^{k-\frac{1}{2}(k+1)})$$

subintervals, each of which is respectively of length

$$O(P^{k-1}),\ O(P^{k-2}),\cdots,\ O(P),\ O(1).$$

By Lemma 11.15 (take $Q = P$) we know that the number of sets of x_{i1} $(1 \le i \le k)$ is $\ll P^{k-(k+1)/2}$. Hence the number of sets of x_{i1} and x'_{i1} $(i = 1, \cdots, k)$ is

$$\ll P^{2k-\frac{1}{2}(k+1)}.$$

Moreover, we know from (1) and (2) that for fixed x_{ij}, x'_{ij} $(1 \le i \le k,\ 1 \le j \le l-1)$ and x'_{il} $(1 \le i \le k)$ each of the sums

$$\sum_{i=1}^{k} x_{il}^{k},\ \sum_{i=1}^{k} x_{il}^{k-1},\cdots,\ \sum_{i=1}^{k} x_{il}$$

falls respectively within an interval of length

$$O(P^{k(1-a)^l}),\ O(P^{(k-1)(1-a)^l}),\cdots,\ O(P^{(1-a)^l}).$$

From

$$O\left(\frac{P^{k(1-a)^l}}{P^{(k-1)(1-a)^{l-1}}}\ \frac{P^{(k-1)(1-a)^l}}{P^{(k-2)(1-a)^{l-1}}}\cdots\frac{P^{(1-a)^l}}{1}\right) = O(P^{(k-\frac{1}{2}(k+1))(1-a)^{l-1}})$$

and Lemma 11.15 (take $Q = P^{(1-a)^{l-1}}$) we know that the number of sets of x_{il} $(1 \le i \le k)$ is

$$O(P^{(k-\frac{1}{2}(k+1))(1-a)^{l-1}}).$$

Hence for fixed x_{ij}, x'_{ij} $(1 \le i \le k,\ 1 \le j \le l-1)$ the number of sets of x_{il} and x'_{il} is

$$O(P^{(2k-\frac{1}{2}(k+1))(1-a)^{l-1}}).$$

Therefore the number of solutions of (1) under the restriction (2) is

$$\ll P^{(2k-\frac{1}{2}(k+1))(1+(1-a)+\cdots+(1-a)^{n-1})}$$
$$= P^{(2k^2-\frac{1}{2}k(k+1))(1-(1-a)^n)}.$$

§5. A LEMMA

Let

$$S_0 = \sum_{n \le 2kP} e(\alpha_k n^k + \cdots + \alpha_1 n),$$

$$S_{ij}(\alpha_k,\cdots,\alpha_1) = \sum_{(2i-1)P^{(1-a)^{j-1}} < n \le 2iP^{(1-a)^{j-1}}} e(\alpha_k n^k + \cdots + \alpha_1 n),$$

where $1 \le i \le k$, $1 \le j \le n$.

Lemma 11.17. *Let* $t = k^2 + 1$ *and*

$$n = \left[\frac{\log (50\, k^3 \log k)}{-\log (1 - a)} \right] + 1.$$

Then

$$\int_0^1 \cdots \int_0^1 | S_0 |^{2t} \prod_{j=1}^{n} \prod_{i=1}^{k} | S_{ij} |^2 \, d\alpha_k \cdots d\alpha_1 \ll P^{2t + 2k^2(1-(1-a)^n) - \frac{1}{2}k(k+1)}.$$

Proof. We divide up the domain of integration in the same way as in the proof of Theorem 15. Since $t \geq k^2 + 1$,

$$\sum_{\mathfrak{M}} \int \underset{\mathfrak{M}}{\cdots} \int | S_0 |^{2t} \, d\alpha_k \cdots d\alpha_1 \ll P^{2t - \frac{1}{2}k(k+1)}$$

(which is obtained by the same process as in the proof of Theorem 15). Hence

$$\sum_{\mathfrak{M}} \int \underset{\mathfrak{M}}{\cdots} \int | S_0 |^{2t} \left| \prod_{j=1}^{n} \prod_{i=1}^{k} S_{ij} \right|^2 d\alpha_k \cdots d\alpha_1$$

$$\ll \max_{\alpha} \left| \prod_{j=1}^{n} \prod_{i=1}^{k} S_{ij} \right|^2 \times \sum_{\mathfrak{M}} \int \underset{\mathfrak{M}}{\cdots} \int | S_0 |^{2t} \, d\alpha_k \cdots d\alpha_1$$

$$\ll P^{2k^2(1-(1-a)^n)} \cdot P^{2t - \frac{1}{2}k(k+1)} = P^{2t + 2k^2(1-(1-a)^n) - \frac{1}{2}k(k+1)}.$$

Furthermore, we know from (7) in §3 of Chapter X that over E

$$S_0 \ll P^{1-\lambda}, \quad \lambda = \frac{1}{50\, k^3 \log k},$$

and from Lemma 11.16 that

$$\int \underset{E}{\cdots} \int | S_0 |^{2t} \left| \prod_{j=1}^{n} \prod_{i=1}^{k} S_{ij} \right|^2 d\alpha_k \cdots d\alpha_1$$

$$\ll P^{2t(1-\lambda)} \int_0^1 \cdots \int_0^1 \left| \prod_{j=1}^{n} \prod_{i=1}^{k} S_{ij} \right|^2 d\alpha_k \cdots d\alpha_1$$

$$\ll P^{2t - 2t\lambda + (2k^2 - \frac{1}{2}k(k+1))\,(1-(1-a)^n)} \ll P^{2t + 2k^2(1-(1-a)^n) - \frac{1}{2}k(k+1)},$$

where we have used

$$\frac{1}{2}\, k(k + 1)\, (1 - a)^n \leqslant t(1 - a)^n < 2t\lambda.$$

This completes the proof of the lemma.

§6. A FURTHER LEMMA

By definition we have

$$\mathfrak{r}_0(\alpha_k, \cdots, \alpha_1) = \sum_{p \leq 2kP} e(\alpha_k p^k + \cdots + \alpha_1 p),$$

$$\mathfrak{r}_{ij}(\alpha_k, \cdots, \alpha_1) = \sum_{(2i-1)P^{(1-a)^{j-1}} \leqslant p \leqslant 2iP^{(1-a)^{j-1}}} e(\alpha_k p^k + \cdots + \alpha_1 p),$$

$1 \leq i \leq k$, $1 \leq j \leq n$. Let $t = k^2 + 1$ and

$$\mathfrak{Q} = \mathfrak{r}_0^{2t+1} \prod_{j=1}^{n} \prod_{i=1}^{k} \mathfrak{r}_{ij}^2 = \sum I'(N_k, \cdots, N_1)\, e(N_k \alpha_k + \cdots + N_1 \alpha_1),$$

where $I'(N_k, \cdots, N_1)$ is the number of sets of solutions of the equations

$$\sum_{i=1}^{k} \sum_{j=1}^{n} p_{ij}^h + \sum_{i=1}^{k} \sum_{j=1}^{n} p_{ij}'^h + \sum_{\nu=1}^{2t+1} p_\nu''^h = N_h, \quad 1 \leqslant h \leqslant k,$$

$$(2i-1)\, P^{(1-a)^{j-1}} \leqslant p_{ij}, p_{ij}' \leqslant 2i\, P^{(1-a)^{j-1}}, \; 1 \leqslant p_\nu'' \leqslant 2kP,$$

with $2kP = N_k^a$.

Lemma 11.18. *We have*

$$I'(N_k, \cdots, N_1) = \frac{b_2 P^{2t+1+2k^2(1-(1-a)^n) - \frac{1}{2}k(k+1)}\, \mathfrak{S}(N_k, \cdots, N_1)}{L^{2t+1+2kn}} \times \left(1 + O\left(\frac{\log L}{L}\right)\right),$$

where

$$b_2 = \int_{-\infty}^{\infty} \cdots \int_{-\infty}^{\infty} \left\{ \left(\int_0^1 e(\gamma_k x^k + \cdots + \gamma_1 x)\, dx \right)^{2t+1} \times \prod_{\nu=1}^{k} \left(\int_{(\nu-\frac{1}{2})a}^{\nu a} e(\gamma_k x^k + \cdots + \gamma_1 x)\, dx \right)^2 \times e\left(-\frac{N_k}{(2kP)^k} \gamma_k - \cdots - \frac{N_k}{2kP} \gamma_1 \right) \right\} d\gamma_k \cdots d\gamma_1.$$

Proof. We have

$$I'(N_k, \cdots, N_1) = \int_0^1 \cdots \int_0^1 \mathfrak{r}_0^{2t+1} \prod_{j=1}^{n} \prod_{i=1}^{k} \mathfrak{r}_{ij}^2\, e(-N_k \alpha_k - \cdots - N_1 \alpha_1)\, d\alpha_k \cdots d\alpha_1.$$

Divide up the domain of integration in the same way as in the proof of Theorem 16. By Lemmas 10.8 and 11.17,

$$\int \cdots_{\mathfrak{N}} \int \left| \mathfrak{r}_0^{2t+1} \prod_{j=1}^{n} \prod_{i=1}^{k} \mathfrak{r}_{ij}^2 \right| d\alpha_k \cdots d\alpha_1$$

$$\ll P L^{-s_1} \int_0^1 \cdots \int_0^1 |\mathfrak{r}_0|^{2t} \prod_{j=1}^{n} \prod_{i=1}^{k} |\mathfrak{r}_{ij}|^2 \, d\alpha_k \cdots d\alpha_1$$

$$\ll P L^{-s_1} \int_0^1 \cdots \int_0^1 |S_0|^{2t} \prod_{j=1}^{n} \prod_{i=1}^{k} |S_{ij}|^2 \, d\alpha_k \cdots d\alpha_1$$

$$\ll P^{2t+1+2k^2(1-(1-a)^n)-\frac{1}{2}k(k+1)} L^{-s_1}.$$

In the same way as in Theorem 16 we prove that

$$\sum_{\mathfrak{M}} \int_{\mathfrak{M}} \mathfrak{r}_0^{2t+1} \prod_{i=1}^{k} \mathfrak{r}_{i1}^2 \, e(-N_k \alpha_k - \cdots - N_1 \alpha_1) \, d\alpha_k \cdots d\alpha_1$$

$$= b_2 \mathfrak{S}(N) \, P^{2t+2k+1-\frac{1}{2}k(k+1)} L^{-2t-2k-1} \left(1 + O\left(\frac{\log L}{L}\right)\right),$$

where

$$b_2 = \int_{-\infty}^{\infty} \cdots \int_{-\infty}^{\infty} \left\{ \left(\int_0^1 e(\gamma_k x^k + \cdots + \gamma_1 x) \, dx \right)^{2t+1} \right.$$

$$\times \prod_{v=1}^{k} \left(\int_{(v-\frac{1}{2})a}^{va} e(\gamma_k x^k + \cdots + \gamma_1 x) \, dx \right)^2$$

$$\left. \times \, e\left(- \frac{N_k}{(2kP)^k} \gamma_k - \cdots - \frac{N_1}{2kP} \gamma_1 \right) \right\} d\gamma_k \cdots d\gamma_1 .$$

Then by applying the method employed in the proof of Lemma 9.6, we obtain the required theorem.

CHAPTER XII

OTHER RESULTS

§1. INTRODUCTION

We shall discuss in this chapter certain results and problems whose proof or solution depend upon the application of the methods described in this book. These problems, according to their individual nature, may be divided into four categories as follows:

a) those which include the concept of "almost all" or "to have a positive density;"

b) those which are derived from the following hypothesis: for any predetermined positive integer N there exists an integer A such that the quadratic polynomial

$$x^2 - x + A$$

takes a prime value when $x = 0, 1, \cdots, N$;

c) those which extend the problem in Chapter X to the sum of several distinct polynomials;

d) corollaries derived from the assumption that there exist $\ll c_1(k) P^{k(k+1)/2} (\log P)^{c_2(k)}$ sets of integral solutions for the equations

$$x_1^h + \cdots + x_{\frac{1}{2}k(k+1)}^h = y_1^h + \cdots + y_{\frac{1}{2}k(k+1)}^h, \quad 1 \leqslant h \leqslant k, \quad 1 \leqslant x, y \leqslant P.$$

Some results which do not fall within these categories will be described in §6 of this chapter.

§2. DEFINITIONS

Suppose that $\mathfrak{M}$ is a set of distinct natural numbers, in which $M(x)$ is the number of elements not greater than x. Suppose further that $\mathfrak{N}$ is a subset of the set $\mathfrak{M}$, with $N(x)$ being the number of elements in $\mathfrak{N}$ not greater than x. If

$$\lim_{x\to\infty} \frac{N(x)}{M(x)} = 1,$$

then $\mathfrak{N}$ is said to include almost all the elements of $\mathfrak{M}$. In particular, if $\mathfrak{M}$ is formed by all the positive integers $\equiv l \pmod q$, then $\mathfrak{N}$ is said to include almost all the integers $\equiv l \pmod q$.

Furthermore, if

$$\lim_{x\to\infty} \frac{M(x)}{x} \geqslant \alpha > 0,$$

then $\mathfrak{M}$ is said to have a positive asymptotic density.

Let $h(k)$ denote the least positive integer s satisfying the following condition: the set consisting of all the integers expressible in the form of a sum of s kth powers of primes includes almost all the positive integers $\equiv s \pmod K$. The K here is defined in Chapter VIII. We can prove that

$$h(1)=2,\ h(2)=3,\ h(3)\leqslant 5,\ h(4)\leqslant 8,\ h(5)\leqslant 13,\ h(6)\leqslant 20,\ h(7)\leqslant 28$$

and

$$h(k) \leqslant k+m+4,$$

where m has the meaning defined in §1 of Chapter IX.

Let $f_\nu(x)$ denote s_0 integral-valued polynomials of the kth degree, with s_0 defined by the table

k	1	2	3	4	5	6	7	8	9	10	$\geqslant 11$
s_0	2	3	5	8	13	20	28	36	45	55	$k+m+4$

Then the set of integers which can be expressed in the form

$$f_1(p_1) + \cdots + f_s(p_s) \quad (p \text{ a prime})$$

has a positive asymptotic density.

§3. FORMULATION OF A CONJECTURE

For an arbitrary preassigned positive integer N there must exist an integer A such that

$$x^2 - x + A$$

assumes prime values for $x = 0, 1, \cdots, N$. The following evidence supports the validity of this conjecture. When $x = 0, 1, \cdots, 40,$

$$x^2 - x + 41$$

takes on prime values. Also, the three polynomials

$$x^2 - x + 19421, \quad x^2 - x + 27941, \quad x^2 - x + 72491$$

are particularly rich in prime values (the last one is prime for $x = 0$ to $x = 11000$).[1)]

In other words, the system of $N + 1$ equations for A and the $N + 1$ unknown primes p_m $(0 \leq m \leq N)$

$$m^2 - m + A = p_m, \quad 0 \leqslant m \leqslant N,$$

is solvable. Eliminating the unknown A, we obtain

$$m^2 - m = p_m - p_0, \quad 1 \leqslant m \leqslant N,$$

which is a system of N equations for $N + 1$ unknown primes. The problem, to put it generally, is to find the solution of a set of N simultaneous equations for $N + 1$ unknown primes, namely

$$\sum_{j=1}^{N+1} a_{ij} p_j = b_i, \quad 1 \leqslant i \leqslant N. \tag{1}$$

Naturally, this problem must have a solution if in (1) we require the p_j to be natural numbers and require congruence instead of equality, but to-day the solution of this problem is still beyond the ability of mathematicians, and all we can do at present is to prove that (1) is solvable for almost all b satisfying the condition of "congruent solvability."

But subject to the conditions of positive solvability and congruent solvability, the equations

$$\sum_{j=1}^{2N+1} a_{ij} p_j = b_i, \quad 1 \leqslant i \leqslant N$$

are solvable for all sufficiently large b.

In conclusion we note that these problems contain as special cases the following interesting problems:

I) The Goldbach conjecture. The equation

$$p_1 + p_2 = 2n$$

---

1) N. G. W. H. Beeger, *Report on some calculations of prime numbers*, Nieuw Arch. Wiskunde 20 (1939), 40–50.

is solvable when $n > 1$. (This is a special case of the above mentioned general problems for $N = 1$.)

II) The problem of twin primes. The equation

$$p_1 - p_2 = 2$$

has infinitely many solutions.

III) The problem of triplet primes. The equations

$$p_1 - p_2 = 2, \quad p_2 - p_4 = 4$$

have infinitely many solutions (or

$$p_1 - p_2 = 4, \quad p_2 - p_4 = 2$$

have infinitely many solutions).

§4. APPLICATION OF THE METHOD OF CHAPTERS X AND XI TO A GENERAL PROBLEM

Let $\{f_{i1}(x), \cdots, f_{is}(x)\}$ $(1 \le i \le k)$ denote k sets, each set containing s integral-valued polynomials. The problem now is to solve the equations

$$f_{11}(p_1) + \cdots + f_{1s}(p_s) = N_1,$$

$$\cdots\cdots\cdots\cdots\cdots\cdots\cdots\cdots$$

$$f_{k1}(p_1) + \cdots + f_{ks}(p_s) = N_k.$$

The solution of equations of this type is not very difficult, provided we assume the degree of f is bounded and s is sufficiently large. Generally speaking, we can apply the method of Chapters X and XI, provided we introduce the inequality

$$\int \cdots \int |g_1 \cdots g_s| \, d\alpha_1 \cdots d\alpha_k \leqslant \left(\prod_{\nu=1}^{s} \int \cdots \int |g_\nu|^s \, d\alpha_1 \cdots d\alpha_k \right)^{1/s}.$$

§5. STATEMENT OF A FURTHER CONJECTURE

Conjecture. The number of sets of integral solutions of the equations

$$x_1^h + \cdots + x_{\frac{1}{2}k(k+1)}^h = y_1^h + \cdots + y_{\frac{1}{2}k(k+1)}^h, \quad 1 \leqslant h \leqslant k, \quad 1 \leqslant x, y \leqslant P$$

is $\le c_1(k) P^{k(k+1)/2} (\log P)^{c_2(k)}$.

The truth of this conjecture is obvious in the case of $k = 1$. The case of $k = 2$ has already been proved in Chapter IV (Theorem B_2'), while the case of

$k \geq 3$ is one which remains to be solved. If we could prove this, almost all the theorems contained in this book would be improved. For example, the asymptotic formula for the number of solutions will be true when $s > k(k+1)/2$. Of course, this conjecture also has many applications to the analytic theory of numbers.

§6. FURTHER RESULTS

A description of a number of other results follows:

I) Every sufficiently large integer can be expressed as the sum of a prime and of s kth powers of integers if $s \geq s_0 \sim 2k \log k$.

II) Every sufficiently large integer can be expressed as the sum of a prime and s kth powers of integers if $s \geq s_0 \sim 3(k \log k)/2$.

III) Every sufficiently large integer can be expressed as the sum of s kth powers of integers, each of which has not more than two prime factors, if $s \geq s_0 \sim 3k \log k$.

For the proof of II) and III) we must adopt another of Vinogradov's creative methods. See (especially Chapter 4) I. M. Vinogradov, *The method of trigonometric sums in the theory of numbers*, Trav. Inst. Math. Stekloff 23 (1947), 109 pp.; English transl., Interscience, London and New York, 1954.

APPENDIX

Let $f(x)$ be a polynomial of the kth degree with real coefficients, or be a real function which can be approximated in a certain way by a polynomial of the kth degree. Further, let

$$S = \sum_{x=Q+1}^{Q+P} e^{2\pi i f(x)}.$$

In the applications of estimates for this type of trigonometric sum to the study of the analytic theory of numbers, k and P often simultaneously approach infinity. Therefore, in order to secure a more precise result, we must consider an improvement of the constant factors relative to k in Vinogradov's mean-value theorem. More specifically, we shall prove:

Theorem. *Let $l \geq 1$. Then for*

$$\frac{1}{3} k(k+1) + lk \leqslant s \leqslant 4k^2 \log k$$

we have

$$\int_0^1 \cdots \int_0^1 |C_k(P)|^{2s} \, d\alpha_1 \cdots d\alpha_k \leqslant k^{9k^8} e^{23k^2 l} \log^l P \cdot P^{2s - \frac{1}{2}k(k+1) + \delta_l},$$

where

$$\delta_l = \frac{1}{2} k(k+1)(1-a)^l, \qquad a = \frac{1}{k}.$$

The proof of this theorem is quite similar to that of Theorem 5′, with the exception that in the present case we shall use the following two lemmas instead of Lemmas 4.1 and 4.2.

Lemma 1. *Let $Q = RH$, $R > 1$, $H > 1$ and*

$$1 \leqslant g_1 < g_2 < \cdots < g_k \leqslant H, \qquad g_\nu - g_{\nu-1} > 1, \tag{1}$$

where $g_1, \cdots, g_k$ are integers. Further, let x_ν vary over the interval

$$-\omega + (g_\nu - 1) R < x_\nu \leqslant -\omega + g_\nu R, \qquad 0 \leqslant \omega \leqslant Q. \tag{2}$$

Then the number of sets of integers $x_1, \cdots, x_k$ for which

$$x_1^h + \cdots + x_k^h, \qquad 1 \leqslant h \leqslant k$$

falls within an interval of length $\leq Q^{h-1}$ $(1 \leq h \leq k)$ *is*

$$\leqslant e^{3k^2} k^{-\frac{1}{2}k^2} H^{\frac{1}{2}k(k-1)}. \tag{3}$$

Proof. Suppose that h is an integer satisfying $1 < h \leq k$. Given $x_{h+1}, \cdots, x_k$, assume that $x_1, \cdots, x_h$ and $y_1, \cdots, y_h$ are two sets of integers such that $x_1^r + \cdots + x_k^r$ and $y_1^r + \cdots + y_h^r + x_{h+1}^r + \cdots + x_k^r$ fall simultaneously within a set of intervals of length not exceeding Q^{r-1} $(1 \leq r \leq k)$. Then

$$x_1^r + \cdots + x_h^r - (y_1^r + \cdots + y_h^r) = \theta_r Q^{r-1} \qquad (1 \leqslant r \leqslant h);$$

i.e.,

$$\frac{x_1-y_1}{x_1-y_1}(x_1-y_1) + \cdots + \frac{x_h-y_h}{x_h-y_h}(x_h-y_h) = \theta_1,$$

$$\cdots\cdots\cdots\cdots\cdots\cdots\cdots\cdots\cdots\cdots\cdots\cdots$$

$$\frac{x_1^h-y_1^h}{x_1-y_1}(x_1-y_1) + \cdots + \frac{x_h^h-y_h^h}{x_h-y_h}(x_h-y_h) = \theta_h Q^{h-1},$$

with $|\theta_r| \leq 1$. Treating $x_1 - y_1, \cdots, x_h - y_h$ as variables in these linear equations, we obtain

$$\Delta\,(x_h - y_h) \pm \Delta' = 0, \tag{4}$$

where

$$\Delta = \begin{vmatrix} \dfrac{x_1-y_1}{x_1-y_1} & \cdots & \dfrac{x_h-y_h}{x_h-y_h} \\ \cdots & \cdots & \cdots \\ \dfrac{x_1^h-y_1^h}{h(x_1-y_1)} & \cdots & \dfrac{x_h^h-y_h^h}{h(x_h-y_h)} \end{vmatrix}, \quad \Delta' = \begin{vmatrix} \dfrac{x_1-y_1}{x_1-y_1} & \cdots & \dfrac{x_{h-1}-y_{h-1}}{x_{h-1}-y_{h-1}} & \theta_1 \\ \cdots & \cdots & \cdots & \cdots \\ \dfrac{x_1^h-y_1^h}{h(x_1-y_1)} & \cdots & \dfrac{x_{h-1}^h-y_{h-1}^h}{h(x_{h-1}-y_{h-1})} & \dfrac{\theta_h}{h} Q^{h-1} \end{vmatrix}.$$

We rewrite (4) as

$$\frac{1}{\prod_{r=1}^{h}(x_r-y_r)} \int_{y_1}^{x_1} \cdots \int_{y_h}^{x_h} \{\Delta_h(x_h-y_h) \pm \Delta_h'\}\, dz_1 \cdots dz_h = 0,$$

where

$$\Delta_h = \begin{vmatrix} 1 & \cdots & 1 \\ z_1 & \cdots & z_h \\ \cdots & \cdots & \cdots \\ z_1^{h-1} & \cdots & z_h^{h-1} \end{vmatrix}, \quad \Delta'_h = \begin{vmatrix} 1 & \cdots & 1 & \theta_1 \\ z_1 & \cdots & z_{h-1} & \frac{1}{2}\theta_2 Q \\ \cdots & \cdots & \cdots & \cdots \\ z_1^{h-1} & \cdots & z_{h-1}^{h-1} & \frac{1}{h}\theta_h Q^{h-1} \end{vmatrix}.$$

Then we know by application of the mean-value theorem of the integral calculus that there must be a set $z_1, \cdots, z_h$ such that

$$\Delta_h (x_h - y_h) \pm \Delta'_h = 0. \tag{5}$$

Since

$$\Delta_h = \Delta_{h-1} (z_h - z_1) \cdots (z_h - z_{h-1}),$$

if we let σ_{h-r} denote the elementary symmetric function of degree $h - r$ of the variables $z_1, \cdots, z_{h-1}$, we obviously have $|\sigma_{h-r}| \leq \binom{h-1}{h-r} Q^{h-r}$. Therefore, in the expansion of Δ_h, the absolute values of the coefficients of z_h^{r-1} are equal to

$$|\sigma_{h-r} \Delta_{h-1}| \leqslant \binom{h-1}{r-1} Q^{h-r} |\Delta_{h-1}|.$$

Thus

$$|\Delta'_h| \leqslant |\Delta_{h-1}| \sum_{r=1}^{h} \frac{|\sigma_{h-r}|}{r} Q^{r-1} \leqslant |\Delta_{h-1}| Q^{h-1} \sum_{r=1}^{h} \frac{1}{r} \binom{h-1}{r-1}.$$

Hence we obtain

$$|x_h - y_h| \leqslant \frac{Q^{h-1} \sum_{r=1}^{h} \frac{1}{r} \binom{h-1}{r-1}}{(z_h - z_1) \cdots (z_h - z_{h-1})} \leqslant \frac{2^h Q^{h-1}}{R(3R) \cdots ((2h-3)R)}$$
$$= \frac{2^h H^{h-1}}{1 \cdot 3 \cdots (2h-3)} = L_h.$$

Consequently, for given $x_{h+1}, \cdots, x_k, x_h$, we can take at most $L_h + 1 \leq 2L_h$ different values. Therefore, the number of sets of integers $x_1, \cdots, x_k$ satisfying the condition of the lemma cannot exceed

$$2 \prod_{h=2}^{k} \frac{1}{1 \cdot 3 \cdots (2h-3)} \prod_{h=2}^{k} 2^{h+1} \cdot H^{\frac{1}{2}k(k-1)}.$$

Making use of the obvious inequalities

$$\sum_{n=1}^{N} \log n \geqslant \int_1^N \log x \, dx$$

and

$$\sum_{n=1}^{N} n \log n \geqslant \int_1^N x \log x \, dx,$$

we obtain the lemma without difficulty.

Lemma 2. *Let* $c \geq 1$. *By the assumption of Lemma* 1, *the number of sets of integers* $x_1, \cdots, x_k$ *for which*

$$x_1^h + \cdots + x_k^h, \qquad (1 \leqslant h \leqslant k)$$

each fall within an interval of length not exceeding $cQ^{(1-a)h}$ $(1 \leq h \leq k)$ *does not exceed*

$$(2c)^k e^{3k^2} k^{-\frac{1}{2}k^2} H^{\frac{1}{2}k(k-1)} Q^{\frac{1}{2}(k-1)}. \tag{6}$$

The proof is similar to that of Lemma 4.2.

Lemma 3. *Suppose that* s *is an integer satisfying* $2^s \leq Q/(2k-1)(Q^{1-a}-1)$. *Let* $H_s = 2^s(2k-1)$ *and* $R_s = Q/H_s$. *Further, let*

$$Z_{sg_i} = \sum_{(g_i-1)R_s < x \leqslant g_i R_s} e(f(x)), \qquad 1 \leqslant i \leqslant k,$$

and

$$C^* = \sum_{\omega < x \leqslant \omega + Q'} e(f(x)),$$

where $0 < Q' \leq Q^{1-a}$ *and* $0 \leq \omega \leq Q$. *Then when* $g_1, \cdots, g_k$ *is a well-spaced set*

$$\int_0^1 \cdots \int_0^1 |Z_{sg_1} \cdots Z_{sg_k}|^2 \, |C^*|^{2(b-k)} \, d\alpha_1 \cdots d\alpha_k$$

$$\leqslant b^k e^{4k^2} 2^{s[\frac{1}{2}k(k-1)-k]} Q^{2k-\frac{1}{2}(k+1)} \int_0^1 \cdots \int_0^1 |C_k(Q^{1-a})|^{2(b-k)} \, d\alpha_1 \cdots d\alpha_k. \tag{7}$$

The method for the proof of this lemma is similar to that employed in part 3) of the proof of Lemma 4.4.

Lemma 4 (recursive formula). *Let* b *be an integer satisfying*

$$\frac{1}{3} k(k+1) + k < b \leqslant 4k^2 \log k. \tag{8}$$

If

$$\log Q > 4k \log(4k), \tag{9}$$

then

$$\int_0^1 \cdots \int_0^1 |C_k(Q)|^{2b}\, d\alpha_1 \cdots d\alpha_k$$

$$\leqslant e^{23k^3} Q^{2k-\frac{1}{2}(k+1)+2(b-k)a} \log Q \int_0^1 \cdots \int_0^1 |C_k(Q^{1-a})|^{2(b-k)}\, d\alpha_1 \cdots d\alpha_k . \tag{10}$$

Proof. Let η be an integer determined by the inequalities

$$2^{\eta-1} \leqslant \frac{Q}{(2k-1)(Q^{1-a}-1)} < 2^{\eta}. \tag{11}$$

By what is assumed in the lemma we obviously have $\eta \geq 4$.

Split $C_k(Q)$ into $H_s = 2^s(2k-1)$ parts, the length of each part being $R_s = Q/H_s$. Then, by applying the same method as in the proof of Lemma 4.4, we obtain

$$|C_k(Q)|^{2b} \leqslant 2\eta \sum_{s=0}^{\eta} M_s \sum^{M_s} |Z_s'|^2, \tag{12}$$

where the meanings of Z_s' and M_s are the same as in Lemma 4.4, with the exception that

$$M_s = H_s^{k-1}(4(k-1))^b \quad (s>0), \quad M_0 \leqslant (2k-1)^b .$$

When $0 \leq s \leq \eta - 1$, we can prove as in Lemma 4.4 that

$$|Z_s'|^2 \leqslant \frac{1}{b-k} \sum_{i=k+1}^{b} |Z_{sg_1} \cdots Z_{sg_k}|^2 \, |Z_{sg_i}|^{2(b-k)}$$

$$\leqslant \frac{1}{b-k} \sum_{i=k+1}^{b} N_s^{2(b-k)-1} \sum^{N_s} |Z_{sg_1} \cdots Z_{sg_k}|^2 \, |C^*|^{2(b-k)},$$

where

$$N_s = \left[\frac{Q}{2^s(2k-1)} \frac{1}{Q^{1-a}-1}\right] + 1$$

$$\leqslant \begin{cases} \dfrac{Q^a}{2^{s+1}(k-1)} & (s = 0, 1, 2), \\[2ex] \dfrac{Q^a}{2^s(k-1)} & (3 \leqslant s \leqslant \eta - 1). \end{cases}$$

Therefore, by Lemma 3 and the above inequalities, we have

$$\int_0^1 \cdots \int_0^1 \sum_{s=0}^{\eta-1} M_s \sum^{M_s} |Z_s'|^2 \, d\alpha_1 \cdots d\alpha_k$$

$$\leqslant k^{17k} e^{6k^2} Q^{2k-\frac{1}{2}(k+1)+2(b-k)a} \int_0^1 \cdots \int_0^1 |C_k(Q^{1-a})|^{2(b-k)} \, d\alpha_1 \cdots d\alpha_k \,. \tag{13}$$

When $s = \eta$, we obtain, by (11),

$$|Z_\eta'|^2 \leqslant \frac{1}{b-k} \sum_{i=k+1}^{b} |Z_{\eta g_1} \cdots Z_{\eta g_k}|^2 \, |Z_{\eta g_i}|^{2(b-k)}$$

$$\leqslant R_\eta^{2k} \, |C^*|^{2(b-k)} .$$

Hence, by (9), we have

$$\int_0^1 \cdots \int_0^1 M_\eta \sum^{M_\eta} |Z_\eta'|^2 \, d\alpha_1 \cdots d\alpha_k$$

$$\leqslant M_\eta^2 \, R_\eta^{2k} \int_0^1 \cdots \int_0^1 |C_k(Q^{1-a})|^{2(b-k)} \, d\alpha_1 \cdots d\alpha_k$$

$$\leqslant (4k)^{2k} Q^{2k-\frac{1}{2}(k+1)+2(b-k)a} \int_0^1 \cdots \int_0^1 |C_k(Q^{1-a})|^{2(b-k)} \, d\alpha_1 \cdots d\alpha_k \,. \tag{14}$$

The fact that $\eta \leq \log Q$ and the inequalities (12), (13) and (14) prove the lemma.

Proof of Theorem. Let l_0 be an integer determined by the inequalities

$$(1-a)^{-(l_0-1)} \, 4k \log(4k) < \log P \leqslant (1-a)^{-l_0} \, 4k \log(4k) \,.$$

In the case $l_0 \geq l$ we can prove that

$$\int_0^1 \cdots \int_0^1 |C_k(P)|^{2s} \, d\alpha_1 \cdots d\alpha_k \leqslant e^{23k^3 l} \log^l P \cdot P^{2s-\frac{1}{2}k(k+1)+\delta_l} \,. \tag{15}$$

In fact, when $l = 0$, the inequality (15) is obvious. For the case $l > 0$ we can obtain the result by Lemma 4 and through finite induction on l.

If $1 \leq l_0 < l$, we obtain from (15)

$$\int_0^1 \cdots \int_0^1 |C_k(P)|^{2s} \, d\alpha_1 \cdots d\alpha_k \leqslant e^{23k^3 l_0} \log^{l_0} P \cdot P^{2s-\frac{1}{2}k(k+1)+\delta_{l_0}},$$

and since

$$P^{\delta_{l_0}} = P^{\frac{1}{2}k(k+1)(1-a)^{l_0}} \leqslant (4k)^{4k \cdot \frac{1}{2}k(k+1)} \leqslant k^{9k^3},$$

we obtain the Theorem.

For the case $l_0 < 1 \leq l$, we have, since

$$P^{\frac{1}{2}k(k+1)} \leqslant (4k)^{4k\cdot\frac{1}{2}k(k+1)} \leqslant k^{9k^3},$$

$$\int_0^1 \cdots \int_0^1 |C_k(P)|^{2s}\, d\alpha_1 \cdots d\alpha_k \leqslant P^{2s} \leqslant k^{9k^3} P^{2s-\frac{1}{2}k(k+1)}.$$

This completes the proof of the Theorem.

Fundamental Lemma. *Let*

$$f(x) = \alpha_k x^k + \cdots + \alpha_1 x + \alpha_0$$

be a polynomial of the kth degree with real coefficients, and let P be a positive integer satisfying

$$2k\, |\alpha_k|\, P \leqslant 1.$$

Then

$$\sum_{x=Q+1}^{Q+P} e^{2\pi i f(x)} = O\left(e^{32k} P^{1-\frac{A}{k^2 \log k}} \log P\right) + O\left(|\alpha_k|^{-\frac{1}{k-1}}\right),$$

where A and the constants included in the symbol O are all absolute.

Proof. If $|\alpha_k|^{-1/(k-1)} \geq P$, the lemma is obvious. Therefore we may assume that

$$|\alpha_k|^{-\frac{1}{k-1}} < P.$$

Let Y be a constant satisfying $2 \leq Y \leq P$ and let

$$S = \sum_{x=Q+1}^{Q+P} e(f(x)), \qquad S_1(x) = \sum_{y=1}^{Y} e(f(x+y)).$$

Then

$$\sum_{x=Q+1}^{Q+P} \sum_{y=1}^{Y} e(f(x+y)) = Y \sum_{m=Q+Y+1}^{Q+P} e(f(m)) + \left(\sum_{m=Q+2}^{Q+Y} + \sum_{m=Q+P+1}^{Q+P+Y} \right) O(Y)$$
$$= YS + O(Y^2),$$

and accordingly

$$S = \frac{1}{Y} \sum_{x=Q+1}^{Q+P} S_1(x) + O(Y).$$

Therefore we have by Hölder's inequality

$$S \ll \frac{1}{Y} \left(P^{2s-1} \sum_{x=Q+1}^{Q+P} |S_1(x)|^{2s} \right)^{\frac{1}{2s}} + Y.$$

Let

$$f(x+y) = A_k y^k + A_{k-1} y^{k-1} + \cdots + A_0,$$

where $A_k = \alpha_k$, $A_{k-1} = \alpha_{k-1} + k\alpha_k x$. Then

$$|S_1(x)|^{2s} = \sum_{y_1=1}^{Y} \cdots \sum_{y_s=1}^{Y} \sum_{y_1'=1}^{Y} \cdots \sum_{y_s'=1}^{Y} e(\Phi),$$

where

$$\Phi = f(x+y_1) + \cdots + f(x+y_s) - f(x+y_1') - \cdots - f(x+y_s')$$

$$= \sum_{h=1}^{k} A_h(y_1^h + \cdots + y_s^h - y_1'^h - \cdots - y_s'^h).$$

Let $\psi(N_1, \cdots, N_{k-1})$ denote a set of integral solutions of the equations

$$y_1^h + \cdots + y_s^h - y_1'^h - \cdots - y_s'^h = N_h \qquad (1 \leqslant h \leqslant k-1),$$
$$1 \leqslant y, y' \leqslant Y.$$

Then, since A_k is independent of x, we have

$$\sum_{x=Q+1}^{Q+P} |S_1(x)|^{2S} \leqslant \sum_{y_1=1}^{Y} \cdots \sum_{y_s=1}^{Y} \sum_{y_1'=1}^{Y} \cdots \sum_{y_s'=1}^{Y} \left| \sum_{x=Q+1}^{Q+P} e(\Phi) \right|$$

$$= \sum_{N_1=-2SY}^{2SY} \cdots \sum_{N_{k-1}=-2SY^{k-1}}^{2SY^{k-1}} \psi(N_1, \cdots, N_{k-1}) \left| \sum_{x=Q+1}^{Q+P} e(A_{k-1}N_{k-1} + \cdots + A_1N_1) \right|.$$

By Cauchy's inequality, we obtain

$$\sum_{x=Q+1}^{Q+P} |S_1(x)|^{2S}$$

$$\leqslant \left(\sum_{N_1} \cdots \sum_{N_{k-1}} \psi^2(N_1, \cdots, N_{k-1}) \right)^{\frac{1}{2}} \left(\sum_{N_1} \cdots \sum_{N_{k-1}} \left| \sum_{x=Q+1}^{Q+P} e(A_{k-1}N_{k-1} + \cdots + A_1N_1) \right|^2 \right)^{\frac{1}{2}}.$$

Since

$$\sum_{N_1} \cdots \sum_{N_{k-1}} \psi^2(N_1, \cdots, N_{k-1})$$

is equal to the number of sets of integral solutions of the equations

$$y_1^h + \cdots + y_s^h - y_1'^h - \cdots - y_s'^h = z_1^h + \cdots + z_s^h - z_1'^h - \cdots - z_s'^h,$$
$$1 \leqslant h \leqslant k-1, \qquad 1 \leqslant y, y', z, z' \leqslant Y$$

which is given by

$$\int_0^1 \cdots \int_0^1 |C_{k-1}(Y)|^{4S}\, d\alpha_1 \cdots d\alpha_k,$$

we obtain, by the Theorem,

$$\sum_{N_1} \cdots \sum_{N_{k-1}} \psi^2(N_1, \cdots, N_{k-1}) \leqslant k^{9k^3} e^{23k^2 l} \log^l Y \cdot Y^{4s-\frac{1}{2}k(k-1)+\delta_l}.$$

Furthermore

$$\sum_{N_1} \cdots \sum_{N_{k-1}} \left| \sum_{x=Q+1}^{Q+P} e(A_{k-1}N_{k-1} + \cdots + A_1N_1) \right|^2$$

$$\leqslant \sum_{N_1} \cdots \sum_{N_{k-2}} \sum_{x_1=Q+1}^{Q+P} \sum_{x_2=Q+1}^{Q+P} \left| \sum_{N_{k-1}=-2sY^{k-1}}^{2sY^{k-1}} e^{2\pi i k\alpha_k(x_1-x_2)N_{k-1}} \right|$$

$$\leqslant (5s)^{k-1} Y^{\frac{1}{2}(k-1)(k-2)} \sum_{x_1=Q+1}^{Q+P} \sum_{x_2=Q+1}^{Q+P} \min\left(5sY^{k-1}, \frac{1}{\{k\alpha_k(x_1-x_2)\}}\right)$$

$$\leqslant (5s)^{k-1} Y^{\frac{1}{2}(k-1)(k-2)} P \sum_{x=-P}^{P} \min\left(5sY^{k-1}, \frac{1}{\{k\alpha_k x\}}\right)$$

$$\leqslant (5s)^{k-1} Y^{\frac{1}{2}(k-1)(k-2)} P\left(5sY^{k-1} + \frac{2}{k|\alpha_k|} \sum_{x=1}^{P} \frac{1}{x}\right)$$

$$\leqslant (5s)^k Y^{\frac{1}{2}(k-1)(k-2)} P\left(Y^{k-1} + \frac{1}{k|\alpha_k|}\log P\right).$$

From these inequalities we at once obtain

$$S \ll P^{1-\frac{1}{2S}} \left(k^{9k^3} e^{23k^2 l} \log^l Y \cdot Y^{-(k-1)+\delta_l} (5s)^k P\left(Y^{k-1} + \frac{\log P}{k|\alpha_k|}\right)\right)^{\frac{1}{4S}} + Y.$$

If we take $s = [(k-1)^2 \log (k-1)]$, it is easily proved that $\delta_l \leq 1/2$. Therefore we obtain

$$S \ll e^{32k} \log P \cdot P^{1-\frac{1}{4S}} \left(Y^{-(k-1)+\frac{1}{2}}\left(Y^{k-1} + \frac{1}{|\alpha_k|}\right)\right)^{\frac{1}{4S}} + Y.$$

Taking

$$Y = \begin{cases} [|\alpha_k|^{-\frac{1}{k-1}}] & \text{if } 2^{k-1} \leqslant |\alpha_k|^{-1}; \\ [P^{1-\frac{1}{10S}}] & \text{if } 2^{k-1} > |\alpha_k|^{-1}, \end{cases}$$

we have the proof of the lemma.

This lemma is important in the analytic theory of numbers. We mention here several of its applications. These applications essentially involve only the Fundamental Lemma and certain standard methods.

1) $\zeta(1+it) = O(\log^{3/4} t \log\log^{1/4} t)$.[1]

2) $\pi(x) = \mathrm{li}\, x + O(xe^{-A \log^{1/\eta} x \log\log^{-1/\eta} x})$.[1]

3) The domain of applicability of the mean-value formula

$$\lim_{T\to\infty} \frac{1}{T}\int_0^T |\zeta(\sigma+it)|^{2k}\, dt = \sum_{n=1}^{\infty} d_k^2(n)\, n^{-2\sigma}.$$ [2]

4) If $A(x)$ is the number of integral points in the ellipsoid

$$\sum_{i,j=1}^{4} a_{ij} x_i x_j \leqslant x \qquad (a_{ij} = a_{ji} \text{ are integers})$$

and D is the determinant of this quadratic form, then

$$A(x) - \frac{\pi^2}{2\sqrt{D}} x^2 = O(x \log^{\frac{3}{4}} x \log\log^{\frac{1}{4}} x).$$ [3]

---

1) See Hua Lo-keng and Wu Fang, *An improvement of Vinogradov's mean value theorem and some applications*, Acta Math. Sinica **7** (1957), 574–589. (Chinese. English summary)

2) See Davenport, J. London Math. Soc. **10** (1935), 136–138.

3) See Val'fiš, Publications of the Travaux de L'institut mathématique de Tbilisi, 5 (1938), 181–196.